Date Due

The Golden Land

The

GOLDEN LAND

An Anthology
of Latin American Folklore
in Literature

Selected, Edited, and Translated by

HARRIET DE ONÍS

Alfred A. Knopf: *New York*

1 9 4 8

THIS IS A BORZOI BOOK
PUBLISHED BY ALFRED A. KNOPF, INC.

FIRST EDITION

For Juan

Acknowledgments

I wish to express my gratitude to the many authors who have so graciously granted me permission to use the selections I have chosen from their works; to José Olympio of Rio de Janeiro for allowing me to include selections from several of his authors; to Rinehart & Company, and Alfred A. Knopf, Inc. for permitting me to include material I had already translated into English; to Mr. Walter Owen for allowing me to use a selection from his translation of *Faust* by Estanislao del Campo; to Germán Arciniegas and Ciro Alegría for invaluable suggestions; to Herbert Weinstock of the editorial staff of Alfred A. Knopf, Inc. for his interest, encouragement, and patience throughout the course of this work; and very especially to my husband, Federico de Onís, to whom I owe, in great measure, my knowledge of and love for Latin America.

H. de O.

Foreword

As I WAS discussing the plan of this work with a friend one day, his initial bewilderment was suddenly replaced by a look of understanding. "Oh, I see, it is a theory illustrated by an anthology." The phrase struck me as being an excellent description of what I was attempting to do. I shall, therefore, endeavor to set forth the theory.

It must be made clear from the outset that this anthology is in no sense a study of Latin American folklore as such. That is a field for the anthropologist, the historian, the sociologist. My purpose has been to show how persistent the influence of Latin American folklore in its literature has been, how it has served as a source of inspiration, perhaps the most powerful, to its writers from their emergence on the literary scene, more than four hundred years ago, down to our own day. One of the characteristics of Hispanic civilization, both in Europe and America, is that its culture has proceeded from the people upward rather than from a minority of the elite downward to the masses. It has a natural tendency to synthesize the most divergent elements into a harmonious whole, valid alike for ignorant and learned. Folklore is used in its broadest sense, including myths and legends out of America's remote past, tales of African, Indian, or European origin, often combined and fused into something new and different, customs, superstitions, and historical episodes and characters which have taken on a legendary quality with time and the telling. The selections have in every case been chosen for their intrinsic literary value.

For a long time, in the course of my readings in the field of Latin American literature, I had been struck by the way certain themes, certain attitudes, kept repeating themselves throughout the different phases of its development. Particularly impressive is the Antaeus quality about Latin American writers: their strength is proportionate to their union with their own earth. Keyserling has spoken of the telluric force of South America, how man is dominated by the earth, the landscape, to the point of becoming an integral part of it. Tradition plays an equally powerful role. In no sense does this imply that Latin American writers have been closed to outside influence or have been rotating on their own axis. On the contrary, at all times, during colonial days and after the independence, they have been in constant contact with European literature and thought, through both reading and travel. But no matter how strong the external influences of style or technique, the really great works of Latin American literature, with rare exceptions, have been produced when its writers, utilizing all the literary resources at their command, completely attuned to the diapason of their times, have followed this centripetal tendency, have found their inspiration in their own reality and tradition. When, fifty years after the conquest, the Inca Garcilaso, humanist, classic scholar, wrote his *Comentarios reales*, one of the monuments of Hispanic literature, his theme was the vanished empire of his forefathers, and in it he recounted with nostalgic tenderness the legends and tales he had heard from his Inca princess mother and her relatives, as well as the exploits of the conquest that were the favorite topic of conversation of his Spanish father and his friends. In the eighteenth century the eminent Mexican Jesuit Father Clavijero, to refute the insidious reports of certain European writers on the inferiority of America, wrote his *History of Mexico*, in which with great erudition, elegance, and a historical approach not at all usual in his day he presents a picture of Mexican civilization, from its legendary beginnings to the conquest. He, the child of Spanish parents, skillfully defends the Mexicans, to whom he always refers as "my fellow countrymen," and with them, all other Americans, against the attacks designed to prove that Americans were beings of a lower order, devoid of the capacity of reason, honesty, and industry. The inference was that this made them fair game for the Europeans to exploit, and the affirmation of Europe's superiority justified keeping America in a subordinate position.

Two further revealing illustrations may be found in the literature of Argentina, which is often considered, and likes to think of itself, as being more closely linked to Europe than the rest of America. Domingo F. Sarmiento, author of one of the most widely read South American books, *Facundo, or Civilization and Barbarism in the Argentine Republic*, was a leader of the revolt against tradition, which was typified for him in the dictator Juan Manuel Rosas and the gaucho caudillos who had sprung up around him. A passionate admirer of the United States, Sarmiento has rightly been considered the creator of modern Argentina. But the enduring value of his writings does not rest upon his programs for the educational, social, and economic development of his country, valuable though these were for the nation. His fame as a writer is secured by his magnificent descriptions of the life of the gaucho, and his unforgettable portraits of their leaders, who represented for him all that was retrograde and that stood in the way of Argentina's becoming the great nation he envisaged. Yet underneath his scathing criticism there is an admiration for those qualities which characterized the gaucho: his maleness, courage, independence, and austerity which Sarmiento, too, possessed, and which, his culture and progressive ideas notwithstanding, proved that he was cut off the same bolt. With his deep insight, he himself said that one had only to look under the frock coat of an Argentine to find the gaucho. The case of Ricardo Güiraldes, author of *Don Segundo Sombra*, the outstanding Latin American novel of the last twenty years, is similar. Güiraldes belonged to the wealthy landowning aristocracy of Argentina, had received a part of his education abroad and spent much of his life there. He was a consummate artist, aware of all the devices of contemporary literary technique, and employing them with rare skill. Yet the theme of his novel is the traditional Argentine background, the pampas; the language, a combination of Güiraldes's sensitive, imageful prose, and the lean, functional speech of the gaucho; and the hero, the embodiment of the traits with which legend, if not reality, had endowed the gaucho. The book is dedicated to "the gaucho I bear within me, as the monstrance bears the holy wafer." Three books form the cornerstone of Argentina's literature, Sarmiento's *Facundo*, José Hernández's epic poem *Martin Fierro*, and Güiraldes's *Don Segundo Sombra*. All deal with the traditional figure of the gaucho. Not only are they the cornerstone of Argentina's literature; they are milestones in American literature, North and South.

The reasons for the force of tradition in Latin America become readily apparent. Three cultural groups determined the region's formation, and the traditional, folkloric element was unusually strong in all three. Even a superficial examination of the culture of the inhabitants the conquerors found on their arrival in America reveals that their history, religion, and laws were their traditions and myths. Particularly is this true of the highly civilized groups, the Aztecs, Incas, and Mayas, despite the profound differences that existed between them. Tradition was the amalgam that fused their people together, the framework in which their lives were set. There was a sacramental quality about all they did, even the simplest acts of their daily existence. Their lives were hedged about by secular customs and rites, and any suggestion of change, any departure from prescribed habit, could only invite disaster. Such happiness and well-being as were permitted mortals in this life, where they were at the mercy of capricious divinities in constant need of propitiation, consisted in following the old ways; the best future was a continuation of the past. Such fragments of their literature as have been preserved are impregnated with this spirit.

Into this static, structured universe, history catapulted the discoverers and the conquerors. They had broken through the narrow confines of the known world, guided by new concepts, new values, to launch themselves upon one of the most daring adventures the mind of man had conceived. Their vital optimism, their unlimited confidence in themselves, their readiness to embark on any new venture were in sharpest contrast to the Indians' passive acceptance of fatality, to their inability to shape their own destinies, and their cult of the past. Yet to those bold Renaissance wings there still clung many bits of the medieval shell. The conquerors belonged to one of the oldest nations of Europe and one of the richest in folk culture. They were the legatees of a vast and varied popular tradition, which nowhere was stronger, more common to all, or more potent in fecundating powers than in Spain and Portugal. These pioneers of the Renaissance, individualists and innovators, carried within themselves the Middle Ages, too. The magic, the miraculous still formed a fundamental part of life's pattern. Man's soul continued to be the prize for which the powers of light and the powers of darkness eternally struggled, and it was total warfare. The only arm of man, in other respects so daring, torn between his longing for salvation, which allied him with God, and his natural impulses, which too often threw him into the Devil's camp, was his faith and his hope. The power of God manifested itself through the supernatural; the Devil, too, could feign miracles, so man had to be ever on the alert, for the most trivial act or incident might be of deep portent.

To many of the early conquerors the discovery of the New World was less a triumph of the geographer's and navigator's skill than a miracle. To the more religiously minded it was the fulfillment of God's purpose that the gospel might be carried to the heathen. To the more worldly, it was their dreams of wealth, adventure, glory come true. For the peasant tilling his little plot of ground or working the land of another, the artisan, the penniless soldier, the impoverished *hidalgo*, it was as though he had been offered passage to the Arabian Nights. The reports brought back from the first voyages left them with mouth agape. A land flowing with nothing so commonplace as milk and honey, but gold, silver, pearls, spices. . . . It was all the Spanish imagination needed. The one promise of Don Quixote's that Sancho Panza never doubted, even in his most skeptical moments, was that in the twinkling of an eye his master would discover an island and make him its governor. On this he built all his hopes, and it sustained him through the bleakest days of the immortal pair's wanderings—only once was he prepared to throw in his hand, and that was the time Don Quixote forbade him to talk—until in the end it is hard to say which is the madder, or wiser, of the two, Sancho the realist or Don Quixote the visionary. All this is but the form in which Cervantes's genius fleshed the dreams that had been animating the Spaniards during the hundred years between the discovery of America and the creation of Don Quixote, Spain's two greatest contributions to the world.

So many of the dreams did come true in America, and as only the hits were scored, never the misses—and how many there were!—there

seemed no reason why all the legends that sprang up to lead men on
like will-o'-the-wisps should not be true, too. Was El Dorado, the
Fountain of Eternal Youth, the fabulous city of Manoa where the
queen of the Amazons dwelt, a wilder dream than the reality of Mexico,
Peru, the mines of Potosí, the pearls of Margarita? So up and down the
continents these adventurers marched, undeterred by the elusiveness of
the bird in the bush, so much more alluring than any number in the
hand. As one reflects on the hardships, dangers, and disappointments
these "gold seekers" endured, many of whom had already achieved
success that would have satisfied any ordinary man, one can only agree
with the G.I. in his foxhole, that it was a hell of a way to make a living.
Their motto would seem to have been:

> Perhaps the reward of the spirit that tries,
> Is not the goal but the exercise.

Let no one think that the Spaniards and Portuguese were alone in
their credulity. Amerigo Vespucci, that man of multiple talents, might
have been a real-estate promoter, to judge by his glowing, fanciful
descriptions of the new land that was to bear his name. The tales Sir
Francis Drake brought back to England of the wonders of America!
And the poet's eye of Sir Walter Ralegh indeed saw Helen's beauty in
a brow of Egypt when he described the wife of an Indian chieftain of
Guiana: "I have rarely seen a better-favored woman. She was of good
stature, with black eyes, fat of body, of an excellent countenance, her
hair almost as long as herself. I have seen a Lady in England so like her
as but for the difference in color I would have sworn it might have been
the same."

If the world they had discovered was new to the Spaniards, in a very
short time it had become new to the Indians as well. It was not so much
that a new civilization had been forced upon them as that between
them conqueror and conquered engendered a new civilization, containing elements of both its component parts, but as different as a child
from its parents. To use the term coined by the Cuban anthropologist,
Fernando Ortiz, a process of transculturation had set in. And in this
mestizo civilization the law of heredity held true: it was the characteristics common to both parents which became fixed. None more so than
the tendency to cherish the elements of folklore, legend, tradition, those
links with the past which remain when others have disappeared, and
which are dearest to exiles. For at the beginning, both masters and
mastered were exiles, the first strangers in a new land, the second
strangers in their own land. When Hernán Cortés and his handful of
men first glimpsed the city of Mexico, Tenochtitlán, gleaming like a
mirage in the distance, one of them broke into the verses of an old

ballad, "Behold France, Montesinos, Behold Paris, how it lies." They
had all heard it from childhood, and it must have been like a breath of
Spanish air in their nostrils.

To these two groups there was very soon added a third, the Negroes.
They were the most pitiful exiles of all, standing amidst truly alien
corn. The conquerors had come of their own volition, animated by
dreams of gain and glory which often came true beyond their fondest
hopes. Many quickly founded families and homes. If things went too
badly, they could always return to their own country, though they
rarely did. Once America had got into their blood, it was in Europe
that they felt themselves strangers. For the Indians, even though they
were no longer their own masters, the earth, the sky, many of their
customs remained unchanged. But to the African, everything was new,
and besides he was a slave. His only link with his shattered past, with
his home he would never see again, his ancestors, his supplanted religion, was the memory of his gods, his myths, his legends, in a word, his
folklore. This was the only possession he had been allowed to bring with
him.

As time went by, as the process of transculturation proceeded, the
folklore of the three groups tended to fuse. It was comforting to the
Christian neophytes to ascribe to their new divinities many of the attributes of their native gods. The images of the Virgin executed by
native artists acquired Creole features, and became the objects of such
deep devotion as that the Mexicans feel for their dark Lady of Guadalupe. The churches, though European in outward design, grew rich
with motifs of native decoration. The traditional religious festivals were
invested with ceremonies and pageantry reminiscent of the cults of the
supplanted dieties; these the missionaries wisely accepted, just as in the
early days of Christianity many pagan rites continued as before, except
that they were brought under the advocation of some saint. In a six-
teenth-century adaptation of the parable of the Prodigal Son into a
miracle play for the Peruvian Indians, the characters and setting have
become completely American. The elder son says to Kuyaj Yaya, his
old Indian father: "You have welcomed that libertine son of yours . . .
and dressed him in fine clothes, and even slaughtered a fat pig for him.
As for me, who honored my father . . . not even a llama did you offer
me saying here, take this, and invite your friends, the comrades of your
youth, to eat it with you."

When the tumult of the conquest had died down, and everyone
slipped into his proper niche, the sphere to which God had been
pleased to call him, this body of folklore became the mental diet of the
vast majority of the population. Outside the cities there was little education; people depended for their entertainment on the religious fes-

tivals, the tales told around the fire by slaves or servants when their work was done, the wandering minstrel who improvised ballads on every subject to the accompaniment of his guitar. And in this world the supernatural held powerful sway. The superstitions, legends, and traditions of the European settlers were reinforced by the counterpart folklore of Indians and Negroes, and the workaday world was hemmed about by another world charged with mystery, miracle, and witchcraft.

This traditional fare has provided Latin American writers, no matter what their subsequent culture, with their first nourishment, and they have drawn on it for inspiration from the beginning down to our own day. One can hardly mention an outstanding writer of Latin America, during the colonial period or afterwards, who did not drink at this spring. In the cross section of Latin American literature this anthology presents, the reader will find most of the names he had already known along with many he may not have heard before. For four hundred years Latin America has been producing a literature of great originality and richness, with a character peculiarly its own. It has a common Hispanic background, but each nation speaks with its own unmistakable accent. Each selection has a representative value, is typical of a period or a tendency.

When one considers the quality of the writings that comprise this collection, it is impossible not to accord the literature they represent a place among the great literatures of the world. That nations so isolated from one another and from Europe, faced with such harassing political, social, and racial problems; that Brazil, a continent within a continent, which, like Topsy, seems to have "just growed," could have produced an unbroken stream of writers of the caliber of those included here, and the many it has been necessary to omit, is nothing short of miraculous. That nations with such natural barriers to communication, with such limited educational facilities, should have preserved their common language, so that from Patagonia to Mexico they speak and write the same tongue, except for unimportant variations of accent and localisms, which are never the slightest hindrance to understanding; and that within the sprawling confines of Brazil wherever the fearless *bandeirantes* blazed their trail, they left behind them physical and spiritual offspring, Brazilian children and the Portuguese language, is another miracle. But we have already seen that the miracle was part of the Latin American way of life.

It is in this preservation of their folklore and tradition as a perennial and vital source of inspiration that Latin American literature shows its greatest originality in its ability to assimilate the new without ever losing touch with the past. This is its unique quality, and to know the world this literature opens up is to illuminate our understanding of our fellow occupants of these continents, and to add a new dimension to our own minds and hearts. This profound awareness of themselves and their past, so varied and yet so homogeneous, gives its possessors a security of direction and the inner resources to solve the challenges the future will present to them as they are doing and have done in the past. If at times they lose heart, and their vexing problems—problems that beset the entire world—blind them to the steady progress they have made, they have every reason to tell themselves, in the words of their greatest poet Rubén Darío: "*Mas es mía el alba de oro*"—"but the golden dawn is mine."

HARRIET DE ONÍS

Contents

The Golden Land

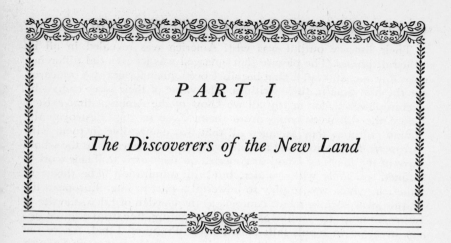

PART I

The Discoverers of the New Land

IN THE BEGINNING were the discoverers, and with them the word. For it is to their *Relations* that the world owes its first knowledge of America and the marvels it encompassed. Every class of society was represented among them, high crown officials, great captains, rude soldiers, dignitaries of the Church, and humble missionaries. A variety of motives had embarked them on the American adventure, but at contact with the new land it was as though the gift of tongues had descended upon them. Beginning with Columbus, their name was legion who had their story to tell of what they had discovered. Everything they saw was tinged for them with wonder, and not the least of the wonders was that so many were rendered articulate who otherwise would have never set pen to paper.

It is not surprising that the Spaniards of this first epoch should have developed something of a God complex, for, in a sense, they had said: "Let there be a new world," and there was. All—the first to arrive and those who followed after—made their discovery of new lands, a new nature, new peoples, new languages, customs, ways of life—a New World. And as though the reality they beheld were not amazing enough, they colored their reports with the legends and myths they carried within themselves, the romances of chivalry in which they were all nourished, the traditions and superstitions of the Indians which they unhesitatingly accepted. At the touch of their exuberant fancy, everything American took on a fantastic character. But with typical Spanish dualism, no matter how lost in the clouds their heads might be, their feet were firmly planted on the earth, and the pursuit of chimeras never interfered with the founding of cities, the subduing of the Indians, and the propagation of the faith.

Their literary output was vast. America was revealed in all its different phases. The picture that emerged was its essential difference from Europe, and much that has since been taken for granted appeared for the first time in their writings. The value of their work cannot be overemphasized, for nearly all we know of the America that existed before the discovery comes from them. Even as they destroyed the Indian cultures, they salvaged all that was compatible in them with European civilization, and in their writings they have left us the whole story of the life they found in America on their arrival. Their work is imbued, not only with wonder, but with admiration. The theme of America, which was to play so powerful a part in later European literature, was born in them: America as the Garden of Eden, the site of future Utopias; the Indian as the child of nature,'free from original sin, not involved in man's fall; America the Promised Land, where the streets were paved with gold, and where, with characteristic Spanish hyperbole, "the dogs were tied with chains of sausage which they did not eat."

These discoverers were the first immigrants. Many of them settled in America, transplanting Old World institutions, creating new ones, fathering children who were the new Americans. Others came and went, but none was the same after knowing America. The New World left its impress on them all. In some ways they were more American than the native-born generation that succeeded them.

GONZALO FERNÁNDEZ DE OVIEDO

(1478–1557)

IN THE TEN YEARS from 1492 to 1502, Columbus had discovered for the world the islands of the Caribbean and had learned that beyond them lay a continent. In the next ten years these islands had become the scene of a bustling activity, where a new world was coming into being. Most important of all at first was Santo Domingo, Hispaniola. All of Spain's colonies in America followed this same pattern. Under the royal governor Ovando, the city of Santo Domingo was transformed in a few years from Bartholomew Columbus's original mud-and-thatch village of 1494 into a comely city of stone and mortar. The crown services and prerogatives were quickly set up, courts of law, church, taxes; and Santo Domingo, not Spain, became the center from which the first expeditions to the mainland were launched. Through it passed all those men who were to become the heroes of the Conquest, Cortés, Pizarro, Balboa, Cabeza de Vaca, Ponce de León, and others who won their fame in a different way. One who rendered an invaluable service was Gonzalo Fernández de Oviedo, whose *General and Natural History of the Indies, Islands and Mainland of the Ocean Sea* is the most entertaining and richest of that whole literary genre known as "histories of the Indies."

Unlike so many of that motley crew of adventurers waiting for their number to come up on fortune's wheel, Fernández de Oviedo was a person of consequence, a former page at the court of their Catholic Majesties, soldier, scholar, and in America, a functionary of the crown. He came out to America in 1513 with Pedrárias Dávila's ambitious and ill-fated expedition to Darien, and was later appointed *veedor*—inspector—of the gold smelteries of the Spanish possessions. *Veedor*—literally the one who sees—was the perfect title for him. Seeing was not only his profession, but his delight, and very little escaped his observation. In the warm tropical nights, probably seeking forgetfulness of his private griefs—he had been three times widowed and had lost his eldest son in the wars in Peru—and of the quarrels and intrigues of the Spaniards (far more dangerous enemies to one another than the Indians), he set down his brisk, fresh account of all he had seen and heard in the Indies. The work contains detailed descriptions of the flora and fauna of the New World, the customs and rites of the Indians, the tall tales and relations of the participants in the various expeditions that set out from or returned to Santo Domingo, some of which ended in disaster, some in stupendous achievement. No detail was too insignificant for his notice, and to him we owe the most complete picture of the new life that was developing in the Indies. Even at that early date he says that many of the things he describes were already disappearing.

He must have begun his work shortly after he came out to America, for the first part was published in 1535, the second in 1557, the year of his death. Practically everything that happened during that period is to be found in it. Rather than an ordered history, it is a storehouse of information. He was a shrewd and intelligent observer in whom good sense rather than imagination predominates, though occasionally his work shows traces of the romances of chivalry he had read, and even translated, in his younger days. The selections that follow give an idea of the variety of his subject matter, his faculties of observation, and the ease and charm of his style.

How the Indians believed the Spaniards to be immortal when they passed over to the island of Sanct Johan, and how they decided to revolt and did not dare attempt it until they had found out whether the Spaniards could die or not.

[GONZALO FERNÁNDEZ DE OVIEDO]

FROM the things the Indians on the island of Sanct Johan had heard of the conquest and the wars waged on this island of Hispaniola, and knowing as they did, that this island is very large and was thickly settled with natives, they reached the conclusion that it was impossible for the Spaniards to have subjugated it unless they were immortal, and did not die from wounds or other accidents. And because they had come from where the sun rises, they fought as they did because they were divine and the children of the sun, and the Indians were not strong enough to resist them. And as they saw that they had already entered the island of Sanct Johan and made themselves the masters of the island, although there were only about two hundred men among them who bore arms, they were determined not to let themselves be subdued by so few, and made up their minds to win their freedom and not serve them, but they feared them and believed them immortal. So the chiefs of the island assembled in secret to discuss the matter, and decided that before they began their rebellion it would be well to experiment first and settle their doubts, and make a test on some Spaniard whom they could come upon by himself and removed from the others. A cacique by the name of Urayoan, the lord of the province of Yaguaca, agreed to find this out, and this is how he went about it. A young man by the name of Salcedo came into his territory on his way to where the Spaniards were, and as an act of courtesy and to help him carry his equipment, this cacique sent fifteen or twenty Indians with him, after having fed him very well and shown him great affection. The young man left, feeling very safe and grateful to the cacique for his kind treatment, and when they came to a river called Guarabo, which is on the west coast and empties into the bay where the town of San Germán now stands, the Indians said to him: "Sir, would you like us to carry you across, so you won't get wet?" And the Spaniard said he would, and was well pleased, which he should not have been, because in addition to the manifest danger into which those fall who trust their enemies, they reveal themselves as lacking in prudence. The Indians set him upon their shoulders, and for this they selected the strongest and most powerful among them, and when they reached the middle of the river, they put him under the water, and those who had been carrying him and the others who had been looking on held him down, because they were all there to accomplish his death, and they drowned him. When he was dead, they dragged him to the shore, and said to him: "Señor Salcedo, arise and forgive us; we fell with you, and now let us continue our journey." And with these remarks and other similar ones they stayed there for three days, until his corpse began to smell, and even then they did not think that he was dead, nor that the Spaniards could die. And after they had proved to themselves that they were mortal, in the manner I have described, they sent word to the cacique, who sent other Indians every day to see if Salcedo had arisen. And still in doubt as to whether they were telling him the truth, he decided to go and see for himself. Meanwhile more days had gone by, and that poor sinner's body was badly spoiled and decayed. Whereupon they took heart and courage for their revolt, and set about killing Spaniards and rebelling and doing what I shall describe in the succeeding chapters.

Which deals with a monkey, the like of which has never been seen until our times, that was part bird and sang like a nightingale or lark.

[GONZALO FERNÁNDEZ DE OVIEDO]

IT has been my habit in these accounts of mine to name the witnesses of those things I have not seen with my own eyes and which I have heard from others; and in connection with what I have said about griffins, I should like to mention something else I have heard of, which strikes me as being no less extraordinary than the griffins. It is said that in the southern land of Peru a monkey has been seen, one of those with long tails, the upper half of whose body, from its forepaws to its head, was covered with brown and different-colored feathers, and the other half, hindquarters and tail, with smooth reddish fur, of a sort of fawn color. This monkey was very gentle and tame, and little bigger than a handspan in size. It belonged to an Indian princess, the sister of the Inca Amaro, brother to the great prince Atabalipa, and this sister, when she came into the power of the Spaniards, was married to a young man, the son of Baptista Armero, a skilled horseman, and in high favor at the court of His Majesty the Emperor. I am giving all these details because this youth is a person of standing. He asked his wife to give him this monkey to send to the Empress, our lady, of glorious memory, with Captain Per Ansurez, and she gave it to him. And this captain was taking it when, through the carelessness of certain of his servants, who were frolicking about, one of them, without meaning to, stepped on the monkey and killed it. I relate this misfortune as an example of the unhappiness of those eyes which had no opportunity to see this animal and give thanks to God who made it so different from all those that exist in the world. Men whose word may be credited have come to this city of Santo Domingo who say that they saw and held this monkey in their hands, and it was as I have described it, and had teeth. And no less to be wondered at than the foregoing is that the monkey, perched on the shoulder of the captain I have mentioned, or where he had it tied, would begin to sing when it felt like it, like a nightingale or a lark, first in a soft warble, and then gradually growing louder than either of these birds, and with as many or more modulations in its song. It was a great pleasure and delight to hear its sweet melody, which lasted for a long time, after the manner of singers. A gentleman named Diego de Mercado, from the city of Madrigal, and another hidalgo by the name of Tomás de Ortega, who made the trip with the aforesaid captain (and who, after they arrived here with fortunes, married in this city, and live here, and are persons whose word can and should be taken for this and much more), were eye-witnesses to what has been related, for they saw this monkey often and heard it sing.

There are those who say that this animal must have been born as the result of the adultery or miscegenation of a bird with a male or female monkey to engender a species of this sort partaking of the nature of both progenitors. But I do not hold with this opinion; and it is my belief (taking into account certain things that one cannot overlook regarding the dissimilarity of the generative organs of birds and monkeys) that this animal was not born as the consequence of such adultery, but belongs to a species of its own, as do the griffins, since the Lord of Creation has wrought other and greater works and wonders, may His name be praised and remembered forever and ever.

I greatly regret that this monkey did not reach this city alive, or dead either, for if I had seen it dead, I would have traded my cape for a little salt to cure it and preserve it so others could see it, too, to praise the wonders of God. And I believe that in Spain it would have been highly esteemed, and wherever there are men of wisdom. In this city of ours there are today four men who saw this monkey alive; and I would rather have seen it than all the rich emeralds I have beheld from those lands of Peru; and I will see as many more before another such animal is seen, unless, in accordance with the opinion I have expressed, others of its species are found in the course of time. I do not doubt that this will be the case, for this great world of our Indies is always revealing new things to those of us who are here, and those who will come after us to contemplate and admire the handiwork of God, to whom nothing is impossible. Therefore, let the Catholic reader recall the words of Hilary: "God can do more than the understanding of man can grasp."

BERNAL DÍAZ DEL CASTILLO

(1492–1581)

LIKE FERNÁNDEZ DE OVIEDO, Bernal Díaz del Castillo had come out to the Indies with Pedrárias Dávila's expedition. He returned to Santo Domingo and from there passed over to Cuba where many of those who had not succeeded in establishing themselves in Hispaniola went to better their fortunes. He accompanied Hernández de Córdoba and then Grijalva on their voyages to Mexico, but neither of them proceeded beyond the coast. Hernán Cortés was destined to be the conqueror of Mexico, and Bernal Díaz was one of those who shared in the undertaking. He went through the entire campaign, and later assisted Pedro de Alvarado in the conquest of Guatemala, where he received a land grant in return for his services and was one of the founders of the city of Santiago de los Caballeros, He wrote only one book, but that has been sufficient to insure him immortality.

When he was an old man, nearing eighty, he came upon the account of the conquest of New Spain written by López de Gómara, Cortés's chaplain, and it filled him with passionate indignation. Gómara, a humanist and scholar, had written his urbane, polished work in the Renaissance manner, which, following the classic prescription, focused all attention on the hero, leaving the rank-and-file soldier in the shadow. Gómara, with his European point of view, completely missed the fact that the conquest had been a democratic achievement, and that Cortés had been elected captain by his own men, a case of *primus inter pares*. According to him, the whole credit for the conquest of Mexico belonged to Cortés. It was the fruit of his genius, his daring. The hardships, courage, fears of Bernal Díaz and his companions, many slain on Indian altars, others dead of their wounds, had been as nothing, merely the anonymous backdrop against which Cortés had moved. So Bernal Díaz wrote the American story, the soldier's account of "that which I have myself seen and the fighting." As Archibald MacLeish puts it in the moving verses of *Conquistador:*

> I am an ignorant old sick man . . .
> > but I
> Fought in those battles! These were my own deeds!
> These names he writes of mouthing them out as a man would
> Names in Herodotus—dead and their wars to read—
> These were my friends, these dead my companions . . .
> What have they written of us, the poor soldiers?

Under the old man's pen, his companions and their deeds of incredible heroism come to life in all the glow of the bright morning that was their youth in Mexico. More than fifty years had elapsed since the conquest, and yet it might have been only yesterday, so vivid is Bernal Díaz's recollection of every detail: the wonder of the new land they had entered; the men, each with his virtues and shortcomings; and not only the men, but the horses—Pedro de Alvarado's bright bay mare, Juan Sedeño's brown mare who foaled aboard ship, Sandoval's Motilla—"when men talk of horses they say as good, or almost as good as Motilla"; and the grim, quarterless fighting. And, like a ritornello, "and it was not the way the chronicler Gómara related it."

In no sense does Bernal Díaz begrudge Cortés all that is his due; but he wants it set down for all to know that a fair share of the glory belonged not only to him and his comrades, but to their Indian allies, without whose aid the conquest of Mexico could never have been accomplished. Of these allies none was more important than Doña Marina, who served them as interpreter, and whose help and devotion to Cortés were of inestimable value to their enterprise. The following description of her meeting with her mother, who had sold her into slavery, has all the quality of a fairy tale, or as Bernal Díaz himself points out, the meeting of Joseph with his brethren in Egypt.

Of the Great Lady Doña Marina Was
[BERNAL DÍAZ DEL CASTILLO]

BEFORE I proceed further in the matter of the great Montezuma and his great kingdom of Mexico and the Mexicans, I should like to speak of Doña Marina, how from early childhood she had been the mistress of lands and vassals. And this was the way of it: her father and her mother were the rulers and chieftains of a town called Painala, and of other villages attached to it some eight leagues from the town of Guazacualco. Her father died when she was a little girl, and her mother married a young chieftain, and they had a son, and it would seem that they loved this child dearly. And the father and mother decided that he should succeed them after they were gone; and that nothing might stand in the way of this, one night, when no one could see them, they handed the girl over to some Indians of Xicalango, and gave out that she had died. At that very time the daughter of an Indian slave who belonged to them died, and they said it was the heiress. The Indians of Xicalango gave her to those of Tabasco, and those of Tabasco gave her to Cortés, and I knew her mother and her half brother, who was by this time grown to manhood and ruled the town with his mother, for the old lady's second husband had died. After they accepted Christianity the old lady received the name of Marta and the son of Lazaro, and I know this for a fact, for in 1523, after Mexico and other provinces had been subdued, and Christoval de Oli had risen in revolt in Higüeras, Cortés went there, and on his way passed through Guazacualco, and most of us who had settled in that town accompanied him. In all the wars of New Spain, Tlaxcala and Mexico, Doña Marina had been such a splendid woman and such a good interpreter, as I shall later relate, and for this reason Cortés always took her with him. And at that time and during that trip she married a hidalgo by the name of Juan Xaramillo in a place called Orizava in the presence of certain witnesses, among them one Aranda, a resident of Tabasco, and he has given an account of the wedding, and it was not the way the chronicler Gómara related it. Doña Marina was a person of great quality, and she enjoyed complete authority among the Indians of all New Spain.

And while Cortés was in the town of Guazacualco, he sent for all the chieftains of that province to tell them of the new doctrine and of the good treatment they might expect from him, and the mother of Doña Marina came, and her half brother Lazaro, and other chieftains. Days before, Doña Marina had told me that she was from that province, and the mistress of vassals, and Captain Cortés and the interpreter Aguilar were aware of this. When her mother came, and her brother, they recognized at once that she was her daughter, because she looked very much like her. They were afraid of her because they thought she had sent for them to have them put to death, and they wept. When Doña Marina saw them weeping she comforted them and told them to have no fear, that when they had handed her over to those of Xicalango they did not know what they were doing, and she forgave them, and she gave them many jewels of gold, and clothing, and sent them back to their village, telling them that God had shown her great favor in freeing her from the worship of idols and making her a Christian and giving her a son by her lord and master Cortés, and marrying her to a gentleman like her husband Juan Xaramillo. And, she added, that even if they offered to make her ruler of all the provinces of New Spain, she would not wish it, for she held serving her husband and Cortés in higher esteem than anything else in the world. And all this that she said I heard with my own ears, and I swear to it, amen. And it seems to me that this resembles what happened to Joseph in Egypt with his brothers, who came into his power at the time of that matter of the wheat. This is what happened, and not that account Gómara gives, who says lots of other things I shall not even mention. Coming back to our story, Doña Marina knew the language of Guazacualco, which is the same as that of Mexico, and that of Tabasco, as Gerónimo de Aguilar knew that of Yucatán and Tabasco, which is all one. They understood them well, and Aguilar translated it into Spanish to Cortés. This was a great advantage for our conquest, and thus we were able to accomplish things successfully, praise be to God. I have wanted to state this here, because without Doña Marina we would not have been able to understand the language of New Spain and Mexico.

GASPAR DE CARVAJAL

(1504–1584)

To THE AMIABLE Dominican friar Gaspar de Carvajal, we owe an eye-witness account of the Amazon woman, one of the most exciting and enduring legends that stirred the imagination of the early discoverers. His description of his encounter with them is so vivid that it is impossible to doubt his sincerity, yet what became of them, those "tall white women," whom nobody else ever saw, but so many sought?

Fray Gaspar came out to Peru from Trujillo in Extremadura, the birthplace of many of the conquistadors, in 1535. When Gonzalo Pizarro set out on his ambitious expedition in search of the cinnamon trees and El Dorado, Fray Gaspar accompanied him as champlain. No preparation or expense had been spared to insure the success of the venture. Spaniards tempered in the conquest of Peru, Indian guides and carriers, horses, dogs, llamas, droves of pigs for food—Gonzalo Pizarro did things in the grand manner. But the mountains and the jungle had the last word. When the party reached the headwaters of the Napo River, most of the Indians and many of the Spaniards were dead, the animals had all died or been slaughtered, and the expedition faced starvation. At a spot that still bears the name of El Barco (The Boat) they managed to build a brigantine, and Francisco de Orellana, governor of Guayaquil, who had sunk all he had in the venture, set out with a party of sixty, which included Fray Gaspar, down the river in search of food. They were to have returned in twelve days, but the stream on which they had embarked grew ever larger and more difficult to navigate, and it was impossible for them to make their way back. For months they sailed through lands no white man had ever seen before, meeting with friendly or hostile Indians, sometimes gorging themselves, sometimes starving, lost in a maze of water and woods, until finally they came out in the sea, the first white men ever to have navigated the Amazon from its upper waters to its mouth.

The Spaniards had been hearing the tale of the Amazons—they supplied the name from classic mythology—ever since they set out from Quito. Somewhere, "over that way," said the Indians, there was a tribe of women ruled over by a great queen. They made war, exacted rich tribute from their vassals, managed their own affairs, and no men were permitted to enter their domain except with their permission and as visitors. "Whoever wishes to see them," an Indian chieftain told Orellana, "must set out as a youth and will return an old man." One could dismiss the story, which seems tailored to the measurements of the Spaniards, as a ruse employed by the Indians to keep the invaders on the move and to get rid of them. But what of Fray Gaspar, that practical, sensible priest, who claims to have actually seen them? One can only conclude that, like so many others, he had come under the spell of the jungle.

Such a chain reaction as the good friar's tale set up! To borrow a phrase from modern science, the different legends began giving off protons and neutrons, which combined to form a new legend. There came into being the fabulous city of Manoa, situated somewhere in the region where Fray Gaspar claimed to have seen the white women warriors, which syncretized the legends of the Amazons, El Dorado, and the kingdom of Paititi, where the last descendant of the Incas was supposed to have taken refuge with a band of followers and vast treasures. It became a land of shattered dreams but undying hopes. Emerging from the Tower of London, Sir Walter Ralegh, who devoured all the histories of the Indies he could come by, made his last voyage to Guiana in search of the city of Manoa. Jiménez de Quesada left this will-o'-the-wisp to his heirs as his most prized legacy. And the others who followed the mirage were legion.

Fray Gaspar, unaware of the seed his tale had sown, came through this perilous adventure none the worse except for the loss of an eye. From Santo Domingo, where the survivors of the expedition dispersed, some to accompany Orellana to Spain (where he claimed and received the governorship of the lands he had discovered but never enjoyed, as he died at the end of the return voyage), others to seek further adventures in America, Fray Gaspar returned to Peru, where he held high posts in his order until his death at an advanced age. There must have been moments in his sober, busy life when his mind turned back to those dangerous exciting months when he and his comrades gazed in amazement on the fabulous "Mother of Waters," as the Indians called the Amazon, and the equally fabulous women he describes.

Encounter with the Amazons

[GASPAR DE CARVAJAL]

THE following Thursday we passed by other small villages, and did not bother to stop there. All these villages are fishing posts of tribes living inland. We were sailing along in this way looking for a pleasant spot to celebrate the feast of the blessed St. John the Baptist, the harbinger of Christ, and God so willed it that as we came around a bend in the river we saw before us on the bank many and large villages, gleaming white. Here we came head on into the fair lands and domain of the Amazons. These villages had received word of our approach, and for this reason the inhabitants came out on the water to meet us, seeming well disposed. When they drew near, the Captain, wanting to make friends with them, began to speak and call out to them. But they laughed and made fun of us, and came closer and told us to go further down the river and they would be waiting for us there, and they would take us all and carry us to the Amazons. The Captain, exasperated by their insolence, ordered us to fire on them with our crossbows and harquebuses to let them know that we had arms to attack them, and in this way we inflicted harm upon them, and they turned and went back to the village to tell what they had seen. We kept moving on and approaching the villages, and before we had traveled more than half a league, there appeared on the water many squadrons of Indians, and as we sailed ahead they assembled and drew near their settlements. In the middle of a village there was a great number of people, comprising a stout squadron, and the Captain ordered the brigantines to draw in where those people were to seek food, and as soon as we approached land, the Indians began to defend their village and shoot at us with arrows, and as there were so many, it seemed as though it were raining arrows. But our bowmen and harquebusiers were not idle; they did nothing but shoot, and although they killed many, it did not seem to matter, because in spite of all the harm we were doing them, some of them kept on fighting and others dancing. We were all on the verge of being lost there, because as so many arrows kept coming, our companions had all they could do to defend themselves from them and were unable to row, and for this reason they did us so much harm that before we could jump ashore they had wounded five of us, of whom I was one, for they got me in the side with an arrow that went through the hollow part of me, and if it had not been for the habit I was wearing, that would have been the end of me. When the Captain saw the danger we were in, he began to encourage and urge on the oarsmen to pull in to shore, and in this way, though with difficulty, we managed to touch bottom, and our companions leaped into the water, which reached to their armpits. There a great and fierce battle took place, because the Indians closed in on our Spaniards who defended themselves so bravely that it was a wondrous thing to see. This fighting lasted for more than an hour, for the Indians were not dismayed, rather they seemed to take heart, although they saw many of their comrades dead, and advanced over their bodies, and fell back only to attack anew. I wish to tell the reason these Indians defended themselves so stoutly. It should be known that they are vassals and tributaries of the Amazons, and when our approach became known, they went to them to ask for aid, and as many as ten or twelve of those women came, and we saw them leading all those Indians in the fighting like captains, and they fought so boldly that the Indians did not dare fall back, and if one of them attempted to retreat before us, they killed him with blows of their clubs, and this is the reason why the Indians defended themselves so bravely. These women are very white and tall, and have very long hair which they wear braided and wrapped around their head, and they are very strong and go naked except for their private parts, which are covered. With their bows and arrows in their hands they fight like ten Indians, and there was one among them who sent an arrow into one of the brigantines a handspan deep, and others less, so our boats looked like porcupines.

To return to the fight, Our Lord was pleased to give our companions strength and courage, and they killed seven or eight of these Amazons, which we saw with our own eyes, whereupon the Indians lost heart and were thrown back and scattered with heavy losses. But many reinforcements were coming from other villages, and they were sure to return, for they were sounding their war cries again, so the Captain ordered his men into the boats with all possible haste, for he did not want to put our lives in danger, and we went aboard, not without difficulty, for the Indians were attacking again, and besides a great fleet of canoes was coming over the water, so we set off downstream and left that land behind.

We had come a thousand and four leagues since we set out and left Gonzalo Pizarro, or probably more, and we did not know how far we were from the sea. In this village we have just spoken of we captured an Indian, a trumpeter, who was about thirty years old, and after we had taken him he began to tell the Captain many things about the land in the interior, and he took him along with us.

Going downstream, as I have said, we let ourselves drift with the current, for our men were so weary that they had no strength to ply the oars. When we had gone about the distance of a bowshot, we saw a good-sized village where there seemed to be no one, and for this reason all the men asked the Captain to put in there, where we might find something to eat, for in the village we had just passed they had not allowed us to get any food. The Captain told them he would rather not, for even though it seemed to them that it was deserted, it would be safer to take more precautions here than in a place where we could see the people. But we all asked him again, and I with our other comrades, as a boon, and although we had already passed the village, the Captain, yielding to our wishes, ordered the ships to turn back to the village, and as we went skirting the shore, the squadrons of Indians, who were concealed among the trees waiting to take us in ambush, were able to attack us, and they began to shoot at us with such ferocity that we could not see one another for the arrows. But as our Spaniards, after the battle with Machiparo, had provided themselves with good shields, they did not do us as much harm as if we had not been armed with this defense. No one was wounded in this village except myself. I received an arrow in the eye which went in and came out on the other side, as a result of which I lost an eye, and I am not without suffering and pain, although Our Lord, not that I deserve it, chose to spare my life that I might mend my ways and serve Him better than I had before. In this brief time the Spaniards in the smaller boat had leaped ashore, and as the Indians were so numerous, they had surrounded them, and if it had not been for the Captain's coming to their help in the large brigantine, they would have been lost, and the Indians would have taken them prisoners. They would have done this anyway before the Captain arrived, had they not fought so skillfully and resolutely, but they were tiring and in great distress. The Captain rescued them, and when he saw that I was wounded he ordered the men into the boats, and so we went aboard, for the Indians were many and so fierce that our men could not withstand them, and the Captain was afraid of losing some of them, and he did not want them to run such risks, for he knew how necessary their aid was to him, as this land was thickly settled, and the lives of all of us had to be defended, for there was not half a league from one village to another, and still less all along the right bank of the river, which is to the south. Moreover, inland, some two leagues, more or less, great cities could be seen gleaming white, and the land is as naturally good, and fertile as in our Spain, for when we came into it on St. John's day, the Indians were already beginning to burn over the fields. It is a temperate land, where much wheat could be harvested and all kinds of fruit raised; besides it is very suitable for the raising of cattle because it has many of the same plants as in our Spain, such as wild marjoram, and thistles, some colored and striped, and many other very good plants; in the woods of these lands there are evergreen oaks, and cork oaks that have acorns, for we saw them, and other oaks; the land lies high and rolling, and is covered with grass that grows no higher than the knee, and there is game of all varieties.

Returning to our voyage, the Captain ordered us to make for the middle of the river to get away from the settlements, which were so numerous that we were filled with fear. We called this province the province of San Juan, because it was on his day that we came into it. I had said Mass that morning as we came down the river in honor of this glorious forerunner of Christ, and I am convinced that it was through his intercession that God spared my life.

That night we were past all the settlements, and we made camp in an oak grove that stood on a broad plain beside the river. We were fearful and alert, because the Indians came to spy on us, and inland there were many villages and roads leading to them, and for this reason the Captain and all of us were on watch against what might befall us.

At this camp the Captain talked with the Indian I mentioned above whom we had taken prisoner, because he could understand him with a vocabulary he had made, and asked him where he was from. The Indian told him he came from that town where we had captured him. The Captain asked him the name of the lord of that land, and the Indian told him he was called Couynco, and that he was a great lord, and ruler of the lands as far as we had come, which, as I have said, was one hundred and fifty leagues. The Captain asked him who those women were that had come to help them and make war on us; the Indian answered that they were women who lived seven days' march inland, and that as this Couynco was their vassal they had come to defend the shore. The Captain asked if these women were married, and the Indian said no. The Captain asked him how they lived; the Indian answered that, as he had said, they lived inland, and that he had been there many times, and had seen how they lived and their homes, for as a vassal of theirs, he had gone there to carry tribute to them when his ruler sent him. The Captain asked him if there were many of these women; the Indian said there were, and that he knew by name seventy villages, and he called them before those of us who were there, and said he had been in some of them. The Captain asked him if the houses were built of straw; the Indian said no, that they were built of stone and had doors, and that roads fenced in on both sides led from one village to the other, and every so often along these roads there were guards posted so no one could enter without paying toll. The Captain asked him if these women bore children; the Indian said they did. The Captain asked him how they conceived if they were not married and no man dwelt among them; he replied that these women had relations with Indians at certain times, and when that desire comes upon them, they assemble a large war party and go out to make war on a very great lord who lives and has his lands contiguous to those of these women, and they bring the men to their lands by force, and keep them with them as long as they want them, and after they have conceived, they send them back to their own land without doing them further harm. When their time comes, if they bear a son they kill him and send him to his fathers; if the child is a daughter they raise her with great care and teach her all the arts of war. He went on to say that among all these women there is one who holds all the others under her sway and jurisdiction, and this lady is known as Coñori. He said that they possess great wealth of silver and gold, and that all the leading women of rank eat only off dishes of gold and silver, and the women of lower class eat out of wooden dishes, except for those in which they cook, which are of clay. He said that in the capital and principal city where the ruling woman lives, there are five great houses that are temples and houses dedicated to the sun, which they call Caranain, and that inside these houses there is wainscoting from the floor to half the height of a man, of thick gold panels covered with paintings of different colors, and many idols of gold and silver in the form of women, and many vessels of gold and silver for the service of the sun. The women wear clothing of finest wool, for in this land there are many sheep like those of Peru; their dress is a blanket clasped below their breasts and reaching to the ground, and on top of this they wear a kind of cloak fastened in front with cords. They wear their hair, which reaches to the ground, loose, and on their head crowns of gold two fingers high. He said it was forbidden for any male Indian to remain in any of these cities after the sun had gone down; and he added that in many provinces bordering on theirs the Indians were subject to them and had to pay them tribute and serve them, while with others they carried on war, especially with the one we have already spoken of, and they bring them in to have relations with them. These men are said to be very large and white and numerous, and the Indian said that all he had described he had seen many times, as one who came and went every day. Everything this Indian told us, and more besides, we had heard when we were six leagues from Quito, for they were well informed about these women there, and many Indians traveled a thousand leagues down the river to see them. For this reason the Indians back there had told us that the man who wanted to go to the land of these women must start as a boy and would return an old man. He said the land was cold and that there is little wood there, and that it abounds in all kind of food. He told us many other things, and each day he reveals more, for he is an Indian of intelligence and very wise, as are all the others in this land, as we have observed.

JOSÉ DE ACOSTA

(1539?–1600)

FATHER ACOSTA'S *Natural and Moral History of the Indies* occupies a place by itself in the books dealing with the New World. The earliest chroniclers, like Fernández de Oviedo, had described the wonders of the Indies and the customs of the natives, but their works were largely compendiums of curiosities. Then came the missionaries, who made a careful study of the customs and rites of the Indians, learned their languages, and studied their history on the basis of the records preserved by them, and from the accounts of the Indians themselves based on their traditions. Utilizing all this material, and his own observations during his fifteen years of work and travels in America, Father Acosta attempted to fit the phenomena of America into their proper setting in the body of universal knowledge. His was a scientific approach to the material, and his work merited the highest praise almost two hundred years later from a person of the insight and attainments of Baron Humboldt. He considered Father Acosta a forerunner in the study of magnetic variations, and said of him: "The magnetic lines of demarcation, whose discovery is attributed to Gassendi, were still a secret even to Gilbert, while Acosta, guided by the reports of Portuguese mariners, had already recognized the existence of four lines without declination over the entire surface of the earth. It was from these four lines that Halley deduced his theory of the four magnetic poles."

It was Acosta who first suggested that man had probably entered America from the north of Asia, crossing from the old to the new continent over some passage that made communication possible. This theory of his, which is still considered the most tenable, is all the more remarkable in view of the fact that the configuration of the continents was largely unknown when he wrote.

Father Acosta loved America, and his attitude toward the Indians anticipates that of his fellow Jesuit, Father Clavijero, by two hundred years. He becomes indignant at those who hold the Indians to be "a brutal and bestial race, devoid of reason," and shrewdly points out that this affords an excellent pretext to exploit and ill-treat them. One of the purposes of his book was to spread a knowledge of their achievements as the best method of combating this mistaken and harmful opinion. But he did not content himself with this. He took the position that a knowledge of their traditions and customs was indispensable to those who govern them, and that they should be allowed to maintain their traditional ways and their own laws in everything not in contradiction with the teaching of the faith.

Like Bernal Díaz del Castillo, Father Acosta was a native of Medina del Campo in the heart of Castile. He came to America in 1571, at the age of 31. He held important posts in his order in Peru, and in the course of his missionary activities traveled extensively through Peru and Mexico, where he had ample opportunity to supplement his source materials with first hand observations.

The *Natural and Moral History of the Indies* was one of the most widely read books of its day. Father Acosta's elegance and lucidity of style, his thoroughly assimilated erudition, lack of preconceived prejudices, and his remarkably modern attitude give his work an interest and freshness that time has not dimmed.

Of the omens and strange portents that took place
In Mexico before the fall of the Empire

[JOSÉ DE ACOSTA]

ALTHOUGH the Holy Scripture forbids us to give credence to omens and vain prophecies, and Jeremiah warns us not to be dismayed at the signs of Heaven, as are the heathen, nevertheless the Scripture itself does teach that in the case of certain changes in the world, and of punishments with which God wishes to chastise us, the omens are not to be ignored, and such events are often preceded by monsters and portents, as Eusebius Cesariense points out. For the Lord of Heaven and Earth orders such manifestations and harbingers in the heavens and elements and among animals and other of his creatures that they may serve in part as a warning to men, and in part as a foretaste of punishment through the fear and terror they cause. In the second book of Maccabees, it tells how before that great disaster and confusion of the children of Israel brought about by the tyranny of Antiochus, surnamed Epiphanes, whom the sacred writings call a wicked root, through all the city of Jerusalem, for the space almost of forty days, there were seen horsemen running in the air, in cloth of gold, and armed with lances, like a band of soldiers, and troops of horsemen in array, encountering and running one against another, with shaking of shields, and multitude of pikes, and drawing of swords, and casting of darts, and glittering of golden ornaments, and harness of all sorts. Wherefore every man prayed that that apparition might turn to good. In the Book of the Wisdom of Solomon it also tells how when God wished to bring his people out of Egypt and punish the Egyptians, they were troubled with strange apparitions, like fires kindled of themselves, very dreadful to see. Josephus, in his book, *The Jewish Wars*, tells of the many and awful omens that preceded the destruction of Jerusalem, and the final captivity of that unhappy people to whom God had so justifiably turned adverse. Eusebius Cesariense and others took this same relation from Josephus. It must also be pointed out that although the devil is the father of lies, notwithstanding the King of Glory often makes him confess the truth, and he himself out of fright or spite sometimes tells it of his own volition. Thus he cried out in the desert, and through the mouth of many possessed of a devil, that Jesus was the Saviour who had come to destroy him, and through the mouth of a certain damsel possessed with a spirit of divination that Paul was the servant of the True God, and he appeared to and tormented the wife of Pilate to make her intercede for Jesus, the righteous man. I have said all this intentionally, that no one may disdain the histories and annals of the Indians which tell of the strange omens and auguries that presaged the end of their kingdom and of the reign of the devil, both of which they adored. They seem to me worthy of credence, because they occurred in times so close at hand, the memory of which is still green, and because it is very reasonable that the crafty enemy of mankind should have feared and lamented when God began to punish such cruel and abominable idolaters. I so consider them, and for that reason I have set them down.

It came to pass that after Motezuma had reigned for many years with great prosperity, and was held in such reverence that he was served and feared and even adored like a god, the Almighty began to chastise him, and in part to warn him, by permitting those same demons whom he adored to give him the lugubrious forecast of the loss of his kingdom, and to torment him with portents unheard of before, until he became so melancholy and bewildered that he was beside himself. The idol of the Indians of Cholola, called Quetzalcoatl, foretold that strange people were coming to seize his kingdom. The king of Tezcuco, who was a great wizard and had a pact with the devil, came to visit Motezuma unexpectedly, and told him that his gods had informed him that great disasters and trials were in store for him and all his realm. Many magicians and soothsayers came to bring him the same news, and among these was one who told him in great detail all that later happened, and while he was talking to him, Motezuma noticed that he had neither thumbs nor big toes on his hands or feet. So exasperated was he by these forecasts that he ordered all the wizards imprisoned; but they quickly disappeared from prison, as a result of which Motezuma flew into such a rage that, unable to avenge himself on them, he ordered their wives and children put to death, and their houses and property destroyed. Harassed by these prophecies, he sought to placate the wrath of his gods, and for this purpose he ordered a huge stone brought in on which to offer up fierce sacrifices. But when many men attempted to move it with their ropes and tackle, they were unable to budge it, although in their attempts they broke many thick ropes. But as they still persisted they heard a voice that came from beside the stone telling them to desist their efforts, that they would never be able to move it because the Lord of the Universe was no longer willing that such things should pass. When Motezuma heard this, he ordered the sacrifices performed there. It is said that the voice was heard again, saying: "Have I not said that it is no longer the will of the Lord of the Universe that this be done? That you may convince yourselves that it is as I say, I shall let you carry me a little way, and then you will no longer be able to move me." And it happened that they moved it easily for a short space, and then they were unable to move it further, until after much supplication it allowed itself to be carried to the entrance of the city of Mexico, where it suddenly fell into a canal, and when they looked for it, they could not find it, for it had returned to the very spot from which they had brought it, where they found it again, which filled them with amazement and fear. About this same time there appeared in the sky a great and dazzling flame, pyramidal in shape, which came into view at midnight, rose higher in the sky, and at dawn, when the sun came up, reached the zenith and disappeared. It showed itself every night for the space of a year, and every time it appeared, the people gave loud howls, as was their habit, for they understood that it was an evil omen. Once, when there was no fire in all the temple, or outside it, and without thunderbolt or lightning, it burst into flame. The guards raised the alarm, and a multitude of people came with water, yet it availed nothing, and the temple was consumed. It was said that it seemed that the fire came out of the wood itself, and that the water made it burn more fiercely. They also saw a comet in the clear light of day, traveling from west to east and throwing off a cloud of sparks; it was said that it had the shape of a tail and what looked like three heads. The great lake that lies between Mexico and Tezcuco, one day when there was no wind or shaking of the earth, or any other reason, suddenly began to boil, and the water rose so that all the buildings near it fell to the ground. About this time it is said that cries were heard, as of a woman lamenting, saying sometimes: "Oh, my children, the hour of your destruction has arrived," and others, "Oh, my children, where can I hide you that you may not all perish?" A number of monsters with two heads appeared, and when they were brought before the king, they vanished. But of all these portents, two stand out above all the others: one was a bird the size of a crane and about the same color, but of a form strange and never beheld, which some fishermen had caught in a lake. They brought it to Motezuma, who at that time was in the palaces known as those of weeping and mourning, and all painted black, for just as he had different palaces for his pleasure, so he had them for times of grief, and his was very great because of the menacing warnings from his gods with their sad presages. The fishermen arrived just at noon, and brought into his presence that bird which had on the crest of its head something shinging and transparent like a mirror in which Motezuma saw the heavens and the stars appear, which amazed him very much, as he cast his eyes heavenward and saw that there were no stars in the sky. Looking into that mirror, he saw soldiers coming out of the east, armed, fighting and slaying. He ordered his soothsayers brought in, of whom he had many, and after they had seen what he saw and were unable to reply to the questions he asked them, the bird suddenly disappeared and was never seen again, which left Motezuma very sad and distressed. The other thing that happened was that a peasant, who was known as a kindly, simple man, came to speak with him, and told him that the day before while he was sowing his fields a great eagle came flying toward him, lifted him up without harming him, and carried him to a certain cave, where the eagle deposited him, saying: "Most powerful Lord, here I have brought you the one you sent me for." And the Indian looked all around him to see whom he was talking to, and he saw no one. Just then he heard a voice that said: "Do you know that man stretched out there on the floor?" And looking down, he saw a man in a deep sleep, with the royal insignia and flowers in his hand, and with a censer of perfume burning before him, as was the custom of the country, and the farmer recognized in him the great king Motezuma. The farmer replied, after looking at him: "Great Lord, this seems to me our king Motezuma." The voice was heard once more: "You have spoken the truth. Look at him, how he sleeps, heedless of the great trials and dangers that menace him; the hour has come for him to pay for his many offenses against God, and the tyranny of his overweening pride, and he is so unmindful of this, and so sodden in his blindness, that he realizes nothing. And to prove this to yourself, take that burning censer and apply it to his thigh, and you will see that he feels nothing. The poor farmer did not venture to do as he was bidden, because of the great fear in which they all stood of their king, but the voice spoke again: "Have no fear, for there is no comparison between me and this king. I can destroy him and protect you; therefore do as I have said." With this the peasant, taking the burning censer from the hand of the king, held it against his thigh, and the king neither moved nor displayed the least feeling. When he had done this, the voice said that since he had seen how deep in slumber the king was, he should go and awaken him, and relate to him all that had happened; and that the eagle, which had been sent by him, would carry him back to the place where it had found him. So in fulfillment of what he had been bidden, he had come to warn him. It is said that when he heard him, Motezuma looked at his thigh, and saw that it was burned. Until that moment he had felt nothing, and he fell into a state of great sadness and despair. It may have been that what the peasant told had happened to him in an imaginary vision. And it is not impossible that God had either ordered a good angel, or had permitted an evil angel, to give this rustic (even though he was a heathen) this warning to punish the king, for we read of similar apparitions in the Holy Scripture, like those that appeared to Gentiles or sinful men, such as Nebuchannezar and Balam, or Saul with the Witch of Endor. And even if these things did not happen exactly as they are related, there is no doubt that Motezuma was greatly affected and distressed by the many and different omens that his kingdom and his law were soon to come to an end.

MARTÍN DE MORUA

(Dates Unknown)

IF, AS A RESULT of the blind, shortsighted zeal of certain of the missionaries and priests who came out to America in the early days of the conquest, many invaluable native documents and records were destroyed with the object of more effectively stamping out idolatry among the Indian converts to Christianity, it was to the vision and understanding of others that we owe most of our knowledge of the history, customs, and traditions of the conquered peoples. The more intelligent among them realized that the only way to win the confidence of the new converts and to understand their psychology was to learn their languages and assimilate their culture. Among the galaxy of names such as Bernardino de Sahagún, Bartolomé de las Casas, José de Acosta, Pedro de Gante, that of Fray Martín de Moura is almost unknown. The reason may be that the manuscript of his work lay for centuries in the library of the Jesuits in Lima, and was not discovered until the end of the nineteenth century. Sir Clements R. Markham succeeded in obtaining a copy of the original on which he drew freely for his *History of Peru*. It is from his *Historia y genealogía real de los Reyes Incas del Peru, de sus hechos, costumbres, trajes y manera de gobierno* that this tale of the shepherd who loved the daughter of the Sun has been taken.

Little can be ascertained of Fray Martín's life and work. He was a Basque, from Azpeitia, a fellow townsman of St. Ignatius Loyola, founder of the Jesuit Order. He joined the Order of La Merced, and must have come out to America in the second half of the sixteenth century, for his book was completed in the year 1590. He was sent first to the city of Cuzco, where he served as priest and then vicar, and was later assigned to a little village called Capachica, on the shores of Lake Titicaca, where he spent many years teaching and converting the Indians and collecting the materials for his work.

Fray Martín must have heard this story from his Indian neophytes, and in his version of it he has preserved the charm and ingenuousness that undoubtedly accompanied the telling of the touching account of this pair of "star-crossed lovers," who, after a brief span of happiness, were turned to stone by the maiden's irate father, the Sun.

The Tale of a Famous Shepherd Called Acoya-napa
and the Beautiful and Discreet Princess Chuqui-Llanto,
Daughter of the Sun

[MARTÍN DE MORUA]

IN the high, snow-clad Sierra called Sabasiray that rises above the valley of Yucay, an Indian from Laris, by name Acoya-napa, tended the flock of white llamas the Incas sacrificed to the Sun. Acoya-napa was a fine, handsome youth who followed his flock, and while it grazed, played his flute, softly, sweetly, indifferent alike to the pleasures and pains of love.

It happened that one day as he was playing his flute there came to him two daughters of the Sun, who had dwellings throughout the earth and guards in all of them. These two daughters of the Sun could wander about the earth all day, gazing upon its green meadows, but they could never be absent from their homes at night, and when they entered them, the guards and shepherds looked them over carefully to make sure they were not bringing in anything that could do them harm. As we said, they came up to the shepherd, who was taking his ease, and had not seen them, and they asked him about the flock and the pastures.

The shepherd, who had not seen them approaching, though greatly confused, knelt before them, believing that they were the four famous crystal springs of the mountains that had taken, or manifested themselves in, human form, and he was unable to speak a word. But they asked him once more about his flock, and told him to have no fear, that they were the daughters of the Sun, the mistresses of all the earth, and to put him at his ease they took him by the arm and told him once more to have no fear. Finally the shepherd arose and kissed the hand of each, astounded by their great beauty, and after talking together enjoyably for a time, the shepherd said it was time to fold his flock, and asked their permission to do so. The older of the princesses, called Chuqui-llanto, had been much taken with the beauty and charm of the shepherd, and to prolong their talk, she asked him his name and where he was from. The shepherd answered that he was from Laris and his name was Acoya-napa. At this point she noticed a fillet of silver that he was wearing about his forehead, which the Indians call *campu*, which shone and rippled with great beauty, and she saw that at the base was a spider, and looking at it more closely, she saw that the spider was eating a heart. Chuqui-llanto asked him the name of that fillet of silver. The shepherd answered saying that it was called a *utusi*, and we have never been able to learn the meaning of this word, and it is amazing that he should have said what is known as *campu* was called *utusi;* there are those who say this means the virile organ, words that in olden times lovers used to invent; but whatever it means, let us get on with our story. The princess returned his *utusi* to the shepherd, and told him good-bye, bearing in her memory the name of the ornament and the spiders; she kept thinking how beautifully they were carved and how they seemed alive eating the heart as we have said. On the way home she talked with her sister about the shepherd until they reached their palace. As they entered, the *pongo camayos* or doorkeepers looked them over carefully to see if they were carrying anything that might harm them, for they had often found that some women carried their lovers inside their shawls, and others, in the beads of their necklaces, and fearing something of this sort, the doorkeepers examined them very carefully. Finally they passed into their palace, where they found the wives of the Sun waiting for them, with all the delicious things the earth yields cooked in pots of gold. Chuqui-llanto went into her room, saying she did not want anything to eat, and giving as an excuse that she was weary and exhausted from walking so much. All the others ate with her sister; if she gave any thought to Acoya-napa, it was not enough to upset her, although she did give a few sighs. But Chuqui-llanto was unable to find any repose because of the great love the shepherd Acoya-napa had aroused in her, and she suffered because she could in no way manifest what was in her heart. Like the very wise and shrewd woman she was, she finally lay down and went to sleep. In this dwelling, which was a great and sumptuous palace of the Sun, there were many richly furnished chambers in which dwelt the wives of the Sun, who came from the four provinces ruled by the Inca, Chinchay-suyo, Conde-suyo, Ante-suyo and Colla-suyo, and in the palace there were four fountains of sweet, crystalline water that welled up and flowed in four directions, and each woman bathed in the fountain that flowed toward her native province. The fountains were called after this manner: that of Chinchay-suyo, which was to the west, *Siclla-puquio*, which means fountain of the blue flower; that of Colla-suyo, which is to the east, *Llallacha-puquio*, which means fountain of the little fish. The one to the north, *Ocururu-puquio*, which means fountain of cress, and the other, to the south, *Chidra-puquio*, which means fountain of frogs. It was in these fountains that those we have spoken of bathed. To return to our story, the beautiful Chuqui-llanto, the daughter of the Sun, was sunk in a deep sleep and dreamed that she saw a nightingale fly from one tree to another, and wherever it came to rest, it sang very gently and sweetly, and after it had sung for some time with great harmony and delight, it settled in her lap, and told her to have no sorrow or sad thoughts. When the princess replied that she was sure she was going to die, and asked for a cure, the nightingale replied that it would help her, and to tell it what was troubling her. Then the princess told her of the great love that filled her heart for the shepherd of the white flock called Acoya-napa, and that she would surely die, for there was no cure for her ill but to see her beloved, and one of the wives of her father the Sun would surely learn of it and tell him, and he would order her killed. Whereupon the nightingale answered that she was to stand in the middle of the four fountains and sing the thing she remembered best, and that if the fountains were in accord and said the same thing that she had sung and spoken, then she could do as she wished, and saying this it departed, and the princess woke up in amazement, and swiftly dressed, and as everyone was sleeping soundly, she was able to get up without anyone hearing her, and she went and stood in the middle of the four fountains and began to say, recalling the spiders and the silver band on which the spiders were eating the heart: *Micuc usutucuyuc Utusi cusin*, which means "Spider eating the moving *utusi*." The four fountains at once began to repeat the same thing in chorus.

When the princess saw that the fountains were favorable to her, she went back to rest, for it was still night.

After the shepherd returned to his hut he could think of nothing but the great beauty of Chuqui-llanto, and with this care he began to grow sad, and the new love that was springing in his carefree, innocent breast made him long to know all the delights of love, and taking up his flute, he began to pipe so plaintively that the rocks were moved, and when he had finished playing it, so heavy was his heart that he fell to the ground like one dead, and when he came to himself, he said, shedding many tears, and making a loud lament: "Woe is thee, luckless and unhappy shepherd, joyless and afflicted, the day of thy death is at hand, for hope denies thee what thy desire longs for. What solace can there be for thee, poor shepherd, when it is impossible for thee even to see thy cure." With these words he returned to his hut, and exhausted and weary with his sufferings, he fell asleep.

This shepherd had a mother in Laris, who through magic means learned of the plight of her son and that his life would soon come to an end if some remedy were not found. When she knew the cause of his misfortune, she took up a beautiful and wonder-working staff, and without pause set out on the road to the mountains and traveled so swiftly that she reached the hut just as the sun was rising, and she went in and saw her son lying like a man dead, and his face covered with tears, and she came over to his side and aroused him, and when the shepherd opened his eyes and saw his mother, he began to weep bitterly. His mother comforted him as best she could, telling him not to grieve, for she would help him before many days had passed. With these words she left and began to gather nettles among the rocks, for these Indians believe them to be a cure for melancholy, and when she had gathered a great many of them, she put them on to cook, and before they were quite cooked, the two sisters, the daughters of the Sun, appeared in the doorway of the hut, for at break of day Chuqui-llanto had clad herself, and as soon as it was time to go out among the green fields of the highlands, she directed her steps toward the hut of Acoyanapa, because her tender heart was full of the thought of him. When they reached the hut they sat down beside the doorstep, wearied with their walk, and greeting the kindly old woman they saw within, asked her if she could give them something to eat. The old woman knelt before them and replied that she had nothing but a mess of nettles, which she seasoned and served to them, and they began to eat with great relish. Chuqui-llanto gazed about the room with tear-filled eyes, without revealing what she longed to see, and she did not see the shepherd, because just as they were approaching he had concealed himself within the staff, as his mother ordered. The princess thought he had gone out with his flock, and did not venture to ask for him. When she saw the staff she said to the old woman that it was a beautiful staff, and how had she come by it, and the old woman answered that the staff long ago had belonged to one of the women beloved of Pachacamac, a famous lord of the plains, and she had inherited it. When the princess heard this she begged her to give it to her, and finally the old woman did. She took it in her hands, and it seemed to her even more beautiful than before, and after spending a while in the hut, she took her leave of the old woman and wandered through the meadows, looking all around to see if she could discover the shepherd she loved so.

We pay little attention to the sister here, because she has nothing to do with our story, and so we shall deal here only with Chuqui-llanto, who grew sad and pensive when she could find him nowhere, and turned her steps homeward full of sorrow at not seeing him. As she entered the palace the guards looked her over carefully, as they always did when the princesses returned, and as they saw nothing new except the staff which she was carrying openly, they closed the doors after her, completely fooled. The princesses entered their chambers and were served there with a splendid, abundant dinner. Later in the evening they all went to bed, and Chuqui-llanto took her staff, and laid it beside her bed, because she admired it very much, and when she was in bed, thinking herself alone, she began to cry, remembering the shepherd and the dream she had dreamed. But she did not remain in this state long, for the staff had turned into the being it was before, and began to call Chuqui-llanto by her name. When she heard this she was greatly surprised, and getting out of bed, she went for a light, which she lighted without making a noise, and when she returned to her bed she saw the shepherd kneeling before her, shedding many tears, and she was amazed. When she made sure it was her shepherd she asked him how he had entered, and he answered that the staff she had carried made it possible. Then Chuqui-llanto embraced him and covered him with her blankets of embroidered gold and silver tissue, and he slept the night with her, and when day was breaking, he went into the staff once more, under the eyes of his Princess and Lady, who, when the sun was bathing all the earth, set forth from the palace of her father, walked through the meadows with her staff in her hand, and entered a ravine among the hills to be with her beloved shepherd who had taken on his human shape again. It so happened that one of the guards had followed her. Finally, although they were in a hidden spot, he came upon them, and when he saw what was happening, he began to shout, and when they heard him, they fled toward the mountains that rise above the village of Calca. Wearied and footsore, they sat down upon a cliff, and there they fell asleep. They were awakened by a great noise and sprang up, she with one sandal in her hand and the other on her foot, looking toward the village of Calca, and they were both turned to stone, and today the two statues may be seen, from Guallabamba and Calca, and many other spots, and I have seen them many times. Those mountains were known as Pitu Siray, and are still so called in our own times.

JOSÉ GUMILLA

(1687–1750)

ALTHOUGH IT WAS not until 1705 that Father Gumilla came out to America, he may fittingly be considered one of the discoverers of the new land, for the basin of the Orinoco, where he was assigned to carry on his missionary work, was the pristine jungle of pre-Discovery days, which much of it still remains. Father Gumilla arrived in Santa Fe de Bogotá from Spain with forty-three other Jesuits when he was only eighteen years old. He spent ten years completing his religious training there, and the remaining thirty-five years in that "green hell."

No explorer would think of entering the Orinoco region today without full medical and scientific equipment; yet Gumilla and his little band of missionaries endured the merciless tropical heat, venomous insects, snakes, wild animals, and the hostile Indians unaided except by their faith and zeal to save the souls of the heathen. He founded six villages along the upper Orinoco, inducing the nomadic Indians to settle there, he studied the native languages, rites and customs, he planted the first coffee trees in this region, and he found time to write one of the most entertaining books containing his observations and experiences, *El Orinoco Ilustrado*.

Never was there such an "elephant's child." His curiosity was insatiable, and his conclusions at times reveal astonishing scientific intuition intermingled with an ingenuousness that is almost incredible in a man of his ability. His theories on the origin of man in America, his stubborn conviction that the Indians are descendants of the ten lost tribes of Israel, in support of which he adduces the most farfetched proof, are in marked contrast to the discerning hypothesis of Father Acosta who preceded him by more than a hundred years. But in his observation of the reality by which he is surrounded, his unflagging interest, his eye for detail he is unequaled. No more graphic account of the manufacture of *curare*, that deadly venom with which the Indians tipped their arrows, has ever been set down than in the selection that follows. He died among the Indians of the Orinoco, whom he sincerely loved in spite of the fact that at times they exasperated him beyond endurance with their stubbornness and their backsliding, in the jungle with which he had so completely identified himself.

How the Indians Make Curare

[JOSÉ GUMILLA]

THE cursed serpent, not satisfied with having infected the whole of mankind with his foul and mortal poison from the days of the Garden of Eden, never wearies or abates his sinister designs, spewing forth new forms of death for sin-ridden souls and bodies in the poisons with which he tempts persons of reason and judgment, and with the hidden venoms he discovered and revealed to the blinded natives of the Orinoco and others like them. I say this in all seriousness and sincerity, for when, from my own observation, I compare the mysterious secrets of some of these poisons with the limited capacity and complete lack of reasoning power of those ignorant Indians, I come to the conclusion, which I think is warranted, that the knowledge and process of manufacture of these poisons cannot have come from their feeble intelligence or their rude industry. These deadly weapons proceed from the implacable hatred with which our common enemy regards the human race, whose complete destruction would be his greatest joy. The demonstration of the fact will be the best proof of my assertion.

The Caberres, the most inhuman, brutish, and bloodthirsty of all the tribes that inhabit the valley of the Orinoco, have a monopoly of the most deadly poison, in my opinion, to be found on the face of the globe. This tribe alone holds the secret, and it manufactures it, and receives a rich income from the other tribes who themselves, or through some third party, come to buy the *curare*, which is the name by which it is called. It is sold in little pots or vessels of clay. The largest of these holds about four ounces of this poison, which is similar in color to boiled honey. It has no taste, nor is it especially bitter. It can be taken into the mouth and swallowed without any danger, provided there is no open wound on the gums or in any other part of the mouth, for all its activity and strength is directed against the blood, to such an extent that for it to touch one drop of blood and curdle all the rest in the body with the speed of lightning is all one. It is amazing to see how a wound from an arrow dipped in *curare*, even though the scratch is no bigger than that of a pin, will make all the person's blood clot, and he dies before he can say the name of Jesus three times.

A soldier, who was later an officer of the guard of our missions, from Madrid, by the name of Francisco Macías, a brave, courageous man, a great student of the nature and properties of plants and animals, and even of insects, was the one who first told me of the instantaneous action of *curare*. I withheld judgment, and waited to see for myself. It happened that a band of yellow monkeys soon came along, which the Indians consider very good eating and which are known in their language as *arabata*. All the Indians got ready to shoot as many as they could. I called one Indian aside and asked him to shoot a monkey that was standing on a palm frond, holding onto the leaf above it with its left paw. It raised its right paw in a movement to try to pull out the arrow (as they do when these are not dipped in *curare*) but even as it made the gesture, without time to get its paw on the arrow, it dropped dead to the foot of the palm tree. I ran over, and, although it was not far away, all the warmth had departed from the outside of the body. I asked to have it cut open from the breast down, and I could find no trace of warmth, not even in the heart itself. Around this organ there was a large quanity of coagulated blood, dark and cold; there was hardly any blood in the rest of the body, and the little I found in the liver was like that around the heart. The outside of the body was covered with an orange-covered cold foam, and I came to the conclusion that the intense cold induced by the *curare* instantly chills the blood, and that this seeks refuge in the heart; not finding sufficient warmth there, it clots and freezes, and this causes the victim to die more quickly, as the heart is smothered.

While I was watching, the Indian cut the monkey into pieces, put it into a pot, and set it to cooking, and the other Indians did the same with their monkeys. My amazement did not come from the fact that they ate that flesh, or because it was a monkey, or because it had been killed by poison. What astounded me was that those clots of blood that contained all the force of the poison also went into the pots and afterwards into the stomachs of the Indians. I asked them a number of questions, and so satisfied was I with their answers that that same day I ate the liver one of them was cooking (and it is as delicious as that of the tenderest suckling pig, unless my hunger deceived me), and from then on, whenever there was a similar encounter with monkeys, I always asked for a liver as my share of the spoils.

I saw the same instantaneous effect of *curare* on jaguars, deer, pumas, and many other wild animals and birds. So powerful is it that an Indian is not frightened even when he comes on a jaguar face to face. Calmly he takes out his arrow, takes aim, and shoots, certain that he will not miss his mark, and even more certain that he has only to wound the animal lightly on the tip of the nose or in any other part of the body and it will give one or two leaps and drop dead.

In view of this unheard-of and deadly poison, and the ease with which all the tribes along the Orinoco and its broad basin manage to secure it, I cannot refrain from giving praise to the infinite providence of the Almighty and calling upon all to bless His fatherly mercy for having so arranged things that those savages should not be fully aware of the invincible weapon they have in their *curare*. Which missionary, which Spaniard, which soldier, could live among them if they did not prefer to the silent fury of their arrows and *curare* the contingent noise of a gun? I say contingent, because of the flint that may not strike; of the aim that is not certain; because of the rain that may put it completely out of condition, when, on the contrary, for the *curare*-dipped point, there is no antidote, no cure, not even time to commend one's soul to God. I say without cure or antidote, because even though an innocent boy revealed to Father Juan Rivero that if one has salt in his mouth *curare* cannot harm him, which he found to be true by performing several experiments on animals, this remedy is not practical for men, because how can they stand salt in their mouth for a long time? And if they have it in their knapsack, the poison does not give them time to get it out.

We have seen, not without astonishment, the unerring power of *curare*. Now let us see the strange process of its preparation. All the poison of *curare* comes from a root by the same name, and such a strange, unique root that it is only root, never producing leaves or stalk, and although it grows, it is always hidden, as though it were afraid to show its secret malignance. And the better to hide itself, it has sought, or the Creator has assigned it, not such soil as other plants commonly grow in, but the fetid, rotten slime of those bayous that have no outlet and whose waters are never drunk except in case of dire necessity, because they are heavy, dark, foul-tasting, and equally malodorous. In the putrid slime upon which these pestilential waters rest, there comes into being and grows the root of the *curare*, a fit offspring of such foul origins. The Caberre Indians dig up these roots, which are brownish in color, and after washing them and breaking them into pieces, they pound them up and put them into large pots over a slow fire. For this task they select the most useless old woman of the tribe, and when she drops dead from the effects of the fumes given off by the brew, as generally happens, they pick another like her in her place. These women make no protest about the work, nor does the community or their relatives object; they all know that this is what old women are for. As the water grows warmer, the poor old woman kneads her death, going from pot to pot and squeezing and stirring the macerated roots, so they can the more freely yield up their poison, and the juice begins to color the water, which must remain tepid, until it is the shade of light honey. Then the old woman, with such feeble strength as she possesses, squeezes the last juice from the roots into the brew and throws them away, useless now, and then adds wood to the fire, and the brew begins to boil hard. After the pots have boiled for a little while, she drops dead, overcome by the fumes, and the second one takes charge. Sometimes the latter escapes with her life, sometimes not.

When the brew has cooked down to its proper consistency and concentration, which is when about one third of the liquid has evaporated, the unfortunate cook calls out, and the chief, accompanied by his captains and all the other people of the village, hastens up to examine the *curare* and see if it is ready or not. (And this is the most astonishing thing about this whole strange operation). The chief dips the end of a stick in the *curare*, and at the same time one of his braves, with the point of a sharp bone, cuts himself in the leg, thigh, or arm (wherever he feels like), and when the blood begins to flow from the wound, the chief holds the point of the stick dipped in *curare* near it. He does not touch it, or bring the *curare* in contact with the blood; he just puts it near it, because if he should touch the blood and it should shrink back, it would infect all the veins and the patient would die at once. If the blood that was about to flow out draws back, the poison is ready; if it remains at the mouth of the wound and does not draw back, it is almost ready; but if the blood flows out, as it naturally would, it needs more cooking. In this case they order the poor old woman to continue with her deadly task, and then they test it again until the blood's drawing back violently from its enemy gives them proof that the *curare* has reached its maximum strength.

If some famous botanist had discovered this root and learned its secret malignancy, it would be nothing to wonder at. If the famous Tritemio or Borri or one of those learned inventors of chemistry, as a result of their experiments and studies, had finally hit upon this singular process, they would deserve great praise, and it would be looked upon as the outcome of their cultivated understanding. But who can believe that all this should be the invention of the most uncouth and barbarous tribe of the whole Orinoco River without admitting that the whole thing, from the discovery of the root to the completion of the poison, was the work of the devil? This is what I believe.

It is also worth remarking how this poison preserves its properties, the obstinancy with which it maintains all its vigor and strength until it is completely used up, even though the Indians take no special precautions with it, not even covering the little pots in which they buy it, and it does not evaporate or lose one iota of its mortal powers. This is surprising, but, after all, as it is there together, and in concentrated form, it is not so strange that it should preserve all its potency. What is most remarkable is that once the arrow points are daubed with it, even though the amount used is so small that each tip receives no more than a smear, yet that small quantity maintains and preserves all its strength for many years, as many as it takes the owner of the arrows to use them up. Until now, so far as is known, no matter how many years these poisoned arrows lie exposed without any protection, the strength of the deadly *curare* does not abate. I noticed one thing, however, on several of my trips through those jungles, and this was that when the Indians took their arrows out of their quivers to kill a monkey or a wild boar, or in case of sudden attack, they always put the poisoned tip in their mouth before fitting the arrow to the bow. When I asked them the reason for this (impelled by my insatiable and natural curiosity), they always answered that with the warmth of the mouth and the moisture of the saliva the powers of the *curare* were activated and the effects of the shot surer, which struck me as being very natural.

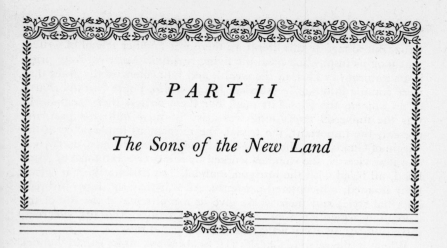

PART II

The Sons of the New Land

THE DISCOVERERS begat children, some pure Spanish, most of mixed blood, the first sons of the New Land, and the epoch of the colony, which was to last three hundred years, had begun. Under the organization and institutions Spain quickly set up, the colony presented a uniform, seemingly static exterior; but beneath the surface the life forces were busily at work, fusing the various racial elements, bringing about adjustments to the new conditions, creating a new type of human being, with an outlook and psychology of his own.

It is not surprising that the descendants, physical or spiritual, of men so given to the written word should have shown literary inclinations. There were many of this first generation who still had strong ties with the Indian world that was disappearing. They had known it in its twilight, and they set down their memories of it, not as something external, but as a precious heritage they bore within themselves. Where the great Indian civilizations had flourished—the Mayan, the Aztec, the Incan—there was an abundance of this type of literature. Sometimes, as in the case of the *Popol Vuh*, it was the reproduction of traditional native literature; sometimes, as in the case of the Inca Garcilaso or Alva Ixtlilxochitl, and so many others, the history of their Indian past based on the tales they had heard from their elders.

As the great urban centers developed, the literary life of the colony flourished. For the most part this literature was a sterile imitation of the rolling periods of classic Spanish literature or the baroque metaphors of Gongora, although occasionally it produced figures like Ruiz de Alarcón, one of the brightest stars in the galaxy of dramatists of the Golden Age, or the exquisitely endowed poetess, Sor Juana Inés de la

Cruz. But alongside this literature there was another school of writers that took its inspiration from the living reality of America, from pride in its natural beauties, in the wealth and refinement of the cities that were coming into being—Mexico, Lima, Quito, Potosí—in the charm of its women, the wit of its men. For these writers their local world was the universe. Everything was grist for their mill: the past, the present, the important, the trivial, the miraculous appearance of the Virgin of Guadalupe, the taking-off of an impenitent sinner, the arrival of a new viceroy, the wonders worked by saints or candidates to saint-hood, all laced with the intrigue, scandal, and tittle-tattle that spiced their isolated, self-centered existence. All this they set down in brisk, informal style, and their works give us a real sense of the life of the colony in which all were collaborating: whites, Indians, Negroes, mixed bloods, of every walk and of every social rank.

When, in the reign of Charles III, Spain shook off its lethargy under the influence of the Enlightenment, the freshening winds blew through America, too. New ideas and new learning spread through the colonies, informing every field of intellectual activity. America began to acquire an awareness of herself and grow restive under the subservient role assigned her by the Europe of the eighteenth century. We find the writers of this period rising to vigorously refute the allegations of the school of thought exemplified in men like Buffon, Raynal, and De Pauw, which was bent on demonstrating America's innate inferiority as compared with Europe. In support of their rebuttal these Americans proudly evaluate their own past, supporting their defense with ex-amples drawn from their native heritage. The American chrysalis was getting ready to break its cocoon.

The Popol Vuh

IT IS NOT SURPRISING that the most important document of American antiquity we possess should be of Mayan origin. None of the native peoples on this continent achieved the degree of civilization the Mayas did. They were in advance of the Egyptians in their knowledge of astronomy; they had worked out the calendar; in sculpture and ar-chitecture they were far ahead of the Aztecs and the Incas; only the finest of Peruvian fabrics can be compared with their textiles; it is to them that we probably owe the development of corn from the wild grasses of the Guatemalan plateau, nor can modern agricultural experts suggest improvements in their methods of cultivation of this vital American cereal. And, perhaps most important of all, they had worked out an industrious, prosperous, equitable way of life, without the fierce imperialism of the Aztecs or the regimented collectivism of the Incas.

After the destruction of Utatlán, the capital of the Quiché kingdom, by Pedro de Alvarado when he suspected that an ambush was being prepared for him there, many of the leading families of the Quichés, one of the most important branches of the Mayas, took refuge in Chichicastenango, in the central highlands of Guatemala. They were a peaceable people who were quickly converted to Christianity by the missionaries, and the town has been an important Indian center ever since.

There in the late seventeenth and early eighteenth century lived a priest of the Dominican Order, Father Francisco Ximénez. During his long cure, by his kindliness, understanding, and real affection for his Quiché flock, he won their trust, and they finally showed him a book they guarded with the greatest secrecy. It was the *Popol Vuh*, variously known as the *Book of the Counsels*, the *Book of the Commune*, the *National Book of the Quichés*, and sometimes referred to as the Mayan Bible.

This book was written shortly after the conquest, around 1550, by a Quiché who had learned to read and write Spanish. It was in the Quiché language, but transcribed in Latin characters instead of the hieroglyphics employed by the Indians. It contains the Quiché myths of the creation of the universe, their traditions, their history and the genealogy of their kings. Beneath the surface of their newly acquired Catholicism, and to a large extent blended with it, the Indians preserved the living memory of their past. As Father Ximénez says: "They drew in these tales and beliefs with their mother's milk, and nearly all of them knew them by heart." And he adds: "Of these books they possessed many."

The identity of the author is a mystery, and the book had remained hidden for a hundred and fifty years until it was shown to Father Ximénez, sometime between the years 1701 and 1703. Being thoroughly conversant with the Quiché tongue, which, in his opinion, far from being a barbarous language, "was the finest there has been in the world," he transcribed the text and made a translation of it into Spanish. The original Quiché version disappeared, but Father Ximénez's transcription and translation in his own handwriting still exists and is the source of our knowledge of this work.

In 1851 the French priest, Brasseur de Bourbourg, during one of his trips to Central America, came upon the work of Father Ximénez, and brought the *Popol Vuh* to the attention of the world. In 1861 he published a French translation of the work, based on Father Ximénez's original. A German translation by Noah Elieser Pohorilles appeared in 1913, and in 1925 Professor Georges Raynaud brought out a new French translation. There have been several modern Spanish translations, that of Villacorta and Rodas, published in 1927, and that of Adrian Recinos, former Guatemalan Ambassador to the United States, in 1947. No complete translation has yet appeared in English, although one is now in preparation based on a new translation being made from Quiché into Spanish.

The following selection is the foreword and the first of the traditions that comprise the book.

Foreword

This is the beginning of the ancient accounts of this region known as Quiché. Here we shall set down and start the ancient accounts, the beginning and the origin of all that was done in the city of Quiché by the tribes of the Quiché nation.

Here we shall set forth the manifestation, the disclosure, and the narration of that which was hidden, the revelation by *Tzacol, Bitol, Alom, Quaholom*, known as *Hunahpú-Vuch, Hunahpú-Utiú, Zaqui-Nimá-Tziís, Tepeu, Gucumatz, u Qux Cho, u Qux Paló, Ah Raxá Lac, Ah Raxá Tzel*, as they were called. And the joint declaration, the narration of the Grandmother and the Grandfather, by name *Ixpiyacoc* and *Ixmucané*, guardians and protectors, doubly grandmother, doubly grandfather, so known in the Quiché narrations, as they all recounted them, and, moreover, all that they did in the dawn of existence, in the dawn of history.

We shall write this now in the Law of God, in Christenhood; we shall disclose it because the *Popol Vuh*, so-called, is no longer seen, in which the coming from the other side of the sea and the account of our darkness are clearly seen, and the vision of life.

The original book, written long ago, existed, but the sight of it is hidden from the investigator and the thinker. Great was the description and the account of how all the sky and the earth was formed, how it was formed and divided into four parts, how it was separated and the sky was measured and the measuring cord was brought and was stretched out in the sky and on the earth, in the four angles, in the four corners, as it was spoken by the Creator and the Maker, the mother and the father of life, of all creation, he who gives breath and thought, who causes children to come forth, who keeps watch over the happiness of the nations, the happiness of mankind, the wise one, who takes thought for all that exists in the sky, on the earth, in the lakes, and in the sea.

Chapter I

THIS is the account of how all was in suspense, in calm, in silence; all was motionless, mute and void the expanse of the sky.

This is the first relation, the first narrative. There was as yet no man, neither an animal, birds, fish, crabs, trees, stones, caves, ravines, grass, or forest. Only the sky existed.

The face of the earth had not yet been revealed. Only the sea was in calm and the sky in all its expanse.

Nothing was joined together that made a noise, nor anything that moved or stirred or made a noise in the sky.

Nothing was upright; there was only the water in repose, the sea placid, alone, at rest. There was nothing endowed with existence.

There was only still and silence in the darkness, in the night. Only the Creator, the Maker, Tepeu, Gucumatz, the Engenderers, were in the water encircled by light. They were hidden under green and blue feathers, for this reason they are called Gucumatz. Great sages, great thinkers, that is their nature. After this fashion existed the sky and likewise the Heart of the Sky, which is the name of God and thus is He called.

Then came the word, Tepeu and Gucumatz met, in the darkness, in the night, and they talked together, Tepeu and Gucumatz. They talked, they took counsel with one another and meditated; they came to an understanding, they combined their words and their thought.

Then it became clear, as they meditated, that with the break of day man should appear. Then they arranged for the creation and growth of the trees and the vines and the beginning of life and the creation of man. In the shadows and in the night it was so arranged by the Heart of the Sky, who is called *Huracán*.

His first manifestation is known as *Caculhá Huracán*. The second is *Chipi-Caculhá*. The third is *Raxa-Caculhá*. And these three are the Heart of the Sky.

Then Tepeu and Gucumatz met; then they took counsel with one another concerning life and light, what should be done that it might grow light and day break, who should be the one to provide food and sustenance.

"Let it be done so. Let the void be filled. Let this water recede and make room, let the earth come forth and find a firm rest." Thus they spoke. "Let there be light, let the day break in the heavens and on the earth. There will be no glory nor greatness in our creation and formation until human beings exist, the created man."

Thus they spoke when the earth was created by them. Verily this is how the creation of the earth came to pass. "Earth," they said, and at once there was earth.

Like mist, like a cloud, like a column of dust, was the creation, when the mountains emerged from the waters, and at once the mountains rose on high.

Only by a miracle, only by magic art was the formation of the mountains and the valleys accomplished; and at once the groves of cypress and pine sprang up together on the surface.

And Gucumatz was filled with joy, saying: "Thy coming has been good, Heart of the Sky; thou, *Huracán*, and thou, *Chipi-Caculhá, Raxa-Caculhá.*"

"Our work, our creation will be concluded," they replied.

First the earth was formed, the mountains and the valleys; the streams of water were separated, the brooks went running freely between the hills, and the waters were divided when the high mountains appeared.

After this fashion was the creation of the earth, when it was formed by the Heart of the Sky, the Heart of the Earth, for by these names those who first generated it are known, when the sky was in a state of suspense and the earth lay submerged within the water.

After this fashion their labor was perfected, when they carried it out after thinking and meditating upon its felicitous conclusion.

GARCILASO DE LA VEGA, INCA

(1539–1616?)

EIGHT YEARS AFTER the Spaniards had conquered Peru, the most gifted, and in a sense the most pathetic of the sons of the new land, the Inca Garcilaso de la Vega was born. His father, Garcilaso de la Vega, was of a noble Andalusian family, a kinsman of the great poet of the same name; although not of the original group that accompanied Francisco Pizarro, he arrived in Peru three years later while the conquest was still under way. His mother was Isabel Palla Huailas, the daughter of the Inca Tupac Yupanqui, brother of Huayna Capac, the last ruler of the Incan empire before the fratricidal struggle for power between his sons Atahuallpa and Huascar began, and with it the end of the empire.

Garcilaso de la Vega received an education befitting the son of a gentleman. He was trained in fencing, equitation, and from the canon of Cuzco, Juan de Cuellar, received a thorough knowledge of the humanities. In his mother's home, as he himself relates, he learned from her and the relatives who came to visit them the Quechua tongue and the glories of the vanished greatness of their ancestors. From his father and his friends he heard again and again the exploits of the conquest, "for in those times their most frequent and usual conversation was re-telling the most notable and boldest episodes that had taken place during their conquests."

Shortly after his father's death, when only nineteen, Garcilaso left Peru for Spain. His father had supported Gonzalo Pizarro in his re-bellion against the crown, and as a result his property was confiscated. One of the objects of Garcilaso's trip to Spain was to petition to have his father's property restored to him. The litigation dragged on, as so often happened in claims of this sort, but the petition was never approved. Garcilaso then turned to one of the two professions for which he was fitted, arms. He fought with the troops of Don Juan de Austria in the campaign against the descendants of the Moors in Granada, rising to the rank of captain. But his real vocation was literature. He retired to Córdoba, where he devoted the rest of his life to study and writing. He never returned to Peru.

His first work was a translation into Spanish of the *Dialoghi di Amore*, one of the outstanding works of the Renaissance, by the expelled Spanish Jew Leon Hebreo (Judah Abrabanel). Fifteen years later he published *La Florida del Inca*, the history of Hernando de Soto's ex-pedition to Florida; and then his masterpiece, *Comentarios reales de los Incas*, Part I, 1602–1604; Part II, 1610–1611. Like the Mexican play-wright Ruiz de Alarcón, who was able to compete on equal terms in Spain with writers like Lope de Vega, Tirso de Molina, and the other great writers of the Golden Age, the Inca Garcilaso won the distinction to which his gifts entitled him among the greatest writers Spain has ever produced.

Garcilaso was an eyewitness of the death of the Incan empire, and the establishment of Spanish dominion over the land of his forefathers. He saw the native masters transformed into serfs and the adventurers become powerful and proud. But in his beautiful, nostalgic account of the history and achievements of his Indian forebears, there is no rancor or bitterness. There are sadness and sorrow for a past that was gone, but he sees and judges with honesty and discernment. One thinks of him, an old man, far from the land of his youth, soothing his home-sickness with this *recherche du temps perdu.* His is the first great work by an American, and it is rightly considered, by reason of its elegance of style, its purity and perfection of language, and the unique insight it affords into a stirring moment of history, a classic of Spanish literature.

What justification there is in fact for his account of the discovery of the New World by Sánchez de Huelva, eight years before Columbus's first voyage, has been widely disputed, but the story was current at the time. *The Strange Adventure of Pedro Serrano* anticipates Robinson Crusoe's experiences by more than a hundred years. And in *The Famous Shrine of Titicaca* he gives a shrewd interpretation of the appearance of the first Inca.

How the New World Was Discovered

[GARCILASO DE LA VEGA, INCA]

ABOUT the year 1484, one more, one less, a pilot of the town of Huelva in the domain of the Counts of Niebla, by name Alonso Sánchez de Huelva, had a little vessel in which he commerced, taking from Spain to the Canary Islands merchandise that sold well there, carrying produce from the Canary Islands to the island of Madeira, and then returning to Spain with a cargo of sugar and preserves. Once while engaged in this his three-way trade, as he was crossing from the Canary Islands to the island of Madeira he was caught in such a wild and roaring tempest that, unable to make any headway against it, he was at its mercy, and was carried along for twenty-eight or twenty-nine days knowing neither where nor whither, for in all this time he was unable to take his bearings either by the sun or by the North Star. The crew suffered greatly from the storm, for it permitted them to neither eat nor sleep. After this long time the wind died down, and they found themselves near an island, nobody knows exactly which, but it is believed that it was the one known as Santo Domingo. This is a strange thing, for the wind that drove that ship on with such violence could have been none other than the Sunwind, commonly called East wind, for the island of Santo Domingo is to the west of the Canary Islands, and this wind on such trips tends to calm storms rather than blow them up. But when the Almighty wishes to perform a deed of mercy, He often works those most mysterious and necessary through their very opposite, as when He drew water from a rock, and returned his sight to the blind man by the mud He laid upon his eyes, that they may be the more manifestly recognized as acts of divine pity and kindness. So He also by His mercy sent His teachings and true light to all the New World, which was so greatly in need of it, for it dwelt, or to be more exact, was languishing in the night of Gentilism and idolatry, barbarous and bestial, as we shall see in the course of this account. The pilot went ashore, took his bearings, and wrote a careful account of all that he saw and all that had happened on the voyage, both going and coming. After taking aboard water and wood, he found his way back, for neither going nor coming, did he know his course, and because of the length of the trip they ran short of water and supplies, for which reason, and because of the trials they had undergone, both coming and going, they began to sicken and die, so that of seventeen men that set out from Spain, only five returned, among them the pilot Alonso Sánchez de Huelva. They came to the house of the famous Christopher Columbus, the Genoese, because they knew that he was a great pilot and cosmographer, and that he made mariners' maps. He received them very kindly, and treated them with great consideration to learn of the things that had happened to them on such a long and strange journey as they told him they had undergone. And as they were in so sorry a state from their sufferings, in spite of everything Christopher Columbus did for them, they did not recover their health, and they all died in his house, leaving him as a legacy the trials that had brought about their death, and that the great Columbus accepted with such courage and resolution that although he suffered others as great, and even greater (for they lasted longer), he succeeded in his effort to give the New World and its treasures to Spain, as he said in the motto on his arms: *A Castilla y a León, Nuevo Mundo dió Colón.* Anyone who wishes to know the great feats of this man should read the *Historia General de Las Indias,* written by Francisco López de Gómara, and he will find them there, though in abbreviated form. I have desired to add this detail, which is missing in the relation of that old historian, who as he wrote far from the spot where these things took place, and heard them from those who came and went, they told him many of the things that happened, but not all. I heard them in my own land from my father and his contemporaries, for in those times their favorite conversation was retelling the most notable and boldest episodes that had taken place during their conquests. They related this we have spoken of, and others we shall tell further on, for as they had known many of the first discoverers and conquerers of the New World, they had heard from them the complete account of such things. As I say, I heard these things from my elders without paying too much attention (being only a child); if I had been more attentive, I could now write many other noteworthy things as befits this account. I shall set forth those I have kept in my memory, lamenting those I have lost. The Very Reverend Father José de Acosta also mentions this tale of the discovery of the New World, but, unfortunately, not in its entirety, for His Reverence lacked a part of the relation of this incident, as have other later writers, for the early conquistadors were gone when His Reverence came out to those lands. It is to this that his words in Book I, Chapter 19 refer: "As it has been demonstrated that it is idle to think that the first inhabitants of the Indies went there sailing a set course for this purpose, it is evident that if they came by sea, it was by chance and as the result of storms that they reached the Indies, which, despite the expanse of the Ocean Sea, is not an incredible thing. For this is what happened in our own days, when that mariner (whose name we still do not know, that such an enterprise may be attributed to none other than God) having as the result of a terrible and unforeseen storm glimpsed the New World, left to Christopher Columbus, in payment of his kind hospitality, the news of so great a thing. Thus it may have been," etc. This is from Father Acosta, as he set it down, wherein His Reverence reveals that he had learned a part of our relation in Peru, and although not all, the most essential part of it. This was the first beginning and the origin of the discovery of the New World, and the credit for this achievement goes to the little town of Huelva, which raised up such a son. Christopher Columbus, convinced by his tale, persisted so in his demands, promising things never before seen or heard, and like a prudent man, keeping the secret of them to himself, although in confidence he related them to certain persons of great influence with Their Catholic Majesties, who assisted him in his undertakings. For if it had not been for this information given him by Alonso Sánchez de Huelva, he would not have been able, merely through his knowledge of cosmography, to promise so much, and with such certainty, as he did, or to have carried out so expeditely the enterprise of the discovery. For, according to Father Acosta, it took Columbus only sixty-eight days to make the voyage to the island of Guanatianico, even though he stopped several days at Gomera to take on provisions; if he had not known from the report of Alonso Sánchez what route to follow in so vast a sea, it would have been almost a miracle for him to have arrived there in so short a time.

The Famous Shrine of Titicaca
and Its Fables and Legends

[GARCILASO DE LA VEGA, INCA]

AMONG the famous temples in Peru dedicated to the sun there was one that rivaled that of Cuzco in ornamentation and in wealth of gold and silver, on an island known as Titicaca, which means ridge of lead. It is made up of two words, *titi*, lead, and *caca*, ridge. Both syllables of the word *caca* must be pronounced far back in the throat, for if the letters are given the Spanish pronunciation, it means uncle, mother's brother. The lake known as Titicaca, where the island is situated, took its name from the island, which is two bowshots distant from the mainland. The island is about five or six thousand feet in circumference, and the Incas say that the Sun put his son and daughter there when he sent them to earth to enlighten the wild and barbarous people who inhabited the land at that time, and to teach them a better way of living. To this fable they add another that antedates it by centuries. They say that after the flood the rays of the sun were first seen on that island and that great lake before they appeared anywhere else. The lake is seventy and eighty fathoms deep in places and has a circumference of eighty leagues. Father Blas Valera wrote that it was impossible for ships to navigate its waters because of the quantity of lodestone they contain, but I cannot express an opinion on this.

The first Inca, Manco Capac, with the help of this old fable and his own intelligence, resourcefulness, and shrewdness, seeing that the Indians believed it and held the lake and island to be a holy place, made up the second fable, saying that he and his wife were the offspring of the Sun, and that their father had placed them on that island that they might go forth throughout the world teaching the people, as we explained at the beginning of this history. The *amautas*, who were the philosophers and sages of the republic of the Incas, brought the first fable within the second, turning it into a prophecy or foretoken, so to speak. They said that the fact that the Sun had shed his first rays on that island in the rekindling of light in the world had been a sign and earnest that he would send his two first-born children to the same place to teach and illuminate the people, bringing them out of their bestial ways, as those sovereigns afterwards did. With these and other similar fabrications, all redounding to their own benefit, the Incas made the other Indians believe that they were the children of the Sun, and with the many good works they carried out they confirmed them in this idea. Because of these two legends the Incas and all their subjects considered that island a holy site, and for this reason they ordered a rich temple built there, all lined with sheets of gold, dedicated to the Sun where each year all the provinces under the rule of the Incas brought great offerings of gold and silver and precious stones as tribute of their gratitude to the Sun for the two boons he had conferred upon them in that place. That temple was served the same as the temple of Cuzco. The reports of the Indians on the amount of gold and silver offerings assembled on the island, aside from that which had been made up for the service of the temple, are more to be wondered at than believed. Father Blas Valera, speaking of the riches of that shrine, and of the quantity that had been left over and piled up about it, says that those Indians transferred from other regions (who are called Mitmacs) that live in Copacabana told him that there was enough gold left over to build another temple of it from foundations to roof, without using any other materials, and that after the Indians learned of the arrival of the Spaniards, and how they were appropriating for themselves all the riches they found, they threw all that gold into the great lake.

I have heard another similar story to the effect that in the valley of Orcos, which is six leagues to the south of Cuzco, there is a little lake that is less than half a league in circumference, but very deep, and surrounded by high hills. It is believed that the Indians threw into it much of the treasure that was in Cuzco when they learned of the arrival of the Spaniards and that among other things was the chain of gold that Huayna Capac ordered made in honor of his son Huascar, which we shall tell about in its proper place. Twelve or thirteen Spaniards who were living in Cuzco, not those holding grants of Indians, but of the merchant and trader class, pricked on by these reports, organized a company to drain the lake and recover the treasure. They took soundings and found twenty-three or twenty-four fathoms of water, not counting the mire, which was deep. They decided to excavate along the eastern shore of the lake, where the river known as the Yucay flows, because in that region the level of the ground is lower than the bed of the lake, and the water could run off, leaving the lake drained. This could not be done on any other side, because it was surrounded by mountains. They did not dig the drainage ditch straight down from the surface (which might have been the better plan), because they thought it would be cheaper to tunnel through the ground. They began their work in the year 1557, with great hopes of coming upon the treasure; but they had not dug more than fifty feet when they hit a very big rock. Although they did everything they could to break it, they found it was of flint, and as they hammered at it, they found that they got more fire than stone. And as they had spent a great part of their capital, they lost heart and gave up the undertaking. I entered the mouth of the tunnel several times when they were working on it. Thus it is common report, as those Spaniards heard it, that the Indians hid innumerable treasures in lakes, caves, and mountains, from which there is no hope of recovering them.

The Inca kings, in addition to the temple with its sumptuous decorations, beautified that island in many ways in honor of the fact that it was the first land their forefathers had set foot upon when they descended from heaven, as they said. They leveled it as much as they could, clearing away rocks and cliffs; they built terraces, which they covered with rich fertile soil, brought from far off, so they could grow corn, because as that whole region is very cold, it is impossible to raise it there. They sowed it on those terraces along with other seeds, and by lavishing great care upon it, they managed to harvest a few ears. These they sent to the king as something holy, and he took them to the temple of the Sun, and some of them were sent to the temple of the virgins in Cuzco, and they sent them to other convents and temples in the land, one year to one, the next year to another, that all might enjoy that grain, which was as though it had come from Heaven. They sowed it in the gardens of the temples of the Sun, and of the houses of the chosen virgins in the provinces where they existed, and the harvest that was garnered was divided among the villages of these provinces. They put a few grains in the granaries of the Sun and of the king, and in the communal storehouses that, like the divine thing it was, it might guard, increase, and free from corruption the grain that was stored there for the maintenance of all. And the Indian who could come by one of the grains of this corn or any other of the sacred seeds believed that he would never lack for bread as long as he lived. They were that superstitious in everything pertaining to their Incas.

The Strange Adventure of Pedro Serrano
[GARCILASO DE LA VEGA, INCA]

SERRANA ISLAND, which lies on the route between Cartagena and Havana, received its name from a Spaniard called Pedro Serrano, whose ship was wrecked near it, and he alone saved himself, being a great swimmer, and reached that island, which is uninhabited, uninhabitable, without water or wood, and by his courage and industry managed to live there for seven years. Before him this island was nameless; as he reported it, it has a circumference of two leagues. This is almost as it appears on mariners' maps, which show three tiny islands surrounded by sand shoals. These waters are full of them, and for this reason ships avoid them to keep from coming to grief.

It was Pedro Serrano's fate to be lost here, and he swam to the island, where he was overtaken by the greatest despondency, for he found there neither water nor wood, nor even grass that he could graze, nor anything else to keep him alive until some ship should pass and rescue him before he perished of hunger and thirst, a death more cruel than drowning, which is quicker. Thus he passed the first night, bewailing his misfortune, as unhappy as one may imagine a man would be in such a plight. When morning came he walked around the island again, and found some animals that had come up out of the sea, such as crabs, shrimps, and other vermin, of which he caught as many as he could, and ate them raw, because he had no fire to cook or roast them.

In this way he managed to exist until he saw some turtles swim ashore, and when they were a distance from the sea, he caught one of them and turned it over on its back, and did the same thing with as many as he could, for it is hard for them to right themselves. With a knife he carried in his belt, and which saved him from death, he cut its throat and drank the blood instead of water. He did the same with the others, and put the meat in the sun to dry so he could eat it, and to have the empty shells in which to catch water when it rained, for, as is well known, this region has a heavy rainfall. In this way he kept himself alive the first days, killing all the turtles he could, and some of them were as big or bigger than the biggest shield, and others smaller, of all sizes. He was unable to turn the biggest ones on their back, for they were too strong for him, and even though he got astride them to tire them out and hold them down, it was no use, for even with him on their back they made for the sea. Experience taught him which turtles he should attack and which he should let go. In the shells he caught a great deal of water, because there were some that held as much as two arrobas. When Pedro Serrano saw that he had a sufficient supply of food and drink, it seemed to him that if he could get fire to cook his food and send up smoke signals when a ship came in sight, he would lack for nothing. With this thought, and being a man who had followed the sea, and these are superior at any task to others, he looked about for a couple of stones to serve as flint, for he planned to use his knife as a steel. And as he could find none on the island, for it was all covered with fine sand, he swam into the sea and dived to the bottom. Diligently seeking what he was looking for in one place and another, he finally found some pebbles and brought up as many as he could. He selected the best of these, and breaking them against each other so they would have edges against which to whet his knife, he tried his scheme. And when he saw that he struck sparks, he tore up a piece of his shirt, shredding it very fine until it was like carded cotton, to serve as tow, and by his persistence and skill, after many attempts, he got fire. When he found he had it, he considered himself very fortunate, and to keep it going, he collected the flotsam washed up by the sea, among which were seaweed, spars of ships lost at sea, shells, fish bones, and other things to sustain the fire. And so that the rain would not put it out, he built a hut of the biggest shells of the turtles he had killed, and with unrelaxing care tended the fire so it should not slip away between his fingers. At the end of two months, and even before, he found himself in the same state as when he was born, because the continual rains, the heat, and the dampness of the climate had rotted the few garments he had. The great heat of the sun made him suffer, for he had no clothes to cover himself, nor was there any shade where he could take refuge from it. When he was very tired he would get into the water until it covered him. With this struggle and effort he lived three years, and during that time he saw some ships go by; but even though he sent up his smoke signals, which on the ocean is the sign of shipwrecked castaways, they either did not see them or were afraid to approach for fear of running aground on the shoals, and they sailed by. Pedro Serrano became so disconsolate over this that he felt like dying and ending everything. Constant exposure to the weather had grown so much hair on his body that it looked like the pelt of an animal, and not just any kind of animal, but a wild boar. His hair and beard hung below his waist.

One afternoon to his great surprise, Pedro Serrano saw on his island a man who had been lost on the shoals the night before and had kept himself afloat on a plank of the ship. When morning came and he saw the smoke of Pedro Serrano's fire, suspecting what it was, he made his way toward it with the help of the plank and his swimming. When the two men came face to face, it would be hard to say which of the two was the more surprised. Serrano imagined that it was the Devil who had come to tempt him to some act of despair. The visitor thought Serrano was the Devil in person when he saw him covered with all that hair, and his long locks and beard. Each fled from the other, and Pedro Serrano called out as he ran: "Jesus, Jesus, save me, O Lord, from the Devil." When the other heard this, he took heart, and running after him, cried: "Do not run away, brother, I am a Christian like yourself." And to reassure him, as he ran, he recited the Creed in a loud voice. When Pedro Serrano heard this, he turned toward him, and they embraced each other with great affection and tears and sighs, seeing themselves as victims of a common misfortune and without hope of remedying it. Each recounted his past life briefly. Pedro Serrano gave his visitor to eat and drink of what he had, and this comforted him somewhat and he began to talk again about his misfortune. They arranged their life as best they could, spending the hours of the day and night looking for shellfish to eat, and seaweed and driftwood and fish bones and whatever else the sea washed up to keep the fire going. They had to keep continual watch over it, taking turns so it would not go out. Thus they lived for a number of days, but not many had gone by before they quarreled and separated and almost came to blows (proof of the slaves we are to our evil passions). The cause of the quarrel was that one said to the other that he was not taking care of things as he should, and this reproach, and the words in which it was voiced, gave rise to the quarrel, and they separated. But realizing what a foolish thing they had done, they asked each other's forgiveness, be- came friends again, returned to each other's company, and lived in this fashion four years more. During this time they saw other ships go by, and sent up their smoke signals, but the ships sailed on without taking notice of them, and the men were so disheartened they felt like lying down and dying.

After these long years a ship happened to sail so close that it saw the smoke and put a boat over the side to bring them in. Pedro Serrano and his companion, who was covered with a pelt like his, when they saw the boat approaching began to shout the Creed and call out the name of Our Redeemer in a loud voice, so that the sailors manning the boat would not think they were devils and flee from them. And their precaution served them well, for otherwise the sailors would surely have turned back, for they did not look like human beings. Thus they brought them to the ship, and all who saw them and heard the trials they had endured were amazed. The companion died on the seas on the voyage back to Spain. Pedro Serrano arrived there, and went to Germany where the Emperor was at the time. He left on the hair with which he was covered as proof of his years as a castaway and the sufferings he had undergone. He could have earned a great deal of money if he had wanted to exhibit himself in the towns he traveled through. Certain knights and gentlemen to whom he had shown himself gave him money for his expenses, and His Imperial Majesty, when he had seen and heard him, conferred upon him a pension of four thousand pesos, which amounts to four thousand, eight hundred ducats, in Peru. As he was coming out here to enjoy it he died in Panama, so he never even laid eyes upon it.

This tale, as told here, I heard from a gentleman called Garci-Sánchez de Figueroa, who had known Pedro Serrano. He said that he had heard it from his own lips, and that after Pedro Serrano saw the emperor he trimmed his hair and his beard, leaving the latter a little above his waist, and at night he braided it, otherwise it got all over the bed and disturbed his sleep.

FERNANDO DE ALVA IXTLILXOCHITL

(1568?–1648)

THERE IS a great resemblance between Fernando de Alva Ixtlilxochitl and the Inca Garcilaso. Like the latter, Alva Ixtlilxochitl descended from a royal house, that of Mexico, and from the conquering Spaniards. Little information is available concerning his grandfather and father beyond the fact that they were Spanish, but on his mother's side he was closely connected with the Emperor Montezuma, and a lineal descendant of Netzahualcoyotl, the great poet and philosopher king. It was with this branch of the family that Alva Ixtlilxochitl felt himself most closely allied. He wrote several historical works in which he related the achievements of the Chichimecas, their legendary origin, their expansion, their subjection to the Aztecs, and the important part they played in Cortés's conquest. Without the help of his Indian allies, chafing under the Aztec tyranny and eager of an opportunity to throw it off, it would have been incomparably more difficult, if not impossible, for Cortés to have effected his victories.

Fernando de Alva, too, received his education in a school that had been established for the education of the sons of Indian nobles by the Franciscan friars, the Colegio de Santa Cruz in Tlatelolco. Although by a royal decree he had been declared the sole heir to the property and titles of his family, his birthright was never restored to him, in spite of his repeated appeals. He earned his living as interpreter in the court that had been established for the Indians.

It was at the request of the viceroy of Mexico that he began to write his history. Some of the picture records of the Indians were still extant in his day, though many of them had been destroyed, some at the time of the conquest, by the Spaniards anxious to destroy the Indians' memory of their past, and others that were in the possession of important native families, by their owners to avoid suspicion of idolatry. Utilizing such of these records as he could discover, and which he knew how to decipher, and supplementing this knowledge with the information of old Indians who recalled preconquest days and the songs the people still sang, in which they related the triumphs or defeats of their heroes, Alva Ixtlilxochitl composed his admirable history.

As in the case of the Inca Garcilaso, Alva Ixtlilxochitl felt himself defrauded of what was rightfully his, an outcast between two worlds. Confronted by the downfall of their former greatness, both took refuge from the present in the evocation of the past. Both glorify the wisdom and perfection of their supplanted civilizations, although both, in what seems like all sincerity, proclaim the incomparable superiority of the true faith. Alva's account of his people is more objective, more factual; it lacks that poetic quality, that tender melancholy which is one of the greatest charms of Garcilaso's work.

In this account of King Netzahualcoyotl's vision of the Unknown God, to whom the idea of human sacrifices, so prevalent among the other Mexican nations, was abhorrent, he gives a picture of one of the last moments of splendor of Indian civilization before it was submerged in the tide of the conquest.

King Nezahualcoyotl and the Unknown God
[FERNANDO DE ALVA IXTLILXOCHITL]

THE cacique Toateuhtli, who lived continually scheming how he could avenge himself on the King and do him harm, had a piece of great good luck. Two princes, sons of King Axayaca, had come from the city of Mexico to Texcuco to visit their uncle, King Nezahualcoyotl; and the two princes, with two of their cousins, sons of Nezahualcoyotl, went out into the fields around the city to hunt, as boys do. The servants, captains, and soldiers of the cacique Toateuhtli had set out to harry the countryside, and they came upon the four princes. As the attackers were many and the princes were unarmed, they captured them easily and brought them before the cacique, who rejoiced greatly at his good fortune, gave thanks to his gods for their favor, and immediately ordered the prisoners sacrificed. He had their hearts torn out and set in gold to make a necklace, which he wore around his throat, and he ordered their bodies placed in the four corners of a great hall in his house where he and his followers assembled for their festivities and dances. In the hand of each prince a metal spoon was placed filled with mallow ointment that burned and illuminated the room. When a captive slave, who was from the city of Texcuco, saw this terrible deed of cruelty, moved to pity by the sight of the four dead princes, her natural lords, and putting aside all fear and the suffering and danger of death to which she was exposing herself if she was missed or overtaken on the way, one night she took the bodies of the four princes and carried them to the city of Texcuco. Entering the palace of the King, their father, with many tears and cries, she spoke to him: "King Nezahualcoyotl, where are the princes and nobles of this court, where is your daring and prowess? Is it you to whom all the nations from one sea to the other bow? It cannot be you, for under your eyes the men of the province of Chalco and a blind old man who is their cacique were powerful enough to capture your two sons, whom I bring to you dead, with their cousins, the sons of the King of Mexico," and she described how she had found them.

When the King and the nobles who were with him saw and heard from the Indian woman this dreadful act of defiance and cruelty, he wept bitter tears, and sent word to the King of Mexico, the father of the two princes, of what had happened. Then King Nezahualcoyotl, considering how little his power had availed him, and the affront done him by the Indians of Chalco under his very eyes, and how useless had been the human sacrifices made to his gods, raising his eyes to heaven, spoke: "Verily the gods I worship, which are idols of stone that neither speak nor feel, could not have fashioned the beauty of the firmament, the sun, the moon, and the stars that adorn it and give light to the earth, nor the rivers, waters, fountains, trees, and plants that are its glory, the people who possess it and all that has been created. Some very powerful God, hidden and unknown, is the Creator of the Universe, it is He alone who can comfort me in my affliction and sustain me in this anguish my heart feels; I would have Him for my helper and protection." And the better to achieve and accomplish his intention, he decided to withdraw, as he did, to his forest of Tezcutzinco, and there removed and apart from all affairs and matters that might distract him, he fasted forty days in honor of the Almighty God, Creator of all things, hidden and unknown, and offered Him, instead of sacrifices, incense and copal at sunrise, at noon, at sunset, and at midnight.

At midnight of the fortieth day one of the pages of his bedchamber, by name Iztapalcotzin, heard a voice from without calling him by his name, and when he went out to see who it was, there stood a beautiful youth, richly clothed and shining with a great light. He was frightened by the vision that he had never seen before, but the youth called him by his name and spoke to him, saying: "Be not afraid. Go in and tell the King your lord to grieve no more and take comfort; the Almighty and Unknown God to whom he has fasted and made offerings these forty days has heard him, and will avenge him by the hand of his son, the Prince Axoquentzin, who will conquer the Chalcas, and capture and take prisoner the cacique, their lord; and the Queen, his wife, will bear a very wise and prudent son who will succeed him on the throne." And saying this, he disappeared, and the page entered the room where the King was making the usual sacrifice of incense and copal, and told him what he had seen and what the youth had said to him. The King at first thought it was a lie and invention of the page, for the Prince

Axoquentzin had never been in battle and was a youth seventeen years old; and the Queen was no longer young and had not borne a child for many years, though, at the same time, the fact that he said the Unknown God to whom he had commended himself and made offerings had promised to favor him heartened and consoled him. To make sure whether it was merely an invention of the page or the truth, he ordered him put in a cage.

That very morning the Prince Axoquentzin and other striplings of the city went out to the lands on the frontiers of Chalco to see his brothers who were in his father's army, and he arrived just as they, who were the principal chieftains of the army, were about to seat themselves to eat upon a great shield, as was their custom before going into battle, which they were preparing to do for the second time. One of the brothers, Acapipiotzi, as soon as he recognized him, was very happy to see him, and asked him how he had come through land where war was being fought without harm. The young prince answered that the desire he felt to see them had given him so much courage that he had felt no fear at all, and the brother bade him sit down and eat with them. But the other brother, Ichautlatoatzin, who was the eldest and the general of the army and of harsh and haughty nature, told him not to sit down, that only captains and brave men like them might occupy that seat. The other brothers insisted that he should let him sit there, as he was their brother and had the courage to risk his life to come to see them, which went to show that he would be a great man and worthy of any honor, but Ichautlatoatzin took the young prince by the arm and pushed him away contemptuously, telling him to go and eat with the women and not at the captains' table. Humiliated and insulted by these words, the boy went into the tent where his brothers had their weapons and armed himself with a shield and a war club. Determined to kill or capture the cacique who had killed his brothers and cousins and offended his father's gray hairs or die in the attempt, alone, without notifying his brothers of his decision or permitting the youths who had accompanied him to go with him, he made for the enemies' camp without the slightest fear, and so quickly that the captains and soldiers of his brothers who followed their King's son to keep him from being lost and harmed were unable to overtake him. He entered the tent of the cacique, calling in his heart upon the Unknown God, to whom his father had commended himself and made offerings, to help him in his undertaking. And it was a miraculous thing that when the Prince saw the cacique sitting in the chair from which he directed his army, as he was old and blind, and surrounded by the men of his confidence, he seized him by the hairs, without one of them stopping him, and dragged him out of the tent into the field.

When the cacique asked him not to treat him in that manner, as he was old and a man of standing, and to honor him as befitted a captive, the Prince raised him by the hand, saying to him:

"Although your great cruelty, Toateuhtli, and the perfidy you showed in sacrificing my brothers and cousins, the sons of such great kings, and the contempt in which you held them, would justify my dragging you before the eyes and presence of my father whom you have offended, I shall show magnanimity toward you, because of who I am, and because a noble should not take cruel vengeance on a vanquished enemy." And in this manner he took him to the city of Texcuco, despite the efforts of the many men of the cacique's army who tried to liberate him. Their determination put the Prince in danger of his life, but his good fortune so willed it that his brother Acapipiotzi, informed of the prince's intention, came with many men to his assistance just as the cacique's followers had him surrounded, and broke through with such violence and uproar that the Chalcas, dismayed and frightened at seeing their cacique the captive of one young boy, turned and fled, and the army of the King of Texcuco pursued them, killing many and capturing the survivors, so that the province ever after was under the domination of the King of Texcuco. The latter, when he heard the joyous news of the victory that the Unknown God had given to his son, as the handsome and dazzling youth had foretold to his page, freed the latter from his prison and gave him rich gifts, and entering a garden of his house, alone and without anyone, he knelt down and bowed his head, without raising his eyes to the sky in token of greater humility, and said:

"I give Thee all thanks, Almighty God and maker of all things, cause that Thou art of all causes, who I truly believe art in the bright and beautiful heavens that illuminate the earth, and from there Thou governeth, watcheth over, and bestoweth Thy blessings on those who call upon Thee and seek Thy favor, as Thou hast done with me, and I promise to recognize Thee as my Lord and Creator, and in payment of the bounty I have received, to build a temple where Thou shalt be reverenced and offerings laid before Thee all the time until, O Lord, Thou deigneth to show Thyself to this Thy slave and the others of my kingdom; and from today on I shall order that no human being shall be sacrificed in my realm, because I believe that this offends Thee."

When he had spoken these words he arose from the ground, happier than he had ever been in his life, and went into the hall where the nobles were waiting to congratulate him on the victory of the prince, and the King said to them:

"I receive these congratulations coming, as they do, from vassals who love me well, but I would be better pleased to have you give thanks for so great a victory to the Almighty God, maker of all things, who gave courage and strength to my son, a child and weak, as you all know, because I hold this God alone in esteem and wish to have Him as my defender, and from this day on, there will be no more human sacrifices, for this Lord is offended by them. And that my son's victory may be known to everyone, go forth to receive him, all of you, with music and dancing and bring him into my presence, and put the cacique in prison until his hour comes."

All did as the King bade them, and when the prince who had won this great victory reached the palace, the King, his father, received him in the hall and embraced him and kissed his face, raising him from the floor where he had knelt down to kiss his father's hands, and taking him to one end of the hall, he seated him beside him and said:

"Even if I were not sure that you are my son, as you are, I would know it from seeing how, aware of the grief suffered by my soul and heart at the doleful sight of your brothers and cousins, dead and outraged in their tender years by so cruel a man, you laid aside all fear and peril of your life to risk it to avenge their death and my dishonor. I believe this determination came from the Unknown God, who, all powerful, went to your aid and support," and with other loving words he begged him to tell him how he had the courage to attempt such an act of daring. The prince answered him:

"Know, my Father and Lord, that one of these past nights when I was sleeping in my room, so much light came into it that it was like day, and awaking, I saw beside my bed a white and very beautiful youth, in shining garments, and fearful of this vision never seen before, I covered my face, and the youth spoke to me and said: 'Prince, have no fear, for I have been sent by the Almighty God who created the heavens and the earth and all this world you see, on whom your father has called and to whom he has made offerings. Arrange things so you arise very early, and without saying anything to your father or any other person, go to the boundaries of Chalco where your brothers are, for you are destined to avenge the dead whom the cacique of that province sacrificed, and if your father learns of it, he will not let you go. Be assured of this which I say to you: that when you need me I will be with you.' And saying this, he disappeared, and the room was as before. In my eagerness to be up early, I slept no more, and as soon as it was light I arose. As I left this palace I met three boys, the sons of caciques, who asked me where I was going, and I told them that I had a longing to see my brothers, and was going where they were. The lads said they wanted to go with me, and we all went to the province and came to the tent of my brothers who were preparing to eat," and he told him what had happened to him with them, and all that we have related and more, "and when I reached the tent of the cacique and saw him and all the people with him, I was grieved and afraid, and did not know what to do. Then the beautiful youth appeared and took me by the right arm, saying to me: 'Be of stout heart and have no fear, for I am here.' With this I felt new courage, and I went to the cacique and took him out a prisoner, and no one molested me, and the youth accompanied me until he left me safe among my own."

The King, in gratitude for the great mercy and honor that had been done him, built a sumptuous temple of stone nine stories high, and the top one was ornamented with gold and precious stones inside, and outside with black pitch and some stars, because the God who had hearkened to him and had blessed him was a hidden, unknown thing. And for this reason he made no statue or image, and he ordered that throughout his kingdom from then on, all should make offering to the Unknown God, the cause of causes and the Almighty, of incense and copal every day, at the same hours that he had done and did it, and that there should be no human sacrifices, under threat of gravest penalties. In that upper story of the temple he built, there were instruments that were played at the hours when the offerings were made, and the principal instrument was known as Cailiztli, which was the name of the temple. And when it was finished, the Queen bore a son to whom his father gave the name Nezahualpilli, which means the "Fasted Prince," in memory of the forty days his father fasted.

JUAN RODRÍGUEZ FREILE

(1566?–1636?)

JUAN RODRÍGUEZ FREILE was the son of Spanish parents who had come out to America with Jiménez de Quesada on his second expedition to New Granada. His father was one of the legion who accompanied Quesada on his disastrous search for El Dorado, losing in the venture, as his son says, "everything but his dreams." In his old age, after having fought as a young man in the wars against the Indians, spending some years with his relatives in Spain, and then settling down to a quiet life farming his lands near Bogotá, an occupation at which he was only moderately successful, Rodríguez Freile wrote one book, *El Carnero*, a picaresque account of the conquest and settlement of New Granada. But in this single work he reveals his exceptional gifts as a narrator and a shrewd, uninhibited observer. He was a born gossip; he knew the private life of everyone in the colony, and he delighted in washing dirty linen in public. No detail escaped his notice, and since much of what he relates he had seen firsthand, his chronicle has great freshness and vivacity. In keeping with the picaresque convention, he mixes in all manner of moralistic observations on human frailty, and especially the snare of beauty, but this is merely a sop to respectability. There is no doubt that in a world where his precepts were obeyed, Rodríguez Freile would have found life very dull.

Along with the historical facts that he narrates with great exactitude, and the colorful day-by-day life of the colony, he intersperses all manner of tales of witchcraft, crimes, miracles.

In the two following selections he gives in the first a straightforward, matter-of-fact description of the ceremony of the Chibcha Indians, who inhabited the region around Bogotá, which gave rise to the legend of El Dorado, and in the other an account of the witchcraft of a certain Juana García which threatened to plunge the leading figures of the colony into a scandal of major proportions, until the governor himself, Jiménez de Quesada, prevailed upon the judge to dismiss the case.

El Dorado

[JUAN RODRÍGUEZ FREILE]

IN my youth I left this kingdom for those of Castile, and there I spent six years. I returned, and have traveled widely in this land, and among the many friends I have had here was Don Juan, the cacique and lord of Guatavita, a nephew of the one the conquistadors found in power when they entered this kingdom, who later succeeded his uncle and who told me all these old tales and those that follow.

He told me that at the time the Spaniards entered by way of Vélez, upon the discovery of this kingdom and its conquest, he was fasting in preparation for occupying the throne of his uncle, for among them the power passed to a nephew, the son of a sister, and this custom continues until our own days. When he entered upon his fast he already had had knowledge of women, and the fast and ceremonies were as follows:

It was the custom among these Indians for the successor and heir to the power or lordship of the uncle he was succeeding to fast for six years, living in a cave that was designated for this purpose, and in all this time he must have nothing to do with women, or eat meat, salt, or hot peppers, or do other things that were forbidden. Among these were that during the fast he must never see the sun; only at night was he permitted to emerge from the cave and see the moon and stars, but he had to return to the cave before the sun should see him. When this fast and ceremonies were over he took possession of the *cacicazgo* or lordship, and the first trip he had to make was to the great lake of Guatavita to make offerings and sacrifice to the devil, whom they held to be their god and master.

The ceremony consisted in making a great raft of reeds, which they prepared and decked out as beautifully as they knew how. They set upon it four lighted braziers in which they burned *moque*, which is the incense they used, and turpentine, and many other different perfumes.

On this occasion the lake, which was very large and deep enough so seagoing ships could sail upon it, was completely surrounded by Indians, men and women, decked out in feathers, and breastplates and crowns of gold, and with bonfires burning all around it. At the same time that the fuming began on the raft, they lighted the fires on land, and so dense was the smoke that it clouded the light of day.

Thereupon they stripped the clothing off the heir, leaving him completely naked, and smeared him over with a sticky mud, and then they dredged him with gold dust and ground gold, so that he was completely covered with this metal. They put him on the raft, standing erect, and at his feet they placed a great heap of gold and emeralds as an offering to their god. Four chieftains, his most important vassals, got on the raft with him, naked too, and adorned with feathers, gold coronets, bracelets, breastplates and earrings of gold, each with his offering.

As the raft moved away from the land the instruments began to resound, horns, conch-shell trumpets, and other instruments, and along with these such yells and cries as deafened the hills and valleys, and continued until the raft reached the middle of the lake, when a flag was hoisted as a signal for silence.

The gold-covered Indian made his offering, throwing all the gold in the pile at his feet into the middle of the lake, and the other chieftains who accompanied him did the same. When this was concluded they lowered the flag that had been flying all during the ceremony, and as the raft started back toward land, the shouting, the trumpets, the horns, began again with dances such as they used. In this fashion they received the newly elected and recognized him as their prince and sovereign.

This is the ceremony that gave rise to that celebrated name of *El Dorado*, which has cost so many lives and fortunes. It was in Peru that the word was first heard. It fell out that after Quito had been conquered, Sebastián de Benalcazar, in the course of his wars and conquests, met an Indian of these of the kingdom of Bogotá, who told him that when they chose a king in his country, they took him to a great lake and covered him all over with gold, and with great ceremonies made him king. As a result of this Don Sebastián said: "Let us go find this golden Indian."

The news spread to Castile and the rest of the Indies, and incited Benalcazar to set out to look for him, and for that reason he had a share in the conquest and foundation of this city.

The Missing Sleeve
[JUAN RODRÍGUEZ FREILE]

ON a ship of the fleets that came and went between Castile and the Indies, a resident of this city took passage to see how he could use his money to better his fortunes. He was a married man, and had a young and beautiful wife who, during her husband's absence, was reluctant to see her beauty wasted without enjoying it. She was careless, she found herself with child, but she thought she would be over her trouble in good time. But before the nine months were up, news came to her of the arrival of the fleet in the city of Cartagena, and the poor soul was greatly distressed, and did everything she could think of to rid herself of her burden, but to no avail.

Whereupon she consulted a crony of hers, Juana García, a free Negress who had come to this kingdom with Governor Don Alonso Luis de Lugo. She had two daughters who were so fine they went about this city in silks and gold, and with more than one gentleman pinned to their skirts.

This Negress dabbled in witchcraft, as afterwards came out. The pregnant woman went to see her, told her the trouble she was in, what she wanted to do, and asked her to help her. Juana García said to her: "Who told you that your husband was with this fleet?" The woman told her that he himself had said that he would be back the first chance he had. The Negress replied: "If that is the case, you wait; don't do anything, for I want to make sure of this news about the fleet, and I'll find out if your husband is aboard. I'll see you tomorrow, and we'll decide what we should do. Now, go with God."

The next day Juana García, who had spent the night making diligent inquiry and had learned the truth, came to see the woman. She said to her:

"My friend, I have taken steps to learn news of your husband; it is true that the fleet is at Cartagena, but I have heard nothing about your husband, nor does anyone say that he is aboard it." The lady was very unhappy, and begged her gossip to give her something to get rid of the child, to which Juana García replied:

"Do nothing until we learn the truth, whether he is coming or no. What you can do—you see that green basin over there?" "Yes," replied the lady.

"Well, gossip, fill it full of water and put it in your room, and prepare dinner for us, for I will come this evening and bring my daughters, and we will pleasure ourselves, and we will think up some cure for your trouble."

With this she took her leave, returned to her home, and when it was dark she went with her two daughters to the home of the woman with child, who had not forgotten to fill the basin with water. She had also invited some other young women, neighbors of hers, to come and spend the evening with her. When they were all together, and the girls were singing and dancing, the lady said to Juana García:

"I am in much pain. Do you want to examine me?"

"I will. Take one of these candles, and let's go into your room."

She took the candle, and they went into the room. Once they were inside, she locked the door and said:

"Mother, there is the basin full of water."

Juana García replied: "Then take this candle and see if you see anything in the water." The woman did as she said, and, looking into the water, began to speak:

"I see a land I do not know, and there is my husband, sitting on a chair, and there is a woman beside a table, and a tailor with a pair of shears in his hand about to cut a dress of scarlet cloth."

The Negress said to her:

"Wait a minute; I want to see that, too."

She came over beside the basin and saw all the other had described. Her friend asked her:

"What land is that?", and she replied:

"That is the island Hispaniola of Santo Domingo." Just then the tailor put his shears to the cloth and cut out a sleeve, which he threw over his shoulder. Juana García said to the lady:

"Do you want me to take that sleeve from the tailor?"

"But how can you take it from him?", the other asked.

"If you want me to, I'll take it away from him." The lady answered:

"Go on, mother gossip, take it from him." The words were no more than out of her mouth when the other said: "Here it is," and handed her the sleeve.

They watched for a while until the dress was cut, which the tailor did in a minute, and then the whole scene disappeared and nothing remained but the basin and the water. Juana García then said to her friend:

"You have seen how much of a hurry your husband is in. You've time to bear this baby and get another one."

The pregnant woman, now very happy, put the sleeve of scarlet cloth into a chest that stood beside her bed, and then they went back to the parlor where the girls were amusing themselves. They set the table, ate a fine dinner, and then they all went home.

Let us digress for a moment. It is a well-known fact that the devil was the inventor of this snare, and that he is powerful over all the sons of man; but he cannot reach their innermost being, because this is reserved only for God. He reaches his goal by conjectures, and guided by the steps man takes and the direction in which he goes. I am not surprised at what he showed these women in the water; because to this I can answer that the one who had the audacity to take Christ, Our Lord, to the top of the mountain, and show Him the kingdoms of the world, and the glory thereof, of which God had no need, because He had it all, and this vision was undoubtedly fantastic, could reveal what he did to the women in the basin of water. But what does surprise me is the rapidity with which he got the sleeve, for the one had no more than said: "Take it from him," than the other answered: "Here it is," and handed it to her. I should add that the devil knew the mischief these women were up to, and was prepared for everything. And now we come to the husband of this lady, who was the one that discovered all this witchcraft.

He had reached the city of Seville just as some relatives and friends of his arrived from the island of Hispaniola of Santo Domingo, who told him of its great wealth, and advised him to buy goods with his money and to return with them to that island. The man did as they suggested; he went to Santo Domingo and did very well there; he returned to Castile, bought more merchandise, and made a second trip to Hispaniola. It was on this second trip that the affair of the scarlet dress occurred. He sold his merchandise, returned to Spain, invested his money, and by the time he returned to this New Kingdom, the child was good-sized, and the wife was bringing it up as an orphan she had taken to raise.

The husband and wife received one another cordially, and for some time they were very happy and in accord, until she began to ask for this piece of finery and the other, while at the same time dropping little hints of jealousy, so the husband was in a bad humor, and never had a peaceful meal, because his wife never neglected an opportunity to throw up to him the love affair he had had in Hispaniola. The husband began to suspect that some friend of his who had been in the island while he was there had said something to his wife. So he hid his feelings and treated his wife very well, to see if he could find out who was making this trouble for him. Finally, one night when they were having dinner, both of them very contented, his wife asked him to buy her an embroidered green skirt. The husband did not agree to this and started making objections, to which she answered:

"By my faith, if it was for the lady of Santo Domingo, just as you gave her the dress of scarlet cloth, you wouldn't make any excuses."

This completely confirmed the husband's suspicions, and to get the whole story out of her, he indulged her in all she wanted, and bought her the skirt and other finery, and she was in the best of humors.

Finally one afternoon when they were together very affectionately, the husband said to the wife:

"Sister, won't you please tell me who told you I had bought a lady in Hispaniola a scarlet dress?"

To which the wife answered:

"You're not going to deny it, are you? You tell me the truth, and I'll tell you who told me."

The husband was now on the trail of what he was after, and he said to her:

"Madam, it is the truth, for when a man is away from his home in a strange land, he has to have some amusement. I did give that dress to a lady."

Then the wife said:

"And tell me something, when they were cutting out the dress, wasn't there something missing?"

To which he replied:

"Nothing was missing."

"What a liar you are! Wasn't there a sleeve missing?"

The husband thought for a moment, and said:

"That's right. The tailor forgot to cut it, and we had to get more cloth for it."

Whereupon the wife said to him:

"And if I were to show you the sleeve that was missing, would you recognize it?"

The husband asked: "Have you got it?"

And she said: "If you come with me, I'll show it to you."

They went into her room together, and she opened the chest and took out the sleeve, saying to him:

"Is this the sleeve that was missing?"

"That's it, woman; and I swear by God that I am going to know who brought it from Hispaniola to the city of Santafe."

And with this he took the sleeve and went with it to the bishop, who was the judge of the Inquisition, and told him of the case. His Reverence went to work on the matter and called the wife before him. He examined her, and she freely confessed all that had happened with the basin of water. The Negress Juana García and her daughters were immediately arrested. She confessed everything and gave evidence against many other women.

The case was tried, and the bishop pronounced sentence against all those involved. It is said that many were caught in the net, and among them persons in high places. Finally the Governor, Don Gonzalo Jiménez de Quesada, Captain Zorro, Captain Céspedes, Juan Tafur, Juan Ruiz de Orejuela, and other people of standing went to see the judge, and prevailed upon him not to order the sentence carried out, asking him to bear in mind that it was a new country, and this would be a blot upon it.

They brought so much pressure to bear upon His Reverence, that he dismissed the case. The only one who paid the penalty was Juana García. She was punished by being made to stand in Santo Domingo, at the hour of High Mass, with a noose around her neck and a lighted candle in her hand; and she wept, saying: "We all did it, and I am the only one that pays." She and her daughters were banished from the country.

ANTONIO DE LA CALANCHA

(1584–1654)

FRAY ANTONIO DE LA CALANCHA was one of the early Creole friars. He was born in Chuquisaca, an important mining center, in Upper Peru (now Bolivia) of distinguished Spanish parents. When fourteen years old, he joined the Augustine order. His lively intelligence and devotion attracted the attention of his superiors, and he was sent to study in the convent of the order in Lima. He was graduated with the degree of Doctor of Theology from the Royal University of Lima, and held many important posts in the order. His lifetime work was a history of his order in Peru, *Crónica moralizada del Orden de San Agustín en el Perú*, *con sucesos ejemplares de esta monarquía*, the first volume of which was published in Barcelona in 1638, and the second in Lima in 1653. But rather than the orderly, dull account its title would indicate, it is a most entertaining rag-bag of fact, gossip, superstition, and miracle.

Shrewd, ingenuous, garrulous, witty, Father Calancha is the complete Creole, though only first-generation American. He displays a passionate love for his country, finding it the embodiment of all excellence. "Never did anyone hear a clap of thunder there or see a ray of lightning," he says.

Like Rodríguez Freile, he had an insatiable appetite for gossip of every sort, and it is not surprising that Ricardo Palma, his fellow countryman, who shared his tastes, should have found him a mine of information when he wrote his *Tradiciones peruanas* three hundred years later.

All who have studied the history of the Incan empire have marveled at how they could have built their imposing temples and monuments, often transporting the materials hundreds of miles, without knowing the use of the wheel; and how they could have kept full records of their past without possessing an alphabet. In this description of the *quipus* Fray Antonio gives a fascinating account of how they employed a most intricate system of knotted threads as a substitute for writing.

The Quipus *of the Indians*

[ANTONIO DE LA CALANCHA]

IN Peru the name *quipus* was given to the writings, archives, records of the Indians of that land; we shall proceed to set forth the eminence they attained in this method of writing. In order to understand how it was possible for them to keep an account of the persons and events of their past, it would be well to describe what the *quipus* were, and the accuracy of their records. *Quipu* means to knot, and these knots (among the Indians this word was used both as noun and verb) were in strands of different-colored wool. Some were of only a single color; some two, some three or more, for the plain colors and the mixed ones all had their own meaning. The strands were tightly twisted, and each consisted of three or four threads, giving them the thickness of an iron spindle, or rope, three quarters of a yard long, and the threads were twisted into one another, as in a fringe. By the color they knew the meaning of each thread; yellow stood for gold, white for silver, red for soldiers. Such things as had no color were placed by order, beginning with those of highest quality and proceeding to those of least, each in its proper place. Thus, when listing the fighting equipment, they put first that which they considered most noble, such as lances, and then javelins, bows, arrows, slings. When referring to the vassals of the empire, they listed the inhabitants of each village, and then those of each province. The first thread represented the old people of sixty years or more, the second, those of fifty, and so on for every ten years of difference down to the babes in arms. Some of these threads had other fine threads of the same color wound in, to indicate exceptions to the general rule; for instance, with the thread of the men and women of such and such an age they put another, to show how many were married, how many widowed, and each strand covered only a single year, and counted only from a thousand to ten thousand. To remedy the defect of not having certain words or figures, there were the *amautas*, who were their philosophers or learned men, and it was their office to give scrupulous account of the event, the tale, or the moral. The *Quipo Camayos*, who were like the secretaries of these archives, learned them by heart, so as to be able to transmit them to the Inca, or the local chieftain, or whomever should come to inform himself. The *Arabicus*, who were their poets, composed brief, succinct poems, dealing with the tale, the event, or the embassy, and these were recited in the villages or provinces where they had occurred. They were handed down from father to son through successive generations. The *Quipo Camayos*, either because of the privileges their office conferred upon them, or because if they did not answer the questions put to them, they incurred severe punishment, spent their whole time studying the signs, numbers, and accounts, teaching them to those who were to succeed them in their duties, and there were many of these secretaries, each of whom had his own special field, and the account, relation, or song had to correspond to the knots that served their memory as index and point of reference. In the same way they kept the record of their laws, statutes, rites, and ceremonies; they recounted the reward or the punishment accorded good and evil acts, the ceremony of each festival in honor of the Sun or the invisible God; they learned with the deepest veneration the histories of their kings, the prophecies, and sacrifices to their idols. Summary death, from which there was no appeal, was the penalty the secretary, or *Quipo Camayo*, paid if he deviated a hair's breadth from the truth, or ignored any detail of what he was supposed to know, or gave a contradictory account of an event, tradition, or prophecy.

Eloquence of the Forms and Colors of the Quipus

[ANTONIO DE LA CALANCHA]

THE Inca Garcilaso does not go into details, but I have made a considerable effort to understand the system of the *Quipus*, and I shall endeavor to illustrate it with this example. Let us suppose that one of these secretaries wanted to say that before Manco Capac, who was the first Inca King, there were in this land no kings, leaders, religion, worship, and that in the fourth year of his reign he brought ten provinces under his sway, and that in subduing certain of them he had to make war, and some of his enemies were killed, and three thousand of his own soldiers, and that he won spoils of a thousand pounds of gold and thirty thousand of silver, and that in gratitude for the victory he ordered a festival to the Sun. The *Quipo Camayo*, or secretary, would record it thus: against a black cord, signifying time, he would put many straw-colored threads, and thousands of knots of the same color, and in the middle of the cord a big knot, through which ran a thread of the finest crimson, which stands for the king, because with wool of this color and seals of gold, forming a kind of laurel wreath, all the Incas were crowned, and under no circumstances did they use any other color. Just as Mahomet selected the color green as befitting his brutishness, so the Inca Kings used crimson as a symbol of their grandeur, a color that has been so highly honored by our popes and cardinals, the royal purple being the sign of grandeur, the proof of majesty and the color of sovereignty. No vassal of the Inca might use this color, and thus it always stood for the person of the King. In this scarlet thread they would tie four little knots to signify that the thing had happened in the fourth year of his reign, and to say that he had brought ten provinces under his sway, out of this knot would come a brown thread with ten little knots in it, and to each would be attached a green thread with the number of opposing Indians who died; first those seventy or older, and the others by age, as we have already explained. And to show which provinces they were from, they would put in strands of different colors, by which they denoted such or such a province, because there was a different combination for each. Then they would add a red thread with as many knots as they had lost men in the war. And to tell that the booty taken amounted to a thousand pounds of gold and thirty thousand of silver, they would twist into the strand representing their opponents a yellow thread having a thousand knots and a white one with thirty thousand. To say that they held a feast in honor of the Sun, they would add a twist of white, blue, and yellow which was like saying: The God who lives in the blue sky and creates the gold and silver, to him was made this first feast, and a knot was tied. If it was the third or fourth that had been celebrated that year, three or four knots were tied. Now those who saw the lower half of this cord, with threads of so many colors and large and small knots, and the first half with only straw colored threads and thousands of colorless knots, would read it thus: The people who were here before this King Manco Capac had no king—for there is no crimson thread—

or overlord or leader to govern them, for there is no purple thread, nor did they have a civilization, for there is no brown thread, or provinces, because there are no strands of different colors, nor did they make war, for there is no red thread, nor did they concern themselves with gold or silver, for there is neither yellow or white thread, nor did they have religion, worship, or sacrifices, for there is no strand of blue, yellow, or white. Before there were kings these people were barbarians. Thus by omission they understood what had not been, and by the *quipus* what had been, and this use of the *quipus* goes back to times immemorial, and begins with the coming into the world of their god, Viracocha, which means the God who came or was born from the sea foam. He must have been the first to settle this land after the Flood, and he had himself worshipped, or afterwards they worshipped him as a God. Thus *quipus* have been found that have first nothing but knots in straw-colored threads to indicate disorder, without head of the government or overlord, and then with strands of purple threads, which mean that now there were chieftains and lords of one or two towns, and after Manco Capac, with crimson threads, to show that there were kings and monarchies. This use of the *quipus*, though it was perfected in the time of the Incas, has its beginning in the immemorial past, having been used in villages, among families, in reductions. They were so skilled and apt at this manner of writing that Father Acosta says: "It is unbelievable what they achieved (he is talking of the *quipus*) in this manner, for everything books can relate of history, laws and ceremonies, and business records, all this was set forth by the *quipus* so accurately that it causes astonishment. I saw a handful of these threads with which an Indian woman had written the confession of her whole life, and she confessed by means of them as she might have done in writing, down to the slightest detail." And Father Blas Valera, another member of the Company of Jesus, one of the first Creoles of this kingdom, a remarkable interpreter and student of its antiquities, discovered in the *quipus* many ballads that the Arabicus had composed relating to events of history, wars, and love. The Inca Garcilaso alludes to some of these in his *Commentaries*. Even today the prominent Indians still employ the use of *quipus*, but they must not be as skillful as in olden times. And why should this be wondered at when the Greeks, where once stood Athens, the lighthouse of the wisdom of the world, are today nothing but fools?

LUIS LASSO DE LA VEGA

(Dates Unknown)

IT HAS BEEN impossible to discover more than the meagerest facts concerning the life of Lasso de la Vega. Neither the place nor date of his birth is known. The first knowledge we have of him is that in 1623 he was studying canon law at the University of Mexico. It is apparent that he entered the priesthood, for in 1647 he was named chaplain of the shrine of Our Lady of Guadalupe and vicar of its jurisdiction. In 1657 he was appointed prebendary of the cathedral of Mexico City.

Lasso de la Vega would have remained one of that anonymous army of clerics who spread and watched over the faith in America had it not been for the account he wrote in the Nahuatl tongue, the language of the Aztecs, of the miracle of the appearance of the Virgin of Guadalupe, the patron saint of Mexico, to the Indian Juan Diego. He wrote it, as he himself says, "so the natives may see and read in their own language what you did for love of them, and how it happened, before the memory of the circumstances is effaced by time."

No matter how wanting in faith a Mexican may be, no matter how lax in his religious observances, in some corner of his heart there is a shrine to the Virgin of Guadalupe. On the day of her festival the devout —and the not so devout—gather from the four corners of the land to worship this dark Mexican Madonna, to ascend on their knees the great flight of stairs leading to her altar to show their devotion and implore her favor. Many of the most notable Mexican writers in all epochs have described her miraculous appearance and the wonders she has wrought.

Lasso de la Vega's account was written in 1649; such copies as existed in Mexico were lost or disappeared, and the first known translation into Spanish, which was made by Primo Feliciano Velázquez from the original Nahuatl and published in Mexico in 1926, was from a copy he discovered in the British Museum.

There are an ingenuousness and simplicity about the tale that remind one of the religious paintings of the early primitives. It is utterly enchanting and utterly Mexican.

How the Queen of Heaven, Our Beloved Lady of Guadalupe,
Appeared in the Place Known as Tepeyacac
Near the City of Mexico

[LUIS LASSO DE LA VEGA]

FROM the time I, unworthy though I am, was put in charge of the temple where we venerate your devout image, you saw when I entered your blessed abode that I made offering to you of my heart. I have diligently fostered your cult, and to this end I have set down in the Nahuatl tongue your miracle. Look not with disfavor but accept with benevolence this relation of your humble slave. Your love did more than this, for in that language you called upon and spoke to a poor Indian, and on his rough cape you set your semblance in the colors of sweet-smelling roses, so they would not mistake you for another, and also that they might understand and carry out your behest and your wishes. This has encouraged me to write in the Nahuatl tongue of your wonderful apparition and of the gift of your image to this your blessed house of Tepeyacac, so the natives may see and read in their own language what you did for love of them, and how it happened, before the memory of the circumstances is effaced by time.

Ten years after the capture of the city of Mexico, the wars came to an end, and there was peace in the land, and the faith began to spread, the knowledge of the true God in whom we live. About this time, in the year 1531, early in the month of December, there was a poor Indian, called Juan Diego, so it is said, a native of Cuautitlán. It was a Saturday, very early in the morning, and he was on his way to church and to do some errands. When he reached the hill known as Tepeyacac, day was breaking, and he heard the sound of singing on the hill; it was like the song of many sweet-voiced birds; at times the singers fell silent, and it seemed as though the hills were answering. The song, so sweet and pleasing, was lovelier than that of the *coyoltototl* and the *tzinizcan* and of other singing birds. Juan Diego stopped to look and said to himself: "Am I hearing right? Perhaps I am still asleep? Have I awakened? Where am I? Could I be in the earthly paradise our forefathers told of? Or could I be in heaven?" He was looking eastward, to the top of the hill, whence the heavenly music was coming, when it suddenly ceased, and there was a silence, and he heard someone calling to him from the summit of the hill and saying: "*Juanito, Juan Dieguito*." So he proceeded to where the voice came from; he was not at all frightened, on the contrary, very happy, and he climbed the hill to see who was calling him. When he reached the top he saw a lady standing there, who told him to come near her. When he approached her he was amazed at her superhuman grandeur: her raiment was resplendent like the sun; the rock on which her foot rested was shot through with radiance, and was like an anklet of precious stones, and the earth all around shone like the rainbow. The mesquites, cactus, and other little plants growing there were like emeralds, their foliage beautiful turquoise, and their branches and thorns gleamed like gold. He bent low before her and heard her speak, in a gentle, polite tone, as though to manifest her love and esteem: "Juanito, littlest of my sons, where are you going?" He answered: "Lady and *Niña mia*, I am on my way to your house in Mexico Tlatilolco, to follow the divine teachings given and taught us by our priests, the representatives of Our Lord." Then she spoke to him and revealed her holy desire. She said to him: "Know the Mother of the True God in whom we live, of the Creator in whom all exist, Lord of Heaven and Earth. I greatly desire that a temple be built me here, that in it I may manifest and give to all my love, pity, help, and defense, for I am your mother, yours and all the dwellers in this land and the others who love me and call upon me and trust in me; here I will listen to their pleas, and remedy their sufferings, griefs, and pains. And to carry out the desire of my clemency, go to the palace of the bishop of Mexico and tell him that I have sent you to reveal to him what I earnestly desire, that here on this spot a temple be erected to me. Describe to him carefully all that you have seen and admired, and what you have heard. Rest assured that I will be very grateful and will repay you, for I will make you happy, and you will deserve that I recompense the effort and the trouble you undergo to do what I ask of you. You have heard my bidding, littlest of my sons; go now and do as I have said." At once he bowed low before her and said: "My Lady, I go to do your errand; for the present I take my leave of you, I, your humble servant." And he went down the hill to do as he was bid, and came out on the highway that follows a straight line into the city of Mexico.

When he reached the city he went without delay straight to the palace of the bishop, who had seen appointed only a short while before, by name Fray Juan de Zumarraga, of the order of St. Francis. As soon as he got there he tried to see him; he begged the servants to announce him, and after a considerable time had elapsed, they came to call him, saying the bishop had said he should come in. As soon as he entered, he bowed and knelt before him, and proceeded to give him the message from the Lady of Heaven. He also told him of the wondrous thing he had seen and heard. After listening to all he had to say, the bishop seemed skeptical, and answered him: "Come again some other time, son, and we'll talk this over more slowly; I will hear all you have to say from the beginning, and consider the message and desire with which you have come." Juan Diego departed sadly, because he had in no wise accomplished his errand.

He went back the same day and climbed to the summit of the hill, where he came upon the Lady of Heaven, who was waiting for him right where he had seen her the first time. As soon as he laid eyes upon her, he knelt at her feet and said: "Lady, littlest of my daughters, *Niña mia*, I went where you sent me to do your bidding; although with difficulty I managed to see the bishop; I gave him your message as you had told me; he received me kindly and listened to me with attention; but when he answered, I could see that he did not believe me; he said: 'You come some other time, and we'll talk this over.' I understood from the way he said it that he thought it was probably an invention of mine that you want them to build you a temple here, and not your behest. So for that reason I beg you, Lady and *Niña mia*, to pick out some important person who is known and respected to carry your message, so they will believe him. Because I am just a little man, a bit of rope, a frail wooden ladder, a fallen leaf, a nobody, and you, *Niña mia*, littlest of my daughters, My Lady, send me to a place where I am not in the habit of going and don't belong. Forgive me for causing you sorrow and arousing your anger, My Lady and Beloved." The Blessed Virgin answered: "Listen, oh littlest of my sons, know that my servants and messengers are many whom I could entrust to bear my message and do my will; but it is absolutely necessary that you, and you alone, solicit what I wish, and that my will be done through your mediation. So I beg you, oh littlest of my sons, and I order you to go again tomorrow to see the bishop. Give him the message in my name and make him know fully my will: that he must erect the temple I have requested. And tell him once more that it is I myself, the ever Virgin Mary, Mother of God, who sends you." Replied Juan Diego: "Lady and *Niña mia*, let no sorrow come to you through me; I will go joyfully to carry out your behest; in no wise will I fail to do it, nor will the road seem long. I go to do your bidding; but it may be that they will not listen to me, or if they do, that they will not believe me. Tomorrow afternoon, when the sun is setting, I shall come to tell you how the bishop responds to your message. For the time being, I take my leave of you, littlest of my daughters, My Lady and *Niña mia*. Rest until I return." And then he went to his home to rest.

The next day, which was Sunday, very early in the morning, he left his house and went straight to Tlatilolco, to hear the divine teachings, and to be there when they took the roll, and see the bishop afterwards. At about ten o'clock, after Mass had been said, and the roll taken, and the people had left, Juan Diego went to the palace of the bishop. After many difficulties he was admitted to his presence. He knelt at his feet, and grew sad and wept as he told him of the command of the Lady of Heaven, saying he hoped he would believe his message, and the will of the Immaculate, that a temple should be built to her in the place she desired. The bishop, to certify himself, asked him many things, where he had seen her, what she was like; and he carefully related everything to the bishop. He even described with great exactness how she looked, and all that he had seen and had wondered at, and in everything it was apparent that she was the ever Virgin Blessed Mother of the Saviour, Our Lord, Jesus Christ. Nevertheless the bishop did not believe him, and told him that not merely because of his talk and desire could his wish be fulfilled; that, in addition, he would have to have some sign to show that he was sent by the Queen of Heaven. As soon as he said this, Juan Diego replied to the bishop: "Sir, tell me the sign you want; and I will go at once and ask the Queen of Heaven, who sent me here, for it." When the bishop saw that he ratified all he had said without hesitating or retracting anything, he dismissed him. He immediately ordered some of the members of his household whom he could trust to follow him and watch carefully where he went and whom he met and talked with. And this was done. Juan Diego set straight out on the highroad; those who were following lost him near the bridge of Tepeyacac, where the ravine is, and although they looked everywhere for him, they could not find him. And they returned, angry at not having accomplished what they set out to do, but desirous of preventing Juan Diego from carrying out his plan. They went to see the bishop, to persuade him to pay him no heed; they told him that he was deceiving him, that he was inventing what he told him, or at any rate he had dreamed it. And they decided that if he came back again, they would punish him severely to teach him not to lie and deceive.

Meanwhile, Juan Diego was with the Blessed Virgin, telling her what the bishop had answered. After the Lady had heard him, she said: "It is well, my son. Tomorrow you will return here and take the bishop the sign he has asked for; with this he will believe you and will no longer doubt or distrust your word. And know, my son, that I will repay your diligence and the effort and fatigue you have endured for me. Go now, and I will be waiting for you here tomorrow."

The next day, Monday, when Juan Diego was to have brought the sign to prove his words, he did not return, because when he reached his house an uncle of his, Juan Bernardino, had fallen mortally ill. He went at once for a doctor, but it was too late, for he was a very sick man. That night his uncle begged him to go the first thing in the morning to Tlatilolco for a priest to shrive him and administer the last rites, for he was sure his hour had come, and he would never more leave his bed or get well.

Early Tuesday morning Juan Diego set out for Tlatilolco to bring the priest. As he was coming to the road that skirts the slope of the hill of Tepeyacac, to the west, which he was in the habit of taking, he said to himself: "I'd better keep right on, in case the Lady may see me, and stop me, and have me take the sign to the bishop, as she said. I'll wait till we are over our sorrow. Now I must hurry and bring the priest, for my poor uncle is anxiously waiting for him." So he went around the hill, on the other side, to the east, to reach the city quickly and so the Queen of Heaven would not delay him. He thought she would not be able to see him where he had turned aside, she who sees everywhere. He saw her come down from the top of the hill toward him, and she said to him: "How are you, littlest of my sons, and where are you going?" Was he chagrined, or ashamed, or frightened? He bowed low before her, and greeted her, saying: "*Niña mia*, littlest of my daughters, Lady, I hope you are happy. Did you have a good night? Are you feeling well, Lady and *Niña mia?* I am afraid I shall distress you. Know, *Niña mia*, that a poor servant of yours, my uncle, is very sick. He has caught the plague, and he is dying. I am now hurrying to your dwelling in Mexico to call one of the priests beloved of Our Lord to shrive him and give him the last rites, for from the moment of our birth we await the sad hour of our death. But be assured that I will come back here to carry your message, oh Lady and *Niña mia*, forgive me, bear with me for a little while, I am not deceiving you. Littlest of my daughters, tomorrow I shall return." After the merciful Virgin had heard Juan Diego's words, she replied: "Listen and hearken to me, littlest of my sons. This that frightens and distresses you is nothing. Let not your heart be troubled. Have no fear of this sickness or of any other sickness or trouble. Am I, your mother, not here? Do you not stand in my shadow? Am I not your health? Are you not in my lap? What more do you need? Let nothing sadden or afflict you; have no concern for the illness of your uncle, who will not die now. Know that he is already cured." (And his uncle became well at that moment, as was later learned.) When Juan Diego heard these words of the Lady of Heaven, he was much comforted and grew content. He begged her to send him as soon as possible to see the bishop and take him a sign and token so he would believe him. The Lady of Heaven then ordered him to ascend to the summit of the hill, where he had first seen her. She said to him: "Go up, littlest of my sons, to the top of the hill; there where you saw me and I gave you my orders you will find many flowers. Cut them, gather them up, and then come back to me with them." Juan Diego immediately climbed the hill, and when he reached the top he was amazed to see that many different roses of Castile had bloomed there before the season for them, because it was bitter cold at the time. They were very fragrant and covered with the dew of the night, which looked like precious pearls. He at once began to cut them and gathered them together in his lap. The summit of the hill was not a spot where flowers grew, for it was all rock, where only thistles, thornbushes, cactus, and mesquites lived. He descended quickly and brought the Lady of Heaven the different kinds of roses he had cut. When she saw them, she picked them up in her hand and then put them in his lap again, saying: "Littlest of my sons, these roses are the proof and token you will take to the bishop. Tell him in my name that they are evidence of my desire, which he must fulfill. You are my ambassador, worthy of confidence. I strictly order you not to open your blanket and reveal its contents to anyone but the bishop. Tell everything as it happened, how I ordered you to ascend to the top of the hill, to cut the flowers, and everything you saw and admired, so as to persuade the bishop to give you his aid to erect and build the temple I have asked." When the Lady of Heaven had spoken, he set out on the high-road that leads straight to Mexico, happy now and certain of success, carrying his burden with great care so it should not slip out of his hands, and solacing himself with the fragrance of the different beautiful flowers.

When he reached the bishop's palace, the butler and the other servants of the prelate came to meet him. He told them to tell the bishop he wished to see him, but none of them would do it, pretending that they had not heard him, either because it was too early, or because they already knew him, and found him troublesome and importunate; besides, their companions, who had lost sight of him when they tried to follow him, had already told them about him. For a long time he waited. Finally when they saw that he had been there a long time, standing, and with his head bowed, waiting patiently to see if he were sent for, and as it seemed that he was carrying something in his blanket, they drew near him to find out what it was and satisfy their curiosity. When Juan Diego saw that he could not hide what he was carrying, and that on this account they would upbraid him, or push him or beat him, he opened the blanket a little and showed the flowers. When they saw the different roses of Castile when it was not the season in which they bloomed, they marveled greatly to see them so fresh, so full-blown, so fragrant and so beautiful. They reached in to take some of them from him, but the three times they tried, they were unsuccessful, for when they went to touch them, they did not find real flowers, but they seemed painted or embroidered or worked in the blanket. They went at once to tell the bishop what they had seen, and to ask him to receive the little Indian who had come so many times and who had been waiting a long while to see him. When the bishop heard this, he realized that the Indian had come with the proof he had demanded. He ordered him to be brought before him at once. As soon as he came in he bowed low before him, the same as before, and once more told him what he had seen and marvelled at, and gave him his message. He said: "Sir, I did as you ordered me, which was to tell my mistress, the Lady of Heaven, Blessed Mary, Precious Mother of God, that you had asked for a sign so you could believe me that you were to build her a temple where she had asked that it be erected. I also told her that I had given you my word to bring you some sign and token of her will. She graciously acceded to your request. Early today she told me to come and see you again; I asked her for the sign so you would believe me, which she had promised me. She immediately fulfilled it. She sent me to the summit of the hill, where I had first seen her, to cut different roses of Castile. After I had cut them I brought them down; she took them in her hand and then put them back in my lap so I could bring them to you and hand them to you in person. Although I knew well that the summit of the hill is not a place where flowers bloom, for it is all rocks, and only thistles, thornbushes, cactus, and mesquite grow there, I did not hesitate. As I came near the top of the hill I thought I was in Paradise. There growing all together were the most varied and exquisite roses of Castile, shining with dew, and these I cut. She told me why I was to give them to you; and I am doing so that you may see in them the sign you asked for and accomplish her will; and also that you may see the truth of my word and my message. Here they are; receive them." Then he unfolded his white blanket in which he was carrying the flowers. And as the different roses of Castile poured out on the floor, on the blanket there suddenly appeared the precious image of the ever Virgin Blessed Mary, Mother of God, as it is preserved today in her temple of Tepeyacac, which is called Guadalupe. When the bishop saw it, he and all those present knelt down; they marveled greatly at it; they arose to see it; they grew sad and grievous, showing that they were looking upon it with heart and mind. The bishop, with tears in his eyes, prayed and begged her forgiveness for not having carried out her wish and her command. When he got to his feet, he untied from Juan Diego's neck the blanket in which the image of the Lady of Heaven had appeared, and carried it into his oratory. Juan Diego remained for another day in the house of the bishop. The next day he said to him: "Come show us where it is the will of the Lady of Heaven that we build her temple." And he invited the others to join them. As soon as Juan Diego had pointed out where the Lady of Heaven wanted her temple, he asked permission to leave. He wanted to go home to see his uncle Juan Bernardino who had been very sick when he left him to go to Tlatilolco for a priest to shrive him, and the

Lady of Heaven had told him that he was now recovered. They did not permit him to go alone, but accompanied him to his house. When he arrived they saw his uncle, who was very happy and in no wise ailing. He was surprised to see the company with his nephew, whom he asked the reason for such a great honor. His nephew answered that when he had set out to call the priest, the Lady of Heaven had appeared to him on Tepeyacac, telling him to be of good cheer, for his uncle was now recovered, which comforted him greatly, and then she sent him to Mexico to see the bishop, so he would build her a house on Tepeyacac. His uncle stated that it was true that he had recovered, and that he had seen her in the same way she had appeared to his nephew, and that he learned from her that she had sent him to Mexico to see the bishop. At the same time the Lady told him that when he saw the bishop he was to reveal to him what he had seen and the miraculous way she had cured him, and that he was to call her, as her blessed image was to be known, the ever Virgin Blessed Mary of Guadalupe. Then the company brought Juan Bernardino into the presence of the bishop to bear witness and give testimony before him. The bishop lodged both of them, uncle and nephew, in his house for some time, until they had built the temple of the Queen on Tepeyacac, where Juan Diego saw her. The bishop took the blessed image of the Queen of Heaven out of the oratory of his palace, and carried it to the cathedral that all the people might see and admire her Blessed Image. The whole city was moved. All came to see and admire the holy image, and pray to it. It was a cause of great wonder that it had appeared by a miracle, for no person of this world had painted her precious image.

The blanket on which the image of the Lady of Heaven appeared was the cloak of Juan Diego. It was of *ayate*, somewhat stiff and of good weave. In those days the clothing of all the poor Indians was made of *ayate;* only the nobles and the brave warriors wore blankets of white cotton. *Ayate*, as everyone knows, is made of the fibers of the maguey. This precious *ayate* on which the image of our ever Virgin Queen appeared is of two pieces, joined by a soft thread. The Blessed Image, from her feet to the crown on her head, is six handspans and one woman's handspan high. Her beautiful countenance is grave and noble, and rather dark. Her precious bust is gently bent over, and her hands are joined over her bosom, near her waist. Her girdle is purple. Only the tip of her right foot can be seen, shod in ashen color. Her outer garments are rose-colored, showing red in the folds, and are embroidered in the buds of different flowers edged in gold. Around her neck is a golden chain edged in black, and in the middle a cross. Her inner garment is soft and white, coming well down over her wrists and with drawn work at the bottom. Her veil on the outside is a pale blue; it covers her head without hiding her face, and falls to her feet, caught in a little at the waist. It has a rather wide golden fringe all around it, and is sprinkled with gold stars to the number of forty-six. Her head is inclined to the right, and upon her veil rests a crown of gold, with broad-based uprights tapering to a point. At her feet is the moon with its tips pointing upward. She stands exactly between them, and in the same way she stands in the middle of the sun, whose rays follow and surround her on all sides. There are a hundred rays of gold, some very long, others very small, some like flames; twelve halo her face and head, and in all there are fifty on each side. Outside them, enveloping her garments is a white cloud. This precious image and all the adornments float upon an angel visible only from the waist up; no other part of it appears, for its feet seem lost in the cloud. In its hands the angel holds the mantle and veil of the Virgin. The angel is robed in red with a collar of gold, and its outspread wings are of long feathers, green and other colors. The angel, holding the hem of her garment in both hands, seems very happy to be conducting the Queen of Heaven this way.

JOSÉ DE OVIEDO Y BAÑOS

(1671–1738)

IF NOT SEVEN CITIES, then three countries could vie for the honor of claiming the distinguished author of one of the great historical works of Latin America, *Historia de la conquista de Venezuela*. José de Oviedo y Baños's father was a Spaniard who came out to America as judge of the Royal Tribunal in Santa Fe de Bogotá, where José, the youngest of seven children, was born. His mother was a member of a distinquished family of Lima, and cousin of one of the viceroys, Count de la Granja. After the death of her husband she moved her family to Lima, and there José received his early education. At the age of fifteen he went to Venezuela under the protection of his uncle, Don Diego de Baños, bishop of Caracas, and there he married and spent the rest of his life. He was highly esteemed by his fellow citizens, was twice elected mayor of Caracas, and held other appointments of distinction.

Like Bernal Díaz del Castillo, like Rodríguez Freile, he was the author of a single book, but this has been enough to insure him a place among the great writers of America. His history of the conquest and settlement of Venezuela, published in 1723, covers the period from the arrival of the first Europeans to 1600. He speaks of continuing the work down to his own time, and this has given rise to the belief that the second part of the work was lost, but there seems to be no evidence to indicate that he ever wrote this second volume.

Not only was Oviedo y Baños endowed with rare historical sense, a sure instinct for separating the wheat from the chaff, but he possessed a style of exquisite limpidity and simplicity, all the more amazing in that period when nearly everyone wrote in the hyperbolical, conceited baroque manner. One sees in him the complete Creole, for whom the native and the European contributions to his country's civilization are equally estimable. With rare justice he gives credit alike to the Spanish conquistador and to the Indians, who, in Venezuela more than anywhere else, resisted foreign dominion and often chose death in preference to the sacrifice of their liberty. Oviedo y Baños knew that bravery and chivalry were not the patrimony of the Europeans alone, and the combats he describes often recall the heroic scenes of the *Iliad*.

It is incredible that the work of this historian should have been almost unknown except for a limited group of scholars, for few writers of the period equal him in justice, impartiality, good will, vividness, and elegance of style. The first revolt of the Negro slaves, which he describes here, anticipated by more than two hundred years the uprising of Toussaint L'Ouverture, Dessalines, and Henri-Christophe in Haiti.

Revolt and Coronation of the Negro Miguel
[JOSÉ DE OVIEDO Y BAÑOS]

THE mines of San Felipe were of no small profit to the inhabitants of the newly founded city of Segovia, who began to experience through them considerable improvement in their fortunes, and encouraged by the gains they enjoyed, arranged to put some eighty Negro slaves, assisted by Indians from the allotments, to work in them under the supervision of Spanish miners in the capacity of foremen. One day in the year 1553 one of these miners attempted to punish a Negro named Miguel, a slave of Pedro del Barrio, who was as proficient in the Spanish tongue as he was deep-dyed in wickedness. When they attempted to catch him to flog him, to save himself from this punishment, he seized a sword that he happened to lay his hands upon, and defending himself with it, caused such a tumult that in the confusion, he managed to get away and take refuge in the hills. He would come out at night and communicate secretly with the other Negroes working in the mines, attempting to persuade them to throw off the yoke of slavery and recover the liberty of which the Spanish tyranny had despoiled them. Although most of them refused to follow his evil counsels, and continued their work without heeding him, through his powers of persuasion he finally managed to win over twenty of them, and with these he suddenly fell by night on the mining camp, killing some of the miners in the first assault and taking the rest prisoner to prolong their martyrdom, for he put to death with severest cruelty all those with whom he or his companions had a score to settle (either because they had flogged them, or for other reasons), and then he set the others free. So puffed up with pride and arrogance had he become that he ordered them to go to the city and notify the inhabitants to be ready, for he soon intended to go there and crown his victory by putting them all to death, and he wished to make his prowess the more noteworthy by having forewarned them.

The fame of this exploit and the unremitting efforts of Miguel to induce the other Negroes and Spanish-speaking Indians to join him, in the hope of gaining their freedom in the favor of his fortunes, gradually won over all the others who worked in the mines; so he soon found himself accompanied by one hundred and eighty companions, with whom he retired to the inner fastness of the hills. There he selected the spot he considered most suitable, and built a town, surrounded by strong palisades and moats, to set up his tyranny, for once he was feared and respected by his followers, he changed their support to vassalage, having himself acclaimed king, and a Negress named Guiomar, by whom he had a little son, Queen. That the boy, too, might share in that fantastic monarchy, and have his role in the farce, he was sworn in as prince and heir apparent to the mad dreams of his father. Overcome with the majesty of his new state, and that the outward display might be in keeping with the importance of the position, Miguel organized the royal household, appointing all such officials and ministers as he had heard were customary in the palaces of the kings. And not to limit his jurisdiction merely to the temporal domain, he also named a bishop, selecting for this high office one of the Negroes he judged best fitted, and who really had a claim to this consideration, and had covered much of the ground to achieve it, for when he worked in the mines they all called him the "Canon," because of the pompous folderol he talked. Once in his see, taking thought like the good shepherd for the spiritual welfare of his dusky flock, he built a church, where he pontifically celebrated Mass every day and preached to his sheep such nonsense as his absence of faculties and ignorance dictated.

Once Miguel had ordered such things as seemed most necessary for the proper government of his new republic, and had provided the Indians with bows and arrows, and the Negroes with lances beaten out of hoes, and a few swords he was able to come by, not to spend all his time in the delights of the court, he drew his men up in military array, and with a lengthy harangue exhorted them to carry on the task they had begun, and to assure their freedom with their bravery by marching on New Segovia and razing it to the ground. The strategy employed by his squadrons was to entrust their hopes of success to the horrors of a dark night when, unperceived, they entered the city, attacking it at the same time on two sides, and setting fire to various houses. Although in the confusion of that surprise attack they killed a priest named Toribio Ruiz and two or three other dwellers, the rest quickly armed themselves, and a band of forty made a stand against the Negroes, attacking them with such determination that after killing some and wounding many, they forced them to flee in disorder to the protection of the near-by hills, where they reformed their ranks. Our men, feeling that caution was the better part of valor, decided not to pursue them further lest they lose the fruits of victory through some unforeseen contingency in the shape of a prepared ambush.

The inhabitants of New Segovia had never believed that Miguel would be so bold as to dare attack the city, although he had announced his purpose, and their failure to heed his threat was the reason he had caught them off guard. But having learned their lesson by experience, they realized that they would have to stamp out that rebellion quickly before it had gone too far to be remedied. As they did not feel equal to undertaking this by themselves, as soon as day came they sent word to Tocuyo of what had happened that night, and of the danger in which they all stood, asking for reinforcements to proceed against the Negroes. This petition was acceded to with such promptness by the inhabitants of Tocuyo that without delay they assembled the men in the city under the command of Diego de Losada, who, because of his long military experience and well-known valor, was accepted in this capacity by those of New Segovia as well. The two forces were incorporated, and set out so swiftly on the trail of the Negroes that before Miguel had word of their approach, they were before the stockade of his village.

The Negroes were not dismayed by this sudden attack, and following their king, who with his voice and example encouraged their defense, they made the victory very doubtful because of the determination with which they fought, until with Miguel's death as the result of two wounds he had received, his soldiers' courage came to an end. Disheartened at finding themselves bereft of their leader, they began to retreat in fear, making it possible for our men, killing some and taking others prisoner, to bring to an end, by the rout of all, that revolt which had taken on such fearful proportions because it had been disregarded at the start. And the farce ended in tragedy, with the return of the Queen Guiomar and the prince, her son, to their former state of slavery, where they suffered the changes of their fickle fortunes, bowed in chains when they had believed themselves raised to a royal throne.

BARTOLOMÉ MARTÍNEZ Y VELA

(Dates unknown)

THE OUTSTANDING FIGURES in the literature of the province formerly known as Upper Peru (now Bolivia) during the eighteenth century were Bartolomé Martínez y Vela and his father Bartolomé Arzay Sánchez y Vela. They were the authors of *The Annals of the Imperial Villa of Potosí* and of the *History of the Imperial Villa of Potosí,* but it is impossible to distinguish their individual contributions. According to the Bolivian bibliophile Vicente Ballivián y Roxas, who brought out the first edition of the *Annals* in Paris in 1872, Bartolomé Martínez y Vela was the author of this work, which represented an abridgment and compendium of the *History,* written by the father during the years 1705–36, and then continued by the son to the end of the eighteenth century. However, there seems to be no way of definitely establishing the authorship of each. Only one volume of their joint work has been published; the others are still waiting for an editor.

The *Annals* might be said to be the first scandal sheet of America. It gives an intimate and exciting account of Potosí, a city that might have come out of the Arabian Nights, during the days of its splendor and wealth and turbulence as one of the great mining centers of the world. Martínez y Vela could have named his own salary on a modern tabloid. What a nose for news! Not a detail escaped his notice—the comings and goings of governors, officials, and lesser fry; the discovery of new mines, marriages, births, deaths, murders, fires, flood; and along with these factual details, and related in the same tone, all manner of major and minor miracles.

The picture he paints of colonial days differs radically from the conventional conception of a placid, uneventful existence. Life was lived dangerously. The only phrase that adequately describes it is: "Such goings-on!" Life was a series of calamities, earthquakes, landslides, almost uninterrupted; and savage fights that bordered on civil war between rival factions in the city; and, above all, the constant intrusion of the supernatural. Nothing was what it seemed. A knock at the door might herald the visit of a divine or demoniacal emissary. A troublesome swarm of flies might be a troop of demons waiting to drag an unrepentant sinner off to enternal torment. Nor were the women those fragile sheltered flowers one might have imagined. They needed no men to avenge their honor; they could take care of themselves, shooting, stabbing, choking triflers with their virtue, sometimes burning down a seducer's place of business as a final fillip.

This day-by-day—perhaps "blow-by-blow" would be a more accurate description—account of life in Potosí is a banquet for a lover of gossip. It reveals all the splendor and squalor, the religious fervor and the libertine indulgence of colonial life.

The life of Vela is a complete mystery. Not even the dates of his birth and death are available. It has been said that he was a parish priest, but there seems to be no way of confirming this.

Annals of the Imperial City of Potosí

[BARTOLOMÉ MARTÍNEZ Y VELA]

1462. This year Guayna-Capac, the eleventh monarch of Peru, while on a trip to secure silver from the rich mine of Porco, which lies at a distance of seven leagues from Potosí, was lodged in Cantumarca. When he gazed upon the beauty of the hill of Potosí, he said that in his opinion there must be rich deposits of silver in that hill, and shortly afterwards he sent laborers to dig there. Just as they were about to begin, Providence so willed it that a horrendous noise was heard, like a clap of thunder, and then a fearsome voice saying: "Do not dig the silver from this hill, for it is meant for another." The laborers were so terrified that they gave up the attempt and returned to Porco. They told the monarch what had happened, and when they came to the part about the noise, they said: "Potojsí," which means: "There came a great noise," and this was the origin of the name of Potosí, with a change of one letter. From then on, the hill was known to the natives by the name of Potojsí. This is the version given by Garcilaso de la Vega, although there are others who say the origin of Potosí comes, not only from the aforementioned event, but also because the natives, before they received the true faith, called the hill Potojchi, which means "fountain of silver."

1545. This year, the Church being under the rule of the Holy Father Paul III, and the Spanish monarchy under that of the great Emperor Charles V, about the middle of January the famous mine of Potosí was discovered by an Indian named Gualca, who, according to certain authors whom I shall quote in the General History that I have in preparation, was traveling with his flock from the vicinity of the Porco mine, which had been discovered by the Spaniards the preceding year of 1544. He decided to spend the night on the hill, and tied his rams to clumps of hay. In their eagerness to get loose and seek pasture, they tore up the hay by the roots, discovering the silver lode.

Others say that the Indian, chasing a deer that was running past, to save himself from falling, grabbed hold of a clump of hay, and it came away in his hands, revealing the lode. Still others say, and this seems the most likely version—as I shall set forth in my aforementioned History—that the Indian had been following a ram that had strayed away from Porco. He caught up with it about seven o'clock on the hillside, tied it up, and lighted a fire to protect himself from the cold; when day broke, he saw that the fire had melted the silver and it had run out in little streams.

This same year, in the month of April, the Indian Gualca, who had kept the secret of his discovery to himself until then, quarreled with another Indian by the name of Guanca, who told Captain Juan de Villarroel about Gualca's discovery of the great Potosí. Guanca took his master Villarroel to the hill, and he was the first Spaniard to see the rich vein, and the first to stake out his claim. He went into partnership with Captain Diego Centeno, and they began to work that monstrous rich vein known as "Centeno's Lode."

1579. This year General Don Juan Pereira married off his daughter, Doña Plácida Eustáquia Pereira to a fine gentleman, who was later in command of the armed forces in Chile, where he was killed by the Indians. The reason I mention this marriage is to call attention to the splendor of Potosí. According to certain authors, whom I shall quote in my History, she brought to the marriage a dowry of 2,300,000 pesos in gold, silver, jewels, and pearls. This same year, during the absence of General Pereira, Don Martín de Loyola, a nephew of St. Ignatius Loyola, acted as interim governor of Potosí. He was married to the Indian princess who was the heiress to the throne of Peru.

1589. At the beginning of this year, His Excellency, Don Garciá Hurtado de Mendoza, Marquis of Cañete, eighth viceroy of Peru, having learned of the factions and deaths among the inhabitants of Potosí, in the hope of improving conditions, sent letters on the subject to the Royal Tribunal of Chuquisaca and to the Mayor of Potosí. This same year, at the urging of the Viceroy, Captain Diego Ponce de León recruited seventy good soldiers in Potosí to go to the aid of the sorely beset garrisons of Chile, for the Araucanian Indians were defeating the Spanish troops. General Caupolicán was using the skull of Don Pedro de Valdivia, the conqueror of that region, as a drinking-cup, and the Indians had destroyed the city of Concepción, completely sacking it.

This same year some men who had been notorious evildoers in Potosí were on their way to Cuzco. As they passed through the ravine of San Bartolomé, the name by which it is known today, a league distant from Cuzco and the gateway and road for all those coming from the lower provinces, the two cliffs came together at their narrowest point, killed them all, and then opened up again. According to certain writers, whom I shall mention in my History, both before and after this event other terrible things had happened there; when travelers were riding through on muleback, the mules went so wild that they kicked their riders to pieces; and others had died as they passed through the ravine, all due to the evil arts of a devil who lived in a near-by cave. This went on until the Fathers of the Company of Jesus carried an image of St. Bartholomew there and placed it in a cave, whereupon the devil, who lived in an adjoining cave, rushed out with a roar and dashed himself against the side of the cliff, leaving it all covered with a greenish-black stain. The stain can still be seen. Nothing further happened after the visit of the saint.

1610. This same year in the month of May there took place in Potosí that astounding miracle worked by the Blessed Christ of the Pillar in the church of Our Lady of Mercy. A priest was hearing a sinner's confession, and he was so shocked by the abomination of his many sins that he refused to grant him absolution, which distressed the penitent greatly. Whereupon the Blessed Christ, who was tied to the pillar, extended a finger of His generous hand, and pointing to the sinner, said to the priest: "Absolve that man, for he hasn't told you what he told Me." And in proof of this miracle the divine finger has remained extended ever since.

1615. This same year, one day when the blessed Father Fray Vicente Bernardo was helping the prior celebrate Mass in the main church of the Society of Jesus, suddenly, for no apparent reason, he burst out laughing. The prior noticed this, and when Mass was over, he went into the sacristy with the servant of God, and ordered him under his oath of obedience to tell him what he was laughing at. To which he answered: "Father, the thing that made me laugh was that some women in church were paying no attention to the Mass, but were chattering away; near them stood a devil writing down everything they were saying as fast as he could on a sheet of paper. And as he had used it all up before they finished, the devil took one end of the sheet between his teeth and the other in his two hands, pulling with all his might to stretch it out, and the paper tore, and he fell on his face and gave himself a good crack, and that made me laugh." All those who go to church to talk take note.

1616. This year that miracle took place by which Our Lady of the Candles of the parish of San Pedro, that treasure of beauty and miracles, helped those eight Indians and boys, which has been recounted by different authors, and I shall do the same in my promised History. These Indians had been buried in the mine of Don Pedro Sors de Ulloa in the shaft where they were working, and there was no hope of even recovering their dead bodies. This was the state of affairs on the Saturday sixteen days after they had been imprisoned. As the priest was celebrating a mass in honor of the Virgin the church and the village were thrown into an uproar by the pealing of bells and the news that the Indians had miraculously escaped from their long imprisonment. These beneficiaries of the Virgin entered the church of San Pedro, where they first gave infinite thanks and then told how Our Lady had protected them, first, that they were not buried when the shaft caved in; second, that their piece of candle had not gone out or been consumed in those fifteen days; third, that the same day they were imprisoned, as they were beginning to get hungry, they found, or there was put before them, some loaves of delicious bread, a bite of which satisfied them for hours, and water suddenly welled up, which was also miraculous. Two of them, one named Pedro and the other Cristóbal, awoke to say that in their sleep the Blessed Virgin had told them they would get out of there on Saturday at the hour when Mass was being said in Her church. That morning they suddenly saw through a hole a light so great that it was like day, and they followed it, opening their way, and suddenly they found themselves outside at ground level. As I intend to include in my History the very words in which these good Indians described the miracle, I cannot, nor do I wish, in the brief space at my disposal here, to go into further details, my chief object being to set down the year of the event.

1625. There died this year in Potosí that famous hermit who for twenty years walked its streets, with his begging bag, his long beard, carrying a skull in his hand. He was held by all to be a good, penitent man; at times when he stood gazing fixedly at the skull everyone thought he was meditating on the idea of death. He died having received all the sacraments, and after his death a paper was found inside the skull on which was written these words with his own hand: "I, Don Juan de Toledo, of this city of Potosí, declare to all who have known me here, and to all those who would know of me in the future, that I am that man who because he went about in a hermit's garb was considered virtuous by all, and that is not true, for I am the worst man there has ever been in the world. Know that the wearing of a hermit's attire was not motivated by virtue, but by the most wicked evil. That you may know all, I will say that a little less than twenty years, because of certain offenses committed against me by Don Martín de Salazar of the kingdoms of Spain, by which offenses he infamed the honor God had given me, I took his life with countless knife thrusts. After he was buried I found a way to enter the church by night; I opened his grave and lifted out his body; with my dagger I slit open his breast, tore out his heart, ate it bite by bite, and then I cut off his head and removed the skin. Then I buried him again, and took his skull with me. I dressed myself in sackcloth, as you have all seen, and I have walked with the skull in my hands for twenty years, and I have never had it out of my sight, either at table or in bed. All who saw me held me to be a great penitent, not knowing my deceit, and thinking when they saw me gazing upon the skull that I was pondering upon death, when just the opposite was the case. For men are reduced to the condition of beasts by sin, and I had become the most terrible, turning into a cruel, ferocious crocodile. For just as this animal weeps and moans over the unhappy human he has devoured, not because he has killed him, but because his food is all consumed, so I, fiercer than a wild beast, as I gazed upon the skull of my enemy whom I had killed, lamented the fact that he was dead, for if he had come back to life a thousand times, so many times would I have killed him again. With this cruel vengefulness I have lived for twenty years without ever being able to lay aside my rancour and take pity on myself until this moment, which is the last of my life. Now I repent of all that I have done, and implore God most humbly to forgive me, and I beg all to ask the same of that Divine Master, who forgave those that had crucified Him."

This same year, at the beginning of Lent, a great sinner had withdrawn from the company of a woman, and both were firmly determined to offend God no more. But when Lent was over, he returned to the house of his friend. She was steadfast in her resolve to serve God with all her heart; and zealous of the Divine love, she grew angry with the man and reproved him harshly. But the man persisted in his weakness and solicited her anew, and while the woman was trying to dissuade him from his purpose, she suddenly gave a start and a scream, and said to the man: "Look at that devil, right behind you." The wretch turned his head, saw the devil standing there, and dropped dead.

This same year devils strangled a great sinner in Potosí while he was in bed with a woman. She was saved by the intercession of the Blessed Virgin.

1659. This year, while Juan de Benavente, a miner, was walking by the hovels of the parish of San Pablo, he saw at the door of one the body of a poor Indian, for whom they were asking alms to bury: he had been dead three days, but because he was poor the priest would not bury him. The good miner was moved by the sight, gave the amount necessary for the burial, and told them to remove the body. As he went past the cemetery of San Pablo, an Indian came up to him and told him not to come back that way because a group of enemies was lying in wait to kill him. It was necessary for the miner to return, though he was on his guard. His enemies attacked him, and he would surely have died had not a host of Indians come out of the cemetery and driven away his assailants with sticks and stones. When the grateful miner followed them into the cemetery to thank them, they had disappeared, which made him think that they were souls from Purgatory who had helped him because of the alms he gave. This same year the miraculous image of the Virgin of the Candles, of the parish of San Martín, saved a boy eight years old who had fallen into a well. When after many hours his parents missed him, they began to look for him and came to the well, where they saw his hat floating on the water. They drained the well and brought him out alive. The boy said the Blessed Virgin had stood beside him and had prevented the water from drowning him.

This same year Our Lady of the Candles, whose image is in the church of San Agustín, protected a votary of Hers who had set out on a trip. He was struck by lightning, which melted a locket of silver in which he carried the image of the Virgin of Copacabana. Neither the image nor the man was hurt. This same year General Gómez de Avila, of the Order of Calatrava, arrived in the city, the twenty-first in the number of the mayors of Potosí.

FRANCISCO JAVIER CLAVIJERO

(1731–1786)

FATHER CLAVIJERO was one of that brilliant group of Jesuits who played so important a part in the development of modern thought and science in Spanish America, and who, after their expulsion from the Spanish dominions in 1767 by an edict of Charles III's dissolving the order, worked actively for the cause of Spanish America's independence. Several of Miranda's close associates in his long struggle to win freedom for the Spanish colonies were Jesuits, and another Jesuit, Juan Pablo Viscardo y Guzmán, was the author of a document that has been called the Declaration of Independence of Spanish America.

Clavijero came of a distinguished family. His parents were Spanish; his father held important government posts in Mexico, and a cousin of his mother's became Vicereine of Mexico. Francisco Javier was born in Vera Cruz, and from childhood acquired an intimate knowledge of the Indians and their languages and customs which was to be of great use to him in his later work. He saw for himself the gratitude and devotion of the Indians under his father's jurisdiction, who was unfailingly just and considerate in all his dealings with them. Through this close association Father Clavijero came to read and write the Nahuatl, Otomí, and Mixtec languages like his own.

He was a brilliant student, and received an excellent education. He was conversant with the most advanced scientific thought of his day. In 1748 he professed in the Jesuit order. He had already conceived the idea of writing the book that was to be his masterpiece, *Historia antigua de Mexico*, a history of the Mexican peoples, from their mythical, legendary origins down to the conquest, and he spent five years in the house of the order in Puebla studying the old Indian picture records and learning to decipher the hieroglyphics. After the expulsion he took up his residence in Bologna, which was the refuge of other illustrious Mexicans, such as Abad y Alegre, Cavo y Mañeiro, Castro y Márquez. He gave himself over completely to writing his *History*, utilizing the works of the early historians of the Indies and the missionaries, but above all, the Indian picture records of which there were many in different Italian libraries, particularly that of the Vatican.

In his treatment of his subject matter, Clavijero employs methods of scientific investigation far in advance of his day. To his vast erudition, his painstaking weighing of the evidence, he brings a keen gift of analysis, and a polished, elegant style that is deceptive in its simplicity. He was a great scholar and a true patriot. One of his purposes in writing his book is to vindicate his fellow countrymen, and with them all Americans, against the charges of such European historians as Robertson, Raynal, Paw, and others that America and its inhabitants were inferior to Europe. His defense is brilliant and unshakable, and he shows patently how useful Europeans have found this attitude for their exploitation of America. His book breathes an air of justice, honesty, and nobility.

After writing his book in Spanish, Father Clavijero was forbidden to publish it in that language. He himself translated it into Italian, and it was published with the title *Storia Antica del Messico* in Bologna. After the ban of the expulsion was lifted, the original manuscript in Clavijero's own handwriting was brought back to Mexico, mysteriously disappeared from the library where it had been deposited, and turned up for sale in the United States. A Mexican Jesuit, Father Carlos María de Heredia, raised the price for its purchase, and it was returned to Mexico. A first edition from the Spanish original was published in Mexico in 1945, and the following selections have been made from it.

Journey of the Mexicans to the Land of Anahuac

[FRANCISCO JAVIER CLAVIJERO]

THE Aztecs, or Mexicans, who were the last settlers of the land of Anahuac, and with whom this history principally deals, lived until close to the year 1160 of our era in Aztlan, a territory to the north of the Gulf of California, as is apparent from the route of their travels and from the imformation the Spaniards later acquired from their expeditions to that region. The reason they left their home was perhaps the same as that which impelled the other tribes; but be this as it may, it seems only fair to me to submit to the reader's own judgment what the Mexican writers themselves tell of the reason for this decision.

Among the Aztecs there was, they say, a person of great authority, by name Huitziton, whose opinion carried great weight among them. He took it into his head, for what reason I cannot say, to persuade his countrymen to change lands. While he was engaged in this plan, it is said that he heard a bird in the branches of a tree whose call resembled the Mexican word "*tihui*," which means "let's go." This seemed to him the opportune moment to carry his plan into effect. He called over another person of high standing, by name Tecpaltzin, led him near the tree where the bird was singing, and said to him: "Tecpaltzin, my friend, don't you understand what this bird is saying? This *tihui*, *tihui*, it keeps repeating, what can it mean except that it is time for us to leave this land and seek another? Without doubt this is some friendly spirit that wishes us well. Let us, therefore, obey its voice and not arouse its anger by our disobedience." Tecpaltzin was completely convinced by Huitziton's interpretation, either because of the high regard in which he held his wisdom, or because he shared the same desire, and with these two persons, who wielded so much influence among their people, in agreement, with little difficulty they persuaded them to set out.

I do not give too much credit to this account, not because I consider it unlikely that a person who enjoys a reputation for wisdom could, for religious motives, persuade an ignorant and superstitious people to do what he wishes. It would be harder for me to believe the usual version of Spanish writers, namely that the Mexicans embarked upon this journey at the express behest of the Devil. The naïve historians of the sixteenth century, and those who have copied them, accept as an indisputable truth the close, continuous commerce of the Devil with all the idolatrous peoples of the New World, and they rarely allude to a happening that they do not attribute to his influence. But although it is a fact that this malignant spirit spares no effort to do mankind all the harm he can, and that he has at times taken on visible form to lead them astray, especially those who have not yet been reborn in the Faith, it is not credible that these appearances have been so frequent, or his dealings with those peoples so open and free, as those authors contend. For God, who watches over his children with loving forethought, would not permit this overt enemy of mankind so much freedom. Those readers who have come upon in other works certain of the events I mention in my History should not be surprised at my incredulity on this score. The testimony of the Mexican historians does not suffice for me to attribute any power to the Devil, for I know how easily they could be deceived, partly because of their superstitions, which blind them, and partly because of the cunning of their priests, a thing common among all idolatrous peoples.

The journey of the Aztecs, about which there can be no doubt, whatever its cause may have been, took place, as nearly as can be calculated, about the year 1160 A.D. Torquemada claims to have seen in all the old picture records of this journey an arm of the sea or a great river. If it is true that they contain the representation of a river, it can only be the Colorado, which empties into the Gulf of California, at 32½° of latitude, for it is the largest they would have encountered on the route they traveled. After they had passed it, somewhere above the thirty-fifth parallel, they traveled toward the southeast as far as the

Gila River, where they halted for a time, for even today the ruins of the buildings they constructed along its banks can still be seen. From there they set out again, keeping to almost the same direction, until they came to a point, in the neighborhood of the twenty-ninth parallel, some 250 miles to the northwest of Chihuahua. This spot is known as Casas Grandes, because of the huge edifice that still exists, and which, according to the common tradition of those nations, was erected by the Mexicans during their wanderings. This building was constructed along the lines of those still to be seen in New Mexico, that is to say, of three stories, with a flat roof, and without doors or entrance on the first floor. The door is on the second floor and requires a ladder to reach it. The inhabitants of New Mexico still do this, to make themselves less vulnerable to the attacks of their enemies, using a small ladder that they let down to those they wish to admit to their dwellings. The Aztecs undoubtedly had the same reason to build their homes after that fashion. Casas Grandes has the properties of a fortress, being protected on one side by a very high mountain, and surrounded on the others by a wall almost seven feet thick, whose foundations still stand. Stones as large as ordinary millstones are to be seen here; the beams are of pine and well hewn. In the center of that vast structure there is an artificially constructed mound where, it can be deduced, sentinels were stationed to watch for enemies. Excavations have been carried on at this place, and a number of utensils, such as plates, pots, drinking vessels, and mirrors of the stone known as *itztli* have been discovered.

From this place, crossing the Tarahumara mountains and moving southward, they came to Hueicolhuacan, known at present as Culiacán, situated close to the Gulf of California, where they remained for three years. It is presumable that they built houses and huts there to live in, and that they sowed the grain they carried with them for food, as they did wherever they halted for any length of time. There they carved a statue of wood representing Huitzilopochtli, the presiding deity of their nation, that he might accompany them on their journey. They also made a chair of rushes and withes to carry it, to which they gave the name *Teoicpalli* (chair of God), and they selected the priests who should carry it on their shoulders, four at a time, and these were called *Teotlamacazque* (servants of God), and the act of carrying it was known as *Neomana*, that is to say, bearing God on the shoulders.

From Hueicolhuacan, after traveling westward for many days, they reached Chicomoztoc, where they stopped. Up to this point the seven tribes of Nahuatlacas had traveled together; but here they separated. The Xochimilcos, the Tepanecas, the Colhuas, the Chalqueses, the Tlahuicas, and the Tlaxcaltecas went on, and the Mexicans remained there with their idol. The latter say that the separation was made by direct order of their god; but it seems more likely that some discord had sprung up among the tribes. The site of Chicomoztoc, where the Mexicans lived for nine years, has not been determined; nevertheless, I believe that it must have been some twenty miles to the south of Zacatecas, at a spot where today the ruins of a vast edifice can be seen, which was undoubtedly constructed by the Mexicans during their stay; for the Zacatecas, the primitive inhabitants of this region, were completely barbarous, and had no houses, and were ignorant of the manner of constructing them; therefore those remains discovered by the Spaniards can be ascribed only to the Aztecs. The reduction of their numbers as a result of the separation of the other tribes was undoubtedly the reason why they constructed no more buildings during the course of their wanderings.

From the land of the Zacatecas, keeping southward, through Ameca, Cocula, and Zayula, they came to the maritime province of Colima, and from there to that of Zacatula where, turning westward, they ascended to Malinalco, a place in the mountains surrounding the valley of Toluca, and turning north here, in 1196, they reached the famous city of Tula.

In their journey from Chicomoztoc to Tula they stopped for a brief time at Coatlicamac, where the tribe divided into two factions, between which an eternal rivalry developed, and they did each other great harm. The reason for this discord, according to report, was the discovery of two bundles or parcels that appeared in miraculous fashion in the midst of the camp. When some of the people went to examine them, they discovered in one a precious jewel, and this gave rise to a great dispute, for each group claimed it, believing it a gift from their deity. When they opened the other bundle, they found in it only two pieces of wood. At first sight they disdained them, believing them worthless, but apprised by the wise Huitziton of their value, for they could secure fire from them, they held them in far higher esteem than the jewel. Those who took possession of the jewel were the ones who after the founding of Mexico were called Tlatelolcos, from the site where they settled near that city; those who took the pieces of wood were the ones known as Mexicans or Tenochcas. This relation is not a true account, but a fable invented to teach that the useful should be preferred to the beautiful. The Aztecs many centuries before had discovered how to kindle fire by rubbing two pieces of wood together. In spite of their enmity, the two groups continued their journey together because of their interest in the imaginary protection of their divinity.

It is not surprising that the Aztecs should have wandered so far afield, and should have traveled so many more thousands of miles than was necessary to reach Anahuac, for they had no definite goal in mind, and were only looking for a land where they could enjoy the comforts of life. Neither is it to be wondered at that in certain places they constructed vast edifices, for undoubtedly they believed that each place at which they stopped was the end of their travels. At first many of these spots seemed suitable to settle, and later they abandoned them after having experienced the disadvantages they could not have foreseen. Wherever they stopped, they erected an altar to their god, and when they departed, they left behind their sick, and probably others to look after them, and those who, wearied of their long peregrination, preferred not to undergo new hardships.

They stayed in Tula nine years, and then eleven in other spots not far removed, until in 1216 they came to Zumpanco, a city of some size in the valley of Mexico. Tochpanecatl, the lord of that city, received them with extraordinary kindness; and not content with giving them comfortable lodgings and an abundance of food, asked the leaders of the people for a maiden of noble family as wife for his son Ilhuicatl. The Mexicans, appreciative of his kindness, gave him Tlapacantzin, who shortly afterward was married to the distinguished youth, and from this union the Mexican kings descended.

After remaining in Zumpanco for seven years they departed with young Ilhuicatl to Tizayocan, a city not far removed. There Tlapacatzin gave birth to a son, who was named Huitzilihuitl, and at this time they gave another maiden to Xoquiatzin, the lord of Cuauhtitlan. From Tizayocan they went on to Tolpetlac and to Tepeyacac, where the village and the famous shrine of the Virgin of Guadalupe is today. All these places are along the banks of Lake Tezcoco and very close to the site of what was to be Mexico. There they lived for twenty-two years.

From the time the Mexicans arrived in that land they were accepted by order of Xolotl, who was ruling then, and who, having nothing to fear from them, allowed them to settle where they could. But as they were much harassed in Tepeyacac by Tenancacaltzin, the chief of the Chichemecas, they withdrew to Chapoltepec, a mountain on the west bank of the lake, a scant two miles from the place where Mexico was founded. This withdrawal took place about the year 1245, in the reign of Nopaltzin, not Quinatzin, as Torquemada and Boturini say.

The persecution they suffered there at the hands of many chieftains, and especially the war lord of Xaltocan, obliged them to leave, after remaining there for seventeen years, to find safer refuge in Acocolco, which was a group of islands at the southern end of the lake. There they dragged out fifty-two years of a most miserable existence. They lived on fish, insects, roots, and covered themselves with the leaves of a plant called amoxtli, which grows abundantly there, because their clothes were completely worn out and they had no way of replacing them. Their dwellings were the poorest huts, made of the canes and rushes that grew along the lake. It would seem incredible that they could have lived so many years in such an uncomfortable place and endured such a woeful life, were it not for the fact that this is borne out by the testimony of their historians and by the events that later took place.

Enslavement of the Mexicans in Colhuacan

[FRANCISCO JAVIER CLAVIJERO]

THERE, at any rate, though poverty-stricken, they were free, and freedom somewhat softened their misfortune. But in 1314 to their other trials there was added that of slavery. Historians are not in agreement on this point. Some say that the lord or king of Colhuacan, a city not far from the place where the Mexicans lived, incensed over the fact that they were living in his territory without paying tribute, made war on them, and having defeated them, made them slaves. According to others, that chieftain sent them an embassy with this message: that having taken pity on their misfortunes and the trials they endured on those islands, he was willing to grant them a more comfortable site where they could live more at ease, and that the Mexicans, eager to improve their condition, accepted his offer unhesitatingly and left the place where they had been living. No sooner had they come forth than they were attacked by the Colhuas and made prisoners. However this came about, the fact is that the Mexicans passed as slaves to Tizapan, which at that time belonged to the state of Colhuacan.

After some years of being enslaved, a war broke out between the Colhuas and the Xochimilcos, their neighbors, which went so badly for the former that they were defeated in every encounter. Dismayed at their losses, they decided to utilize their prisoners, whom they ordered to prepare for war. But they did not supply them with the arms they needed, either because they had all been used up in the earlier battles, or to leave them free to arm themselves in their own fashion. The Mexicans, realizing that this was an excellent occasion for them to win the favor of their lords, prepared to come to their defense with the utmost valor. They armed themselves with long, stout staffs, firing the ends to harden them, which could be used, not only to attack the enemy, but to vault from shoal to shoal if they should have to fight in the water. They made themselves knives of stone and shields of reeds. They decided not to stop to take prisoners, as was their custom, but just to cut off one ear, and let them go without further harm. With these preparations, they took the field and fought for the Colhuas against the Xochimilcos on land, along the banks of the lake, or on water, in boats, throwing themselves recklessly against the enemy, using their staffs in the water, and cutting an ear off their prisoners, collecting them in baskets they carried along for this purpose, but killing those that resisted. Thanks to them, the Colhuas won so complete a victory that the Xochimilcos not only abandoned the field, but fled to the hills, afraid to remain in their city.

When the battle had ended so gloriously, the Colhuan soldiers presented themselves to their general with the prisoners they had taken, for among them the bravery of the troops was not judged by the number of enemies they left dead upon the field, but by the number of live prisoners they could lead before their chief. It must be admitted that this practice was in keeping with the concepts of reason and humanity. If a prince can uphold his rights and defeat his enemies without killing them, humanity demands that he preserve their life. And from the practical point of view, while it is true that a dead enemy can do no harm, neither can he be of any use, whereas a live prisoner may be turned to good advantage. As far as the glory is concerned, it requires more valor to deprive an enemy of his liberty than to kill him in the heat of action. In their turn the Mexicans were called to show how many prisoners they had taken; but as they presented none (the four they had captured they had hidden for the purpose we shall soon see), they were called cowards by the general and reviled by the Colhuan troops. Whereupon, bringing out the baskets full of ears, they said: "Judge from the number of these spoils how many prisoners we could have taken if we had wanted to; but it did not seem wise to waste time tying them up, and we preferred to speed the victory." At this answer the Colhuans were taken aback, not only by the shrewdness of their slaves, but by their bravery.

When the Mexicans had returned to their dwelling place, which seems to have been Huitzilopochco, they built an altar to their guardian divinity; and wishing to offer him some precious object in its dedication, they asked their master to send them something. Whereupon he contemptuously sent them a dirty sack of coarse cloth in which was a dead bird and other filth. This the Colhuan priests laid upon the altar and withdrew without speaking a word. Despite the indignation of the Mexicans at such an act of disdain, they decided to put off their vengeance until a more opportune moment, and laid upon the altar, in the place of that filth, a stone knife and sweet-smelling grass. On the day of the ceremony the chieftain and the nobility came, not to honor the festival, but to scoff at their slaves. The Mexicans began the ceremony with a solemn dance for which they had attired themselves in their best garments. When the onlookers were most engrossed, they brought out the four Xochimilco prisoners whom they had hidden until then, and after making them dance for a while, they sacrificed them upon a stone, slashing their breasts with the stone knife and tearing out their hearts, which, still warm and throbbing, they offered up to their god.

This inhuman sacrifice, the first of its kind performed in that land, so far as we know, produced such horror among the Colhuans that they returned immediately to Colhuacan, determined to get rid of their cruel slaves, who in time could become very dangerous to them. In consequence, Coxcox, as their chieftain was called, ordered them to leave his territory and go wherever they wished. The Mexicans, happy to be released from bondage, set out toward the north and reached a place between the two lakes known as Acatzitzintlan, to which they gave the name of Mexicaltzinco, which means the same as Mexico, and they gave it this name for the same reason they afterwards gave it to the capital, as we shall later see. But not finding the comfort they were seeking there, and desirous of putting more distance between themselves and the Colhuans, they moved on to Iztacalco, coming closer to the site of Mexico. There they built a mound of paper, which probably represented Colhuacan, and spent the night dancing around it, chanting their victory over the Xochimilcos and giving thanks to their god for having freed them from their servitude to the Colhuans.

After living for two years in Iztacalco, they finally passed over to that part of the lake where they were to found their city. There they found a cactus growing out of a rock, and on the plant, an eagle; and for this reason they gave to that land, and afterwards to their city, the name of Tenochtitlaan. All, or nearly all, the historians of Mexico say that those were the signs given by the oracle for the founding of the city, and to this they add other supernatural details, which I omit, because they seem to me fabulous, or dubious, to say the least.

The Memorable Experience of a Mexican Princess

[FRANCISCO JAVIER CLAVIJERO]

PAPANTZIN, a Mexican princess, the sister of Moteuczoma, was married to the governor of Tlatelolco; after his death, she lived on in her palace until the year 1509, when she too died of a natural death. Her obsequies were celebrated with the pomp that befitted her lineage, in the presence of the king, her brother, and the nobility of both nations. She was buried in a cave or subterranean grotto in the gardens of the palace where she had lived, close to a pool in which she had been in the habit of bathing, and the opening was closed with a stone. The next day a little girl, five or six years old, who lived in the palace, took it into her head to go from her mother's apartment to that of the steward of the dead princess, which was across the garden. As she passed by the pool she saw the princess sitting on the steps leading down to it, and heard her call to her using the word *"cocoton,"* which they employ in that country to address children affectionately. The little girl, who was too young to reflect on the death of the princess, and thinking that she was going to bathe, as was her custom, went to her without hesitation, and the princess told her to call the wife of the steward. The child did as she was bid; but the steward's wife, smiling and caressing her said: "My child, Papantzin is dead, and yesterday we buried her." But as the girl insisted, and even tugged at her dress, which among them is called *huepilli*, the woman, more to satisfy her than because she believed what she was saying, followed her to the place, and as soon as she laid eyes on the princess, she fell to the ground in a faint. The child went for her mother, and she came to the aid of the steward's wife with two other women; but when they beheld the princess, they were so terror-stricken that they would have fainted, too, if she had not reassured them, telling them that she was alive. She sent them for the steward and told him to tell the king, her brother, what had happened; but he was reluctant to carry out her orders for fear the king would not believe him, and without investigating further, would punish him with his usual severity. "Then go to Tezcoco," said the princess, "and in my name ask King Nezahualpilli to come to see me." The steward obeyed and the king did not long delay in coming. Meanwhile, the princess had gone into one of the rooms of the palace. Filled with fear, the king greeted her, and she entreated him to go to Mexico and tell her brother the king that she was alive and that she needed to see him to reveal to him certain matters of the greatest importance. Nezahualpilli carried out the commission, and Moteuczoma could hardly believe his ears. Nevertheless, not to show himself remiss in the respect due his ally, he went with him, accompanied by many Mexican nobles, to Tlatelolco, and entering the room where the princess was, he asked if she was his sister. "Lord," she replied, "I am your sister Papantzin, she whom you buried yesterday; I am really alive, and I wish to disclose to you what I have seen, because it is of great importance to you." When she had said this, the two kings sat down, and all the others remained standing, amazed at what they were seeing.

Then the princess began to speak again, and said: "After I departed this life, or if that seems impossible to you, after I was deprived of consciousness and motion, I suddenly found myself on a vast plain, extending without limit as far as the eye could see. In the middle of it I saw a road, which divided into several paths, and along one side ran a great river, whose waters made a terrifying noise. I was about to plunge into it and swim to the other bank when there appeared before my eyes a handsome youth of graceful bearing, dressed in a long tunic, white as the snow and gleaming like the sun. He had two wings of beautiful feathers, and on his forehead was this sign (as the princess said this, she made the sign of the Cross with her fingers). Taking me by the hand, he said to me: 'Stop, the hour has not yet come for you to pass this river. God loves you, even though you do not know it.' Then he led me along the bank of the river, on which I saw many skulls and human bones and heard such piteous cries that I was moved to compassion. Then I looked back at the river and saw on it great ships and in them many men unlike those of these lands in dress and color. They were white and bearded; they had banners in their hand and helmets on their heads. 'God,' the youth said to me, 'wishes you to live to bear witness to the revolutions that are going to take place in these lands. The cries you have heard along these banks are the souls of your forefathers who are living, and will always live, in torment as punishment for their sins. Those men you see approaching in those ships will make themselves the masters of these regions by force of arms, and with them will come the tidings of the true God, maker of Heaven and earth. When the war is over, and the baptism has been promulgated that washes sin away, you will be the first to receive it and guide with your example the inhabitants of these lands.' When he had thus spoken, he disappeared, and I found myself restored to life; I arose from the tomb in which I was lying, rolled the stone away, and came into the garden where my servants found me."

Moteuczoma was speechless with amazement as he heard these details, and his mind was grieved with sad forebodings. He arose and went to a palace he had for times of mourning, without speaking a word to his sister, or to the king of Tezcoco, or to any of those who had accompanied him, although some fawning courtiers, to calm him, tried to tell him that the illness the princess had suffered had upset her mind. He did not wish to see her again, not to distress himself anew with the melancholy omens of the downfall of his empire. The princess lived for many years, leading a life of complete retirement and penitence. She was the first to receive holy baptism in Tlatelolco in the year 1524, and from that time on she was known as Doña María Papantzin. During all the years she lived after her rebirth, she was a perfect model of Christian virtues, and her death was in keeping with her life and her marvelous religious vocation.

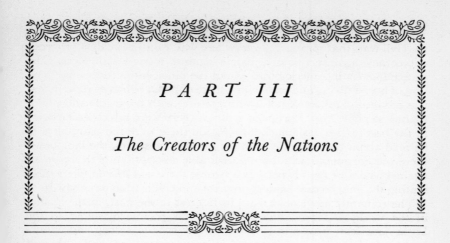

PART III

The Creators of the Nations

ONCE THE SPANISH colonies had achieved their independence, the different worlds that had been germinating under the outwardly unified exterior came to the surface, and Bolívar's dream of a united Spanish America disappeared as reality asserted itself. In spite of the many things they possessed in common, there were deep differences between the various regions—geographical, racial, social—and these physical and psychological variations manifested themselves in the literature of the young republics. As before the independence, the men of letters were mentally attuned to Europe, and their work reflected the literary movements of the day. But the people, the masses, who until this moment had played a negligible role in America's literary life, now made their appearance on the scene. It was they who had fought the war of independence, and were to fight the long series of civil wars that followed. Men who before would have spent their lifetime in the circumscribed area of ranch or village were now marching over the length and breadth of America. Men who might have lived out their days with their herds or behind the counter of a country store were transformed into leaders and generals. Old established barriers of caste and race were overthrown in these restless years. A literature of the people came into being, often anonymous or by authors who had captured its spirit, giving the point of view and reflecting the reactions to the changes that were taking place of these newly minted citizens. They had fought for freedom, but it meant something very different to them than to the political theorists. "Long live freedom, and now to slaughter the cattle!" was the cry of the Venezuelan *llaneros*, whose lances had carried Bolívar to victory. The issues being threshed out in the civil wars that sprang up everywhere was tradition against progress, democracy against tyranny, native against foreign influences. The problem of Latin America throughout the nineteenth century has been that of harmonizing and reconciling these opposed points of view. There was a cultured school of political literature, with programs and philosophies straight from European sources; there were novels and poetry in the best foreign fashion. But alongside these were the pamphlets to be read about the campfire or in the tavern, the satires, the lampoons; there was Sarmiento, with his unforgettable descriptions of the *caudillos*, against whom he used his pen as a sword; there was *Martín Fierro*, presenting the gaucho case against progress and civilization as he saw it.

The romantic movement, with its interest in the past, in the exotic, in the world of legend and tradition, was peculiarly suited to the Latin American temperament, and its influence was deep and enduring. One of the themes of romanticism was America, and although many Americans wrote as though they were viewing their own reality through the eyes of Chateaubriand or Bernardin de Saint-Pierre, nevertheless it strengthened their awareness of themselves and made them realize the rich vein of inspiration their past and their folklore represented. Interest in the heroic tradition went hand in hand with interest in the typical, the quaint, the picturesque, and the school of genre writing flourished, tying in perfectly with this same type of literature which had been so abundant in the colonial epoch. The advent of the realistic and naturalistic movements, with their emphasis on medium and environment as the determining forces of life, led Americans to focus their attention more than ever before on their own reality. All these factors were combining to bring about the independence of American literature, just as in the preceding epoch awareness of their essential difference from Europe had helped to bring about their political independence.

GERTRUDIS GÓMEZ DE AVELLANEDA

(1814–1873)

ONE of the greatest figures the romantic movement produced in Latin America, and perhaps the greatest woman writer in its history was the Cuban poetess, dramatist, and novelist Gertrudis Gómez de Avellaneda.

Although she left Cuba when she was eighteen, and spent nearly all the rest of her life in Spain, she never lost her Creole outlook, and her work has the brilliance, richness, and color that characterizes Cuban literature. She followed with the closest attention and interest everything that happened in the political and literary life of her beloved island.

It was in the field of poetry and the drama that she won her greatest laurels, and she enjoyed the friendship and admiration of the outstanding Spanish writers of her day. Although she wrote a number of novels and legends, her vein was too predominantly lyrical for this type of literature. But in this fragment from her novel *Guatimozin* (1845), which is the only part of the work that she cared to preserve, she shows great understanding of the tragic conflict that took place between Guatimozin—Cuauhtemoc—, who became for a brief time Emperor of the Aztec kingdom after the death of his uncle Montezuma, and Hernán Cortés.

Guatimozin is the symbol of Mexico's resistance to foreign domination, the leader of his people's desperate stand against the invaders, and a great national hero. It is not to be wondered at that even today Mexicans find it difficult to appraise Cortés at his true value, and to accept the fact that he contributed as much, or more, to forming modern Mexico as Guatimozin; it is Queen Boadicea who is a heroine in England, not the Roman generals who brought the island into the orbit of civilization, and it is to Viriatus, not Scipio Africanus, that one finds monuments in Spain.

In this legend dealing with the execution of the Mexican Emperor and the tragic death of his beautiful widow, Gómez de Avellaneda, basing her tale on a few noncommittal lines from Bernal Díaz del Castillo's account of the conquest of Mexico, has drawn a moving picture of the period, and has done justice alike to victor and vanquished.

An Anecdote from the Life of Cortés

[GERTRUDIS GÓMEZ DE AVELLANEDA]

THREE years, more or less, had elapsed since the memorable day when, defeated and a prisoner, the young, heroic emperor Guatimozin had yielded up to the force of Spanish arms the splendid capital of the Mexican empire after ninety-three days of bitter siege. Three years, and yet Cortés the triumphant leader, in spite of his genius and his luck, had not been able to completely subdue all the provinces of the vast region of New Spain which his sword had brought under the dominion of the ancient crown of Castile. But there had been time enough, and more, for the intoxicating sweetness of triumph to become embittered with intimate sacrifices of his own heart and the shameful defection of some of his most trusted followers.

It must have been a bitter pill for that proud spirit to swallow to yield to the demands of his rough, undisciplined troops and the barbarous hordes of his native allies, placed at his service by the hate-blinded Tlascaltecas and other Mexican nations. It was compliance with their demands that stained the famous conquest with such blots that—in the words of Cortés himself—"Never have such lamentable horrors or such relentless cruelty been seen." It was their demands that tarnished the luster of his glorious achievements, and made him consent to the shameful torture of his royal captives in an attempt to drag from them the confession of the hiding place of supposed concealed treasure, torture that has made forever famous the indomitable spirit of the imperial martyr, who, while he was being grilled over a slow fire, said those memorable words to the king of Tacuba, who was suffering the same torment, when the latter let a groan escape his breast: "Coward, am I in a bed of roses?" And it was their demands that made the captain of Extremadura silence the voice of pity in his breast and regard with seeming indifference the sight of the daughter of his protector Motezuma, the beautiful Gualcazintla, the unhappy consort of Guatimozin, in chains.

But all these shameful concessions to the barbarous spirit of those bloodstained times were not enough to satisfy his victorious followers. The superiority of genius is never exercised with impunity; those men who dominate their fellows solely by their mental gifts never manage to inspire that submission that is tributed to noble birth without reserve.

Hernán Cortés, one of the greatest figures on the roster of history;

Hernán Cortés, who perhaps has not been given his due, even by his most fulsome eulogists, who have distorted the true outlines of the man in their attempts to deify him; Hernán Cortés, the representative of his nation in those days when it was great, heroic, fanatical, and indomitable . . . Hernán Cortés, as was inevitable, suffered the fate of all geniuses. Envy pursued him, slander blackened his name, treachery and perfidy dogged his footsteps, harbored in those very hearts that had learned from his never to flinch from the innumerable dangers in which they all won undying fame.

The treason of the infamous Villafaña, even though discovered and punished, had left behind it seeds that seemed to sprout at every turn. At the time of which we are speaking, there had been no word for a long time from Captain Olid, who had been sent by his leader to subdue certain of the nations of Mexico who still refused to yield, and there were many rumors that he and his troops had revolted. Another officer, who was sent with troops after the presumptive rebel, as far as could be judged, had not carried out his orders either; and it was even whispered through the army that instead of opposing Olid, he had made common cause with him.

Cortés, therefore, finally had to set out himself to punish them, if evidence of their insubordination was established, and at the same time subdue the provinces that were still resisting.

He was accompanied on that expedition, not only by the bulk of his army, but by the most important of the captive Tlatoanis, or princes. Among these was the Emperor himself and his wife, whom three years of captivity and untold misfortunes had been unable to deprive of her amazing beauty, although they had so affected her mental faculties that the soldiers referred to her as "the sad mad woman."

To be sure, for the work that faced Cortés on the expedition, a retinue of prisoners was not the most fitting addition; but he was afraid to leave his royal captives anywhere in the fallen empire without a powerful guard, and he could ill spare the men.

Finally, the enforced company of those shackled princes, the sight of whom, particularly the young Emperor, deeply stirred the native settlements through which they passed, became so awkward and such a source of worry to him that he ordered his troops to halt at a village in the province of Acala. There he held a secret conference with his captains, some of whom had held from the beginning of the journey that at any cost they ought to rid themselve of these "stumbling blocks" as quickly as possible.

Outside the council nobody knew what had been discussed; but a rumor began to spread quickly to the effect that a terrible conspiracy had been discovered, plotted by the Mexican monarch and his brother the king of Tacuba, to kill Cortés and arouse the natives against the invaders.

Strange as it may seem, those hapless prisoners, worn out by hunger, surrounded by a powerful army, defenseless, exhausted with fatigue, appear to have aroused such fear in the bold heart of Cortés that he proceeded to pass judgment on them without observing any of the formalities demanded by law.

II

It was early morning on one of those beautiful winter days that come only under the tropic sun, and all the inhabitants of the little town in which the invading army had made camp streamed out of their modest homes to watch the warriors of the East (as they called them), who, for some reason they could not fathom, were blocking off the few streets of the village, all of which opened into a square where a squad of cavalry was assembled.

The people, intrigued by the novelty of the sight, managed to slip through the soldiers, and from the turrets of their temple, the Teocali, and the roofs of the near-by houses, they anxiously scanned every corner of the square, in the hope of discovering the reason for the warlike array of the Spaniards.

Suddenly the eyes of the curious multitude came to rest on a strange new object. It was a gallows that had been erected during the night in the center of the square.

Instinctively the sight of it sent a shudder through the amazed inhabitants of Acala, and some ran off in terror to hide in the hills.

Meanwhile on the esplanade of the temple, where the remains of the god Huitzilopochtli's razed altar could still be seen, two well-favored women, neither of them yet thirty, had settled themselves comfortably to watch the dreadful sight soon to be staged. Both were dressed in Spanish fashion, but it was easy to see that this was not the usual costume of one of them. The color of her skin, the cast of her features, her tiny hands and feet, her halting pronunciation when she spoke Spanish, all pointed to the fact that she was of native origin. The other was a dark-eyed Andalusian to whom the spectacle she was about to witness brought back pleasant memories of autos-da-fé and bullfights which had been the delight of her early years.

"How fine and gallant our soldiers look," remarked the Spanish lady. "They are like high-carat gold, Doña Marina, that comes out purer and more beautiful when its dross has been melted away in the fire. All the trials and hardships they have suffered on this long, fatiguing journey, over rugged mountains, chill uplands, fever-ridden swamps, enduring cold and heat, thirst and hunger, have not dampened the courage of those Spanish hearts."

"It is only fitting that they should follow the example of their leader, my dear Doña Guiomar," answered the Indian. "After so many battles and victories, that hero was entitled to a rest. But you see for yourself how he has to contend against the disloyalty of his captains."

"If Olid has really rebelled he should be shown no mercy," replied the Andalusian; "but I must confess that, like others, I still have my doubts. What is apparent to all is the perversity of these Indians who have dared to conspire against the life of our general. Their abominable crime is going to cost the authors of this base scheme dear. I can't even speak of it, Doña Marina, without getting into a rage."

Doña Marina lowered her eyes, and a smothered sigh escaped her. Then she answered in a voice that trembled a little:

"There are circumstances that make harsh measures inevitable; I realize that he who was the sovereign of all these nations, the mere sight of whom has aroused the people as we have seen, must die; but I do not know how much proof there is of the conspiracy whose punishment we are about to witness."

"It distresses me to hear you suggest that the death sentence of the great cacique was dictated more by expediency than by justice," said Doña Guiomar.

"That is not what I meant to imply," answered Cortés's mistress. "Whatever *Malinche* does cannot but seem good and right to his slave who loves him; but you must realize, dear friend, that I cannot calmly accept the fact that the illustrious descendant of the heroes of Atzcapuzalco, the mighty monarch on whose brow the great crown of Acamapit has rested, is to die on the shameful gallows."

"You are a native of the country over which this man reigned," observed the Spanish lady, "and it is not surprising that you should be moved to pity. I, too, felt sorry for him before his crime of conspiracy; for truly his bearing is noble and full of majesty, and he stands out among all the other natives even in his color, which is so light that he might be a European."

"He fought so heroically to save his people from the foreign yoke to which the weakness of his predecessor Motezuma had handed them over," exclaimed Marina in an uncontrollable burst of patriotic pride. "And after succumbing to the designs of fate, he has suffered misfortune with such noble fortitude."

"Not so his poor wife," her vivacious companion interrupted. "The Empress Gualcazintla has lost her mind completely, even though her madness is of such a gentle, quiet nature that one can hardly feel sorry for her."

"Truly it is fortunate for her that her reason is clouded over, especially today when one should give thanks to heaven for this circumstance which will prevent her understanding the horror of this moment of her tragic fate."

"Look! Look!" Guiomar broke in, "I think they are bringing in the condemned men."

So they were; Guatimozin and his brother Netzalc, King of Tacuba, were being led into the square by a numerous escort.

"Apparently," said Doña Guiomar, stretching her lovely neck to see them better, "only those two have been condemned to death, although it was said that the conspiracy was very widespread."

"*Malinche* is compassionate," Marina brought out with an effort, "and he has probably thought it would be sufficient example to punish only the leaders."

As Marina said this, the Franciscan friars, who were walking beside the condemned men, began to exhort them in a loud voice to confess their crime and ask divine and human forgiveness that they might achieve eternal happiness. Guatimozin, whose proud brow, divested of the imperial coronet, seemed even more majestic beneath its aureole of misfortune, turned to them with great dignity. In firm, manly tones that could be heard from one end of the square to the other, he thanked them for their interest in him, adding solemnly: "Once more I proclaim my innocence before heaven and earth, but I bless this death which brings to an end sufferings beyond the power of a man to endure."

Then he ran his serene gaze over the armed troop that filled the square, letting it rest for a moment on the gallows that was awaiting him, as though to familiarize himself with it. Then raising his eyes to the sky with an expression that was truly sublime, he forgave his enemies, embraced his brother, and with firm step ascended the fatal stairs.

At this, exclamations of admiration and pity were heard from among the Spanish ranks, and Netzalc bent low over the footprints of the royal martyr, kissing them and murmuring in fervent tone: "Happy am I to die with you, great prince, and side by side we shall both enter the palaces of the Sun."

Meanwhile the executioner had laid hold of his victim; the name of Gualcazintla floated through the air, and the tender farewell was cut short by a shrill, piercing cry. The last Emperor of Mexico dangled from the ignominious rope. At that very moment his wife, pale, her hair disheveled, appeared on the esplanade of the temple from which Doña Marina and her friend were witnessing the execution.

"God in Heaven! The mad woman!" exclaimed the latter jumping up from her chair.

"Why didn't they take care to prevent her seeing this horror?" asked the Mexican, rising too and going toward Gualcazintla. "Come, Doña Guiomar, in the name of charity let us take her away from here."

"Gladly," answered the Spanish lady. "Her madness has never taken violent form, and besides we've seen everything there was to see."

She was right. Netzalc's sentence had likewise been carried out by the executioner.

While the two women came over to Gualcazintla's side, she looked on with dry eyes at the body of her husband, writhing in the air in the last convulsions of the death agony. But strangely enough, the sad expression and the apathy that characterized her mental disorder had disappeared, and her face, usually so gentle, was set in a fierce rage and despair.

The supreme blow she had just received seemed to have aroused all her benumbed faculties.

"Princess," said Doña Marina, taking her gently by the hand, "I was born in your father's dominions, I was his subject, and I feel it my duty to shelter you in the desolation that has come upon you. Will you come and live with me, under the protection of the great and victorious general Hernán Cortés?"

"Cortés! Cortés!" repeated Gualcazintla, turning her eyes from the gallows and fixing them on Marina. "I remember that name; he is the stranger who deceived my father and debased him, making him pay homage to the sovereign of the East. He is the man who profaned our temples, cast down our gods, destroyed our city, and put the brand of slavery on the brow of our princes. He is the man who ordered the sacred person of the Emperor, my husband, put to the torment, and has just had him killed like a common criminal. And you, his slave, his concubine, ask me to accept your patronage."

Marina and Guiomar stared at one another in amazement, for they had not expected to hear such sane words from the lips of a mad woman. Then the former interposed, to mitigate the bad impression they might have produced in the Spaniard: "You are talking nonsense, poor Gualcazintla, and all I can answer, since you seem to understand, in spite of your disordered mind, that you have lost your husband and that you are alone in the world, is that you must resign yourself to the will of heaven and forget the past forever. If you accept my offer, from today you shall be at my side, as though you were my sister, and I have no doubt that with time you will do justice to our glorious ruler, whose protection I can guarantee you."

Guatimozin's widow listened to her words with a strange expression, and then, as though some sudden inspiration had brought her to a decision, she pressed Marina's hand tightly, and said: "Very well, I

shall do as you wish since my destiny so orders it. You live beside
Hernán Cortés, and I shall live with you. Let us go," and she cast
one last look upon the still body of Guatimozin, beside which now
hung that of Netzalc. "Let us go quickly, mistress of the conqueror,
to the refuge you offer me."

The troops withdrew to their quarters; the three women left the
temple together, and then went to their different habitations. The two
bodies were cut down shortly afterwards and buried by order of Cortés.

III

Later, when night had covered all with its dark mantle, Hernán
Cortés went to visit his lady, who was lodged in the same vast building
occupied by him, which had been the temple of the goddess Meztli,
the Mexican Diana. Her statues were still to be seen in a spacious hall
that separated Doña Marina's rooms from those used by her lover.

She took advantage of the occasion to present to him her new guest,
and implored him to take pity on her and grant her his protection,
since she was so utterly forsaken.

It must have seemed to her, however, that her entreaties were unnecessary in view of the sudden and manifest impression aroused in
Cortés by the mere presence of the beautiful, unhappy woman whom
he had just deprived of the one being she loved who remained to her
in the world.

The acts of cruelty that expediency forced the leader of the Spanish
troops to commit or tolerate found secret but instant punishment in
his own noble heart. Under the influence of the remorse that had
gnawed at him every since he accepted as inevitable the necessity of
sacrificing his two most distinguished prisoners, he displayed toward
Gualcazintla such marked and tender affection—as though to soothe
his conscience a little—that Marina, infatuated and jealous, began to
take alarm.

While she, perhaps, was repenting her impulse to bring into close
association with the man she loved the recently bereaved princess,
attractive, if for no other reason than by the magnitude of her misfortune, Gualcazintla received the affectionate attentions the general
showered upon her with the melancholy, silent indifference that had
characterized her derangement, which she seemed to have shaken off
only momentarily at the sight of the ignominious death of her husband.
The burning indignation that shone on her face and the terrible recollections that the mere mention of the name of Cortés awakened in her
memory had completely disappeared, to judge by her appearance, for

there was no sign that the sight of the man who had wiped out her family caused her the least distress.

This strange reaction contributed to Marina's uneasiness, for in her mad infatuation she could not comprehend that any woman would not, like herself, sacrifice her strongest ties and her most sacred duties to the glory of being loved by the hero of the East.

When Cortés's visit was over and he had given orders to break camp the next day, he withdrew, and Marina, colder toward her guest than she had been during the day, imperiously ordered her to go to bed and get some rest, while she sat, thoughtful and uneasy, beside her lonely bed, which she felt sleep would not visit that night.

But she was not the only one who kept vigil. Cortés could not sleep either. Perhaps the effort it had cost him to sacrifice justice and considerations of humanity to political exigencies had so upset him that it was impossible for him to rest. Perhaps there rose before his eyes, in the midst of the darkness and silence, the shades of his royal victims, demanding an accounting of their shameful sentence. Perhaps, by some mysterious design of the Almighty, the unusual beauty of his unhappy prisoner, whom, until then, he had regarded with indifference, had suddenly so impressed him as to justify in a measure the presentiments that at that very moment were tormenting his jealous mistress.

Be this as it may, Cortés, sleepless and restless, was unable to bear the narrow confines of his room, and went into the adjoining hall, where he began to pace up and down amidst the crudely carved statues of the goddess of the night, barely outlined by the dim light of a distant lamp.

He had kept up this mechanical movement for some time when suddenly he stopped short, his hair rising in superstitious terror. It seemed to him that he discerned, from the end of the hall next to his rooms where he stood, a black phantom at the other end amidst the white marble figures, which at that moment also assumed a fantastic, supernatural quality in his fevered imagination.

In vain he tried to persuade himself that it was a passing hallucination. The black phantom was unquestionably drawing nearer, and suddenly, in the semidarkness of the room and amidst the funereal draperies in which it was swathed, there glittered the polished steel of a dagger.

Despite this, Cortés neither fled nor did his voice falter as he asked the specter: "Who are you and why have you come here?"

"I am vengeance," answered a voice hoarse with rage, "and I have come to do away with you forever, tyrant."

Hardly had the words been uttered when Cortés felt the slash of the steel against his forehead. The blood began to gush out, veiling his sight, but notwithstanding, he was able to recognize the widow of Guatimozin, whose large, beautiful eyes glittered so sinisterly that they could have lighted up the gloom.

The force of her arm had not been in keeping with the strength of her determination, fortunately for Cortés, but she would undoubtedly have followed up her attack had he not managed to wrest the dagger from her.

On finding herself disarmed and caught in the robust arms of her enemy, Gualcazintla was seized by a paroxysm of despair and fainted away. She would have fallen to the floor had he not supported her, and more moved than angry, he carried her silently to the room that had been assigned her in Marina's quarters.

As he was laying the limp body of his beautiful enemy upon the bed, his mistress, who had been unable to sleep and who had caught a faint echo of the noise the scene in the hall had produced, though very slight, came tiptoeing out of her room, making her way through the chamber of idols to the room of her captain.

Her suspicion and jealousy, when she found the room empty and Cortés's bed untouched, can better be surmised than expressed.

Trembling, pale, beside herself, the passionate Mexican retraced her steps, her goal this time being the chamber of her guest. But before she reached it she heard footsteps, and slipping swiftly behind one of the statues, she saw coming out of that door, on which her eyes were fastened, the man for whom she had sacrificed everything, holding a handkerchief to his forehead to stem the blood from his wound, but which to Marina's frenzied mind was nothing but a mask to prevent his recognition if surprised.

Cortés, far from suspecting that he was being spied upon, returned to his room, where he bathed and bandaged his wounded forehead. He had no intention of telling anyone what had happened that night.

But suddenly his door was thrown noisily open, and there stood his mistress with an expression of fury on her face.

"Marina," he exclaimed, unable to disguise his annoyance at this unexpected visit. "Will you never learn the prudence our respective positions make necessary? Will you always give way to your desires, forgetting that we are not free?"

"I have done much to assure your domestic peace, giving the woman who bears your name little cause for complaint," answered the Mexican, folding her arms; "I have also tortured and debased my soul enough, accepting the husband you insisted on marrying me to. And is this abnegation not enough for you? You also want me, ungrateful man, to blind myself to the outrages of your libertinism? You want me to look on indifferently while you dare, faithless to both love and duty, commit the unspeakable villainy of taking advantage of the madness of this unhappy princess, ravishing her the same day you murdered her husband?"

"It is you who are mad, you with your incurable jealousy," answered Cortés, trying to restrain his anger. "Stop tormenting me with your absurd ravings, and go back to your room, for it will soon be day and the sentries will be coming to call me as we break camp."

"You say that I am raving," answered Marina, her eyes blazing. "Ah, *Malinche*, know then that only a few moments ago I saw you come out of Gualcazintla's room. It is not suspicion I have of your crime, but proof. But you will not repeat it, that I swear to you, you will not offend heaven by defiling the bed of the widow of the Emperor of Mexico before his body is cold in the grave. It is my duty to prevent this, and I have done so."

"What have you done?" asked Cortés, seized by a strange misgiving. "What have you done to Gualcazintla?"

"I have strangled her," replied Marina grimly. "Her spirit has gone to join Guatimozin, and together they will demand vengeance against you at the bar of God."

Cortés in horror pushed her away so violently that she fell to the ground. Tearing the bandage from his wounded forehead, he showed her the dagger still stained with blood, saying as he did so:

"The justice of heaven, with which you are threatening me, has just prevented my life coming to an end at the hands of a maddened woman, but less so than you, and I venture to hope that when it judges the faults I have commited, like all men, it will take into account the many obstacles I have encountered and the sufferings I have endured for the glory of planting the cross of Golgotha throughout these vast lands, open from today on to Christian civilization."

The rumors that were whispered among the troops the next day have been set down by Bernal Díaz del Castillo in these lines:

"Cortés was upset and preoccupied after hanging Guatemuz and his relative, the lord of Tacuba, without justice for so doing, and at night he could not sleep. It seems that he left his bedchamber to walk in a room where there were idols, and was careless and fell, wounding himself in the head. He said nothing, good or bad, about the matter, and attended to his wound, suffering everything in silence."

ESTANISLAO DEL CAMPO

(1834–1880)

OUT OF THE folk poetry of Argentina grew one of its richest forms of literary expression, the *poesía gauchesca*, the poetry of the gauchos. Its origins are remote, going back to the poetry of Spain of the fifteenth century, the epoch in which the cities were coming into being. In this poetry, cultivated by some of the finest poets of the period, the peasants spoke in their rustic dialect, and its theme was the criticism of the city and its ways. In the eighteenth century, too, with the revival of regional literature, a dialectal poetry developed which was a vehicle of social and political criticism. This poetry existed throughout the Hispanic world, but it flourished with especial vigor in Argentina. There it was anonymous, the creation of the *payador*, or wandering minstrel, who was a familiar figure about the ranches and wayside taverns, composing his ballads and accompanying himself on the guitar. Some of these *payadores* became legendary figures, like Santos Vega, who is said to have challenged the Devil himself to compete with him. With the beginning of romanticism, this anonymous and purely folk poetry was adopted by cultured poets of great distinction and ability as their medium of poetic expression. Much of this poetry was written during and following the independence of Argentina, and it became a form of political literature.

From the beginning the problem of Argentina was the city against the country; Buenos Aires against the provinces; foreign, European ways against native customs; in a word, what Sarmiento called "civilization and barbarism." In this poetry the gaucho was the critic of the new against the traditional ways, the champion of the country against the innovations the government, represented for him by the city Buenos Aires, would introduce. This was the theme of Ascasubi's poems, of Hidalgo's, both distinguished cultivators of this type of poetry; and although in Estanislao del Campo's *Faust* the political problem is not touched upon, it does express the reactions of the gaucho in the face of a purely urban and cultured form of entertainment, the opera. In his own language, and giving it his own interpretation, the gaucho Anastasio describes to his friend Laguna a performance of *Faust* he saw in Buenos Aires. There is no doubt in the mind of either that what Anastasio saw was the gospel truth, and the dealings of Dr. Faust with the Devil had a perfectly familiar ring in their ears. All the philosophical connotations of Goethe's work have disappeared; all that remains for them is a man seeking the Devil's help to further a love affair, and offering his soul in payment. Both gauchos are horrified at the idea, though it is not new to them, and amazed that a man as smart as the doctor should think any good could come from pacting with the Devil.

Estanislao del Campo was one of the most cultivated of the group that employed this form of poetry. He came of a distinguished family that had played an important role in the history of the Argentine for generations, and he himself fought in the battles that finally liberated his country from the tyranny of Rosas. He was active in politics, a journalist, and the author of a number of poems in the romantic manner. But his literary fame rests on this witty, satirical portrayal of the gaucho's psychology. The following selection is from the excellent translation by Walter Owen of Buenos Aires.

*Faust**

[ESTANISLAO DEL CAMPO]

I had bare sat down and looked around,
When the band with a bang let go,
Behind a fence, down on the ground
Where the stage was, for the show.

And a big tarpaulin they gave a haul,
With such a rush, I tell you true,
Would have bowled you over, horse and all,
If it caught you goin' through.

And behind the screen a chap appeared,
A doctor by vocation,
Called Fowst, it seems—for so I heer'd—
And well-known by reputation.

* Reprinted from *Faust* by Estanislao del Campo, adapted from the Spanish and rendered into English verse by Walter Owen, by permission of Walter Owen, Copyright 1943 by him, Buenos Aires.

—It's Curnel Fowst, I understand,
Or my mem'ry's gettin' dim;
The Uruguayan—no doctor him—
Why, I served in his command!

—O shucks! I knew the Curnel good;
He's cold meat now, God save him;
It's many the time he cinched his wood
On a chestnut hoss I gave him.

To find two broncs the same hair and size,
Ain't nothin' unheard of, brother,
Don't trouble the Fowst that's in Paradise;
I'm talkin' about this other.

—I never knew gaucho wag his chin
As smart as you, *aijuna!*
—Just give me a swig at that crock of gin,
Before I go on, Laguna.

Well, this doctor comes on, as I said before,
And begins a long oration,—
Confidin' the crowd that he's feelin' sore,
And the why of his tribulation.

He told us that all the pile of books
He had read till his eyes were dim,
Weren't helping his case with a goldy-locks
That hadn't no use for him.

He kept snoopin' around her grazin' patch,
Neglectin' his sleep and food,
And bleatin' all night outside her thatch,
But it didn't do no darn good.

When at milkin'-time that gal came out,
As dainty and fresh as dew,
He hobbled the cow, and stood about;
But nix!—So, says he, I'm through!

It wasn't worth livin' life that way,
She'd not see his face again;

He'd pizen himself that very day—
He was checkin' out there and then.

Then he sloshed his hat on the floor and fell
To cussin' worse than double,
And wound up by callin' the Fiend of Hell
To fix his particular trouble.

He should have thought twice! He'd barely spoke,
By Christ, what a scare I got!
For there in a cloud of stinkin' smoke,
The Devil was on the spot!

Yes, crossin' yourself won't harm you, pard,
At the time I did it too.
—Why didn't the doc start trackin' hard?
—That's just what I'm askin' you!

You ought to have seen the Devil, my word!
Skin and bone, in a flappin' coat,
A hat with a feather, cats-claws, a sword,
And a beard like an old buck-goat.

He was rigged for legs like a bloomin' stork,
With socks right up to his very fork,
For eyes, in his face he had two black holes,
With sparks inside like burnin' coals.

Said the Devil—"I'm at your service, doc,
Just order yours most truly."
But the doctor was showin' signs of shock,
Like his wits were goin' woolly.

—"I'm aimin' to help, said the Evil One;
There ain't nothin' to be afraid of;
Whatever you order's as good as done—
I'll show you the stuff I'm made of."

The doc was scared, and he asked him quick,
To get goin' for good,—and pronto;
And wasn't he wise?—You betcha, Chick,
—But the Devil he didn't want to.

He claimed that in trackin' into town,
He'd had travellin' expenses,
And ended by calmin' the doctor down,
And makin' him lose his senses.

—But how could the Devil drop his rope
On a doctor with all that learnin'?
—Once you listen to Satan, there ain't no hope,
The next thing you know, you're burnin'.

Then the Devil again says most polite,
"Now what can I do for you?
There ain't the least call for takin' fright;
Call your orders—I'll put them through.

If you want *dinero*—I don't talk rash—
But I'll do you proud and proper;
When I'm done with fixin' you for cash,
Anchorena'll look a pauper."

—Says Fowst: " 'Tain't because I ain't livin' rich,
That right now I'm feelin' hurt;
I'm wantin' something beside of which
Gold's just so much yellow dirt."

'Whatever you like,' says the King of Hell;
'I reckon that's what you heard;
D'you want the Government? Good and well,
You're it, if you say the word.'

' 'Tain't power nor money I'm pinin' for,'
Says Fowst; 'let's quit palaver;
I'm nuts on a gal, my good señor,
And my trouble's that I can't have her.'

So soon as those words the Devil hears,
He busts loose with such ugly laughter,
That it kept on ringin' in my ears
The rest of the evenin' after.

He stamps the floor, and the solid wall
Cracks open top to bottom,

And standin' there was the doctor's gal—
I guess the doc thought he'd got 'em!

—By cripes! Is all I'm hearin' true?
You ain't aimin' at kiddin' me?
—I ain't one, Laguna, to fib to you.
Half the town was there to see!

That gal was a topper for looks, my son,
Pure peach, with locks like flax;
I thought I was settin' eyes on one
Of them Virgins they make from wax.

She'd a blue dress on—no frills or frays,
Just tucks around the hem—
And her hair was gold like the beard of maize,
That's fresh plucked off the stem.

She'd skin like curds of cream, old pard,
When the cow-food's lush and rich;
Beside a Madonna 'twould have been hard
To pick out which was which.

She'd teeth like pearls fresh from the sea,
Two mornin' stars for eyes,
And a red-rose bud where her mouth should be,—
No, chum, I'm not tellin' lies.

The doctor gave hisself his head,
Makin' tracks in her direction;
But Satan headed him off, and said:
"Not so fast!—she's in my protection."

If you're ready, I'll only be too pleased
To put things in black and white.
You give me your soul; and you'll find all greased
For smooth-workin' . . . you got me right?"

"Okay," says the doctor on the spot,
"Just show me where I sign."
And the Devil flips out a bill he'd brought,
And gets Fowst on the dotted line.

—A doctor!—and signin' a bond like that!
—Do you wonder he met disaster?
"Diamond cut diamond" fits here just pat;
For the Devil's the lawyer's master.

You must know that the doc hadn't seen his youth
For a longish interval,
And a trifle shaky and long in the tooth
To go pawin' around a gal.

So he says to the Devil with a wink,
As he hands back the contract, signed,
"Can't you fix me up with some witchin' drink?
You know what I've got in mind . . ."

The Devil was hot-stuff, I'll allow,
Old Fowst had no sooner said it,
Than the Devil did somethin'—don't ask me how—
And Gee!—it's hard to credit . . .

Did you ever chance to see a grub
Turn into a butterfly?
That's somethin' how as Old Beelzebub
Made over that crocked old guy.

Old bag-coat, night-cap, and silvery hair,
Went poof! and no more were seen;
And there was the doctor, standin' there,
As good as he'd ever been.

—Am I hearin' right? What's that you said?
The doctor got back his youth?
—Listen matey; may lightnin' strike me dead,
If it ain't pure gospel truth.

The Devil then waved the gal to quit;
And with some kind of magic knack,
He mended the wall where he'd busted it . . .
And they pulled the tarpaulin back.

And now, please pass that talkin-juice;
My talk-box is gettin' wheezy.
—Here you are; give your pipes a double sluice,
And go on when they work more easy.

DOMINGO F. SARMIENTO

(1811–1888)

"YOU ARE NOT A MAN, you are a nation," said Mrs. Horace Mann to her friend Domingo F. Sarmiento, and no one could have a clearer claim to such a title. He was born the year after Argentina declared its independence; he grew up during the turbulent years when it was trying to establish itself, harassed by external enemies and internal discord. As a young man he went into exile as a protest against the tyranny of the dictator Juan Manuel Rosas. From Chile he maintained relentless warfare against him with his pen, and it was in the columns of a Chilean newspaper that his masterpiece, *Facundo, or Civilization and Barbarism in the Argentine Republic*, was first published. When, after many years, the opposition to Rosas came to a head under General Urquiza, Sarmiento joined his troops and was present at the victory of Caseros, which ended Rosas's rule.

No one man did so much to shape the future of his country as Sarmiento, and yet he was always alone. More than anyone else it was he who brought Argentina to the position it holds today; it was he who urged the opening of the country to immigration, it was he who planned and introduced agricultural reforms, the canalization of its rivers, the development of new industries, but, above all, the founding of schools, the extension of education to all. By his dogged determination, his ability to surmount every obstacle, he managed to convert his dreams into reality, but all his life he was known as "*el loco Sarmiento*." He had a vast admiration for the United States, and it was during his ambassadorship in this country that he was nominated and elected President of Argentina. With that same fearless independence, that unshakable faith in himself that had characterized him all his life, he presided over his country's government, putting through his most cherished plans, suppressing the forces of reaction wherever they raised their head, and always building more schools. His lifelong fight had been against what he called "barbarism," represented for him in the stubborn clinging to the past, in the unwillingness of many, the country-folk particularly, to throw off their traditional ways and habits of thought and action in favor of new and modern customs. It was the old struggle between the city and the country, Buenos Aires and the rest of the Argentine republic. But despite the fact that he fought it without quarter, Sarmiento himself was a product of this tradition; he bore it within himself, he found his inspiration in it, and there is admiration under the fury with which he excoriates the archrepresentatives of this tradition, Rosas and the gaucho *caudillos* who supported him. Instead of attacking Rosas directly, he symbolizes all that Rosas stood for in the figure of Facundo Quiroga, one of his supporters who, when he threatened to become a rival, was assassinated, probably at Rosas's orders. Yet Sarmiento could never have left us the unforgettable picture he did if he had not understood Quiroga as one can understand only what forms a part of one's self.

Facundo Quiroga may be considered the archetype of the countless *caudillos* that have flourished in every Latin American country. They are popular leaders who spring up from the people, incarnating their protests and their hopes, but who invariably—if they live long enough —wind up as dictators. These anecdotes of Quiroga, so admirably recounted by Sarmiento, might have been, or perhaps have been, told of many others—Páez, Castro, Gómez, Porfirio Díaz, Pancho Villa. Even during their lifetime these men became legendary figures and supermen; their sayings and their exploits came to form part of their nations' folklore.

Three Anecdotes of Juan Facundo Quiroga

[DOMINGO F. SARMIENTO]

THERE lies between the cities of San Luis and San Juan a vast desert that, because of its complete lack of water, has received the name of "the crossing." The aspect of this lonely stretch is for the most part dreary and desolate, and the west-bound traveler never fails to fill his canteens with water as he passes the last well or cistern on the route. In this desert there once took place the strange scene that follows. The knife play so common among our gauchos had obliged one of them to leave the city of San Luis with all the speed he could muster, and make for the desert on foot, his saddle on his shoulder, to escape the clutches of the law. Two of his friends were to meet him as soon as they could steal horses for the three of them. In those days hunger and thirst were not the only menaces in that desert; for a year a man-eating tiger had lurked in wait for travelers, and more than eight had fallen victim to its fondness for human flesh. It often happens that in those countries where man and beast vie to see which shall get the upper hand, the former falls beneath the latter's bloody claws; when this happens, the tiger develops a preference for human fare, and receives the appelation of *cebado* when it takes to hunting this new quarry, man. When this occurs the judge of the vicinity where it is carrying on its depredations calls upon such as are most skilled in the chase, and under his authority and guidance they undertake to hunt down the man-eating tiger, who rarely evades the death sentence.

When the fugitive from justice had traveled some six leagues, it seemed to him that he heard the roar of a tiger in the distance, and a chill ran through him. The roar of a tiger is a grunt, similar to that of the pig, but shrill, prolonged, strident, and even when there is no reason for fear, it sends an involuntary shudder through the nerves, as though the flesh were trembling of itself with a premonition of death. A few minutes later the roar sounded more clear and close at hand; the tiger had picked up the scent. A considerable distance away a small locust tree reared itself. It was necessary to hurry, to run, in fact, for the roars were following close upon one another, each clearer and fiercer than the last. Finally, tossing his saddle away, the gaucho made for the tree he had glimpsed, and despite the slenderness of its trunk, fortunately of a considerable height, he managed to climb into the upper branches and partly conceal himself among the leaves, though the tree kept swaying back and forth. From this refuge he was able to observe what took place on the road: the tiger bounded along, its nose to the ground, its roars increasing as it scented the proximity of its prey. It passed the spot where the latter had left the road, and there it lost the trail. At this the tiger flew into a rage, turning this way and that, until it spied the saddle, which it ripped to pieces with one blow of its paw, scattering the different parts through the air. This disappointment further enraged it; it turned back until it picked up the trail again, finally discovering the direction the gaucho had taken, and lifting its head, saw its prey, whose weight was making the frail tree sway back and forth, like a river reed when a bird settles on its tip. With this the tiger's roars ceased; it covered the space between them with leaping bounds, and in less time than it takes to tell, its huge paws were resting two yards above the ground against the slender trunk, jerking it back and forth in a way that was anything but soothing to the nerves of the precariously seated gaucho. The beast gave a futile leap into the air; then it began to circle the tree, measuring its height with eyes reddened by the lust for blood, and finally, roaring with rage, it lay down at the foot of the tree, lashing its tail incessantly, without for a moment taking its eyes from its prey, its mouth panting and dry. This horrible scene had gone on for two mortal hours; the strained position of the gaucho, and the terrifying fascination the bloodshot, unwinking stare of the tiger, from which he found it impossible to withdraw his eyes, exerted upon him had begun to weaken him, and he foresaw the moment when his benumbed body would drop into the beast's maw. But at that very moment the distant echo of galloping hoofbeats brought him hope of salvation. As a matter of fact, his friends had seen the track of the tiger and were hurrying to him, but without much hope of arriving in time. The scattered fragments of the saddle revealed to them the spot of the encounter, and setting spurs to their horses, unrolling their lassos and throwing them over the stubborn, infuriated tiger, was the work of a second. The beast, caught and stretched flat by the two lassos, fell a victim to the repeated knife thrusts with which its near victim avenged his long-drawn-out torment. "It was then that I learned the meaning of fear," said General Juan Facundo Quiroga, describing the episode to a group of officers.

He, too, was known as the Tiger of the Plains, and in faith the name fitted him well.

. . . An illiterate man, a friend of Quiroga's in his childhood and youth, who supplied me with many of the facts I have set down here, included in his account these odd observations in speaking of Quiroga's early years: "That he was not a thief before he became known as a public figure, that he never robbed, however desperate his straits; that he not only liked to fight, he would pay for a chance to do so, and to challenge those held in most awe; that he had a deep dislike for respectable people; that he never touched a drop of liquor; that as a young man he was very reserved, and he not only wanted to frighten people, but to terrify them, and for that reason he gave out to those in his confidence that he had supernatural powers and could read the future; that he treated like slaves all those with whom he had dealings; that he never went to confession, prayed or attended Mass—once after he was a general he saw him at Mass—and that he himself said he did not believe in anything." All Quiroga's public career seems to me to be summed up in these statements. They reveal a great man, a man of genius despite himself, without even realizing it, a Cæsar, a Tamerlane, a Mahomet. He was born so, it was not his own doing. He descended in the social scale to command, to dominate, to combat the power of the city, of the organized police. He was offered a commission in the army, but he disdained it, because he had not the patience to wait for promotion, and because there was too much discipline, too many stumbling blocks in the way of his personal liberty; there were generals above him, a gallooned uniform that hampered his movements, tactics that mapped out his course of action. All this was intolerable. Life on a horse's back, a life of danger and strong emotions, had steeled his spirit and blunted his heart. He had an instinctive, an invincible hatred of the laws that had been invoked against him, against the judges who had sentenced him, against all that society from which he had withdrawn from early childhood, and which he regarded with suspicion and contempt. Facundo was an example of primitive barbarity; he rebelled against control of any sort; his anger was that of the wild beast: his jet-black, curly hair fell about his forehead and eyes like Medusa's snaky locks; his voice grew hoarse, his glances turned to daggers. In a fit of rage he killed and kicked N.'s brains out over a gambling dispute; he tore both ears off one of his mistresses because she asked him for thirty pesos for her marriage to which he had agreed; he laid open with an ax the head of his son Juan because he could not make him stop talking; in Tucumán he beat up a pretty girl whom he was unable to seduce or ravish. In all his acts he revealed himself as a man who had not emerged from the brute stage, without being on this account either stupid or devoid of ideals. As he was unable to arouse admiration or regard, he liked to make himself feared, to the point where the mainspring of all his acts was to inspire fear, among civilians as among soldiers, in the victim facing a firing squad, or in his wife and children. Lacking the capacity to employ the means at the command of civil government, he used terror as a substitute for patriotism and self-sacrifice. Though an ignorant man, by surrounding himself with an air of mystery and aloofness, and taking advantage of a native shrewdness and a gift of observation far above the average, he claimed to have a prescience of coming events, which give him prestige and fame among the ignorant.

The repertory of anecdotes in the memory of the regions where he operated is inexhaustible; his sayings, his decisions have a stamp of originality which give them a certain Oriental quality, a tinge of Solomonlike wisdom in the opinion of the masses. As a matter of fact, what difference is there between that famous order to cut the child in two to find out who was the real mother, and this which follows, to determine a thief?

Some object had been stolen in a company of soldiers, and all attempts to discover the thief had been futile. Quiroga assembled the troop and ordered wands all the same size cut, one for each soldier. He then had them distributed among them, and said in a loud, firm voice: "The one whose wand tomorrow morning is longer than those of the others is the thief." The next day he assembled the troop again, and Quiroga had the wands examined and compared. There was one soldier whose wand was shorter than the others. "You wretch," shouted Facundo in a voice that struck terror to the heart, "you're the thief." And so he was; his confusion revealed his guilt all too clearly. The trick was very simple; the credulous gaucho, fearful that his wand might grow, had cut off a piece. But it requires a certain superiority and a certain knowledge of human nature to employ such methods.

Someone had stolen some parts of a saddle from a soldier, and a careful investigation had failed to reveal the thief. Facundo assembled the troop and had them march past him. He stood with his arms folded, his eyes steady, searching, terrifying. Beforehand he had said: "I know who it is," with an assurance that left no room for doubt. The men began to march past, one after the other. Many had gone by; Quiroga stood there motionless, the statue of Jupiter Tonans, the image of God on the Judgment Day. Suddenly he leaned forward, grabbed one of the men by the arm, and said in a flat voice: "Where is the saddle?" "Over there, sir," answered the man, pointing to a little grove. "A firing squad of four," shouted Quiroga.

What special revelation was this? Fear and a guilty conscience brought face to face with a shrewd man. On another occasion a gaucho was defending himself against charges of robbery. Facundo interrupted him saying: "That scoundrel is lying; a hundred lashes. . . ." When the criminal was led away, Quiroga turned to one of those present: "You see, *patron*, when a gaucho shuffles his feet around, making marks on the ground as he talks, it's a sign that he is lying." Under the prompting of the lash, the gaucho confessed the truth of the matter, that he had stolen a yoke of oxen.

There are hundreds of similar episodes in the life of Facundo, which at the same time that they reveal a man of superior abilities, endowed him with a mysterious reputation in the eyes of the ignorant, who came to attribute supernatural powers to him.

JOSÉ HERNÁNDEZ

(1834–1896)

SOMEWHAT IN THE MANNER of the Venerable Bede who, according to the schoolboy, retired to a monastery and there became the father of the English language, José Hernández, in a week, in the boredom of a hotel room in Montevideo, during a period of political exile, produced the epic of Argentina, *Martín Fierro*. It is almost a contradiction in terms that a known author in modern times should have composed a work of this sort. The origins of other epics are shrouded in antiquity and anonymity. Yet this is so typical an epic that it stands in the same relation to the Argentine nation as the *Chanson de Roland* to the French and the *Cantar de Mío Cid* to the Spanish.

Like other great works of Hispanic literature, the originality of *Martín Fierro* consists in its lack of originality, in the fact that everything it says has been said before, but never so completely or so well. The themes and the metrical patterns had all been worked out before in the anonymous folk poetry of the *payadores*. The gaucho's protest against the hateful laws promulgated by Buenos Aires, enforced military service, elections, voting, the authority of the police, had all been voiced before. The hostility of the gaucho, the man of the country, toward the city; the scenes, the episodes, the characters, none of these were new. The reason for the book's immediate and immense popularity was that every word it spoke aroused a familiar chord in its hearers. The proverbs, the simple, sententious philosophy, the humor, the religion, were typically, authentically those of the gaucho, but expressed with an ease and exactitude that were beyond him. This was Hernández's rare achievement; he, an educated man, a man of the city, despite the years he had spent as a youth on the family ranch, was able to write, think, and express himself as only a gaucho could have done. And the book is all the history of the Argentina of the moment, the expanding frontiers and the wars with the Indians, the entrance of the gringo immigrants, the growing power of Buenos Aires, and the melancholy submergence of the gaucho in the rising tide of civilization.

No work ever enjoyed such popularity in Argentina. The poem was published in Buenos Aires in 1872, and fifteen editions of it were printed in seven years. Almost by popular demand, Hernández composed and published a second part, *The Return of Martín Fierro*, in 1879. The gaucho felt that it was his book, and it was read wherever he forgathered. Country stores used to order, along with their supplies of maté tea, hardtack, cheese, tobacco, knives, gin, "so many copies of *Martín Fierro*." And those who could not read came to know it by oral transmission. There were singers who earned their living reciting *Martín Fierro* about the countryside. Hernández was a familiar figure in Buenos Aires, and gauchos visiting the city, when they saw him, would say: "There goes Martín Fierro."

The gaucho had fought enthusiastically for freedom in the War of Independence; but he quickly discovered that he had lost the only thing he valued, which was freedom to do as he liked. Liberty to him meant freedom from interference. The following episode is Martin Fierro's fight with the police, pursuing him because he had settled a quarrel in his own way. During this fight one of the squad of police,

Cruz, a gaucho like Martín Fierro, passed over to his side, and with this companionship the tale acquires a new dimension, as when Sancho Panza takes to the road with his master. The fine translation is by Walter Owen.

Martín Fierro*

[JOSÉ HERNÁNDEZ]

Like a hunted fox the gaucho lives,
That has got himself into a scrape,
Till some day he's off his guard, or rash,
And the dogs are on him like a flash;
For no matter how well a man can ride,
From a fall he'll not escape.

At the peaceful hour of the afternoon,
When everything seems to doze;
When the winds lie down on the prairie's breast,
And the whole wide world seems to turn to rest;
To some swamp or brake, with his load of care,
The homeless gaucho goes.

So when evening fell I would take me off,
And some resting-place I found me;
For where the puma can make its den,
A man can hide from his fellow-men,
And I knew if they caught me beneath a roof,
The police would soon surround me.

As I've told, one night on the open plain
I was dozing with one eye skinned,
While I brooded over my mournful lot,
When I pricked my ears up like a shot,
For from not far off the *chajá's* call
Came echoing down the wind.

As flat as a worm I laid me out
And I stuck my ear to the ground,

* Reprinted from *The Gaucho Martín Fierro* by José Hernández, adapted from the Spanish and rendered into English verse by Walter Owen, by permission of Rinehart & Co., Inc. Copyright 1936 by Rinehart & Co., Inc.

And soon in the still of the night I caught
The thud of hoofs at a steady trot.
That they were a tidy bunch I knew,
For I counted them by the sound.

They were coming so soft that it was plain
They weren't just taking the air;
They had tracked me with their dirty spies,
And were coming to take me by surprise.
It isn't the gaucho's way to run,
So I started to prepare.

To make a start I crossed myself,
Then I got out the crock of gin,
I gave my gizzard a thorough soak,
For I thought to myself "If I've got to croak,
To leave good drink for a bunch like that
Would simply be a sin."

I wound my sash, and I fixed it tight,
My drawers at the knee I tied,
I slipped my spurs, to free my feet,
For I knew I'd have to step quick and neat,
And on a clump of prairie grass
The edge of my knife I tried.

My horse I tethered to the grass,
To have him quick to hand,
I tightened his girth; and to know my ground,
I tried with my foot three paces round;
And then with my back against him there,
I quietly took my stand.

Close up in the dark I heard them rein,
And I thought it time to begin;
I could feel my scalp begin to twitch,—
To get to grips I was all of an itch,—
So I said: "If you fellows are nursing a grudge,
I'd hate you to hold it in."

"You're a gaucho outlaw," said one of them,
"And we've come to settle your score;
You killed a nigger at a dance,

And a gaucho in a store;
The Sheriff here has a warrant signed
To lay you in jail tonight;
And we'll lift your stakes, by the holy Jakes,
If you're fool enough to fight."

"Don't come to me," I said to him,
"With a lot of dead men's tales;
The thing we're going to settle now,
Is if you can get me, and when, and how;
You make me tired with your silly talk
Of the law, and police, and jails."

I had scarcely spoke when they tumbled off,
And all in a heap came on.
Six paces off they opened out,
Like a pack of dogs they ringed me about;
I called on the Saints to give me help,
And I whipped out my *facón*.

Then close in front of my eyes I saw
The flash that a musket made;
But before the fellow could curse his luck
At missing me, I leapt and struck,—
And as one spits a sardine, there
I lifted him on my blade.

Another was cramming a bullet down,
But little it did avail;
With a single thrust I made him squeal,
He no sooner felt the touch of the steel,
Than he gave one jump, and made for home,
Like a dog when you step on its tail.

There were two had swords and were better dressed,
And that leaders seemed to be;
Their ponchos round their arms they rolled,
And in front of the others they stepped out bold,
And then like a couple of unslipped hounds,
Together they rushed at me.

I gave them ground to draw them on
From the rest of the yelping pack;

My poncho I trailed,—and when one fool
Put his foot on it, I gave it a pull;
His heels went up, and down he went,
Full length upon his back.

When the other one found himself alone,
He looked a lot less grim;
I leapt at him ere he fetched his breath,—
By the length of a knife he missed his death,—
For he turned, and a pair of lifting heels
Was the last I saw of him.

As luck would have it, the dawn just then
Began to tint the sky,
And I said to myself: "If the Virgin now,
Gets me out of this scrape, I'll take a vow
That from this day on, till the day I die,
I'll never harm a fly."

Just then I felt along my ribs,
A sword-point tap my juice;
It was only a flesh-cut, I could feel,
But I went real mad at the touch of steel,
And from that moment among the bunch,
With a vengeance I cut loose.

The man with the sword nearly had my life
Before I could prevent him;
I gave ground quick,—then I firmed my heel,
And point and edge I gave him steel,—
He twisted his ankle in a pit,
And to the Pit I sent him.

The heart of a gaucho among them then,
A saint must have made rebel;
Above the rest he shouted loud:
"God damn your souls for a cowardly crowd!
Before you kill a man like that,
You'll have to kill Cruz as well!"

And in a jiffy he was afoot,
And into the fight he sprung.
I saw my chance, and in I ripped,
Between us two we had them hipped,

And the fellow Cruz was like a wolf
When you try to take its young.

The two that faced him he sent to hell
With thrusts to left and right.
The ones that were left began to wheel,
You could see they were sick of the sight of steel;
And when we rushed them they scuttled off
Like bugs when you strike a light.

The ones that had stretched their muzzles out,
All stark and stiff they lay;
One rode off swaying from side to side,
While Cruz looked after him and cried:
"You'd better send out some more police
To cart the dead away."

I gathered together their remains,
And I knelt and said a prayer;
I hunted around for two little sticks,
To serve the dead for a crucifix,
And then I asked God to forgive my soul
For killing so many there.

RICARDO PALMA

(1833–1919)

THE WORKS of Ricardo Palma, or, to be more exact, the work—for his
eight volumes of *Tradiciones peruanas* are really one—is the best, and
certainly the most entertaining encyclopedia of folklore to be found in
the Spanish language, and perhaps in any. He took his materials
wherever he found them, from old wives' tales, musty convent chroni-
cles, dry-as-dust volumes of history, legal archives, and out of them he
fashioned his tales, which have been the delight of the Spanish-speaking
world since he first began their publication in 1872. He covered every
period of Peru's history—pre-invasion, conquest, colony, independence
—but his favorite moment was the days when Lima, "thrice-crowned
city of the kings," was the seat of the viceroyalty. He painted this world

with such skill and penetration that it acquired continental proportions.

No worshipper of the great was Palma. All the important figures of Peru's history are to be found in his pages, but they do not appear in the poses ordinarily adopted for immortality. We see the beruffed viceroys and judges of Lima intriguing, jockeying for power, meeting with spies in out-of-the-way spots, or prowling the streets by night like amorous tomcats. Even the saints and aspirants to sainthood in which Lima abounded are shown in their more prosaic moments, Saint Rose of Lima disciplining a swarm of troublesome mosquitoes, Blessed Martin de Porres persuading a cat, dog, and mouse to eat out of one plate.

Every class of society appears before our eyes: great gentlemen and ladies, representatives of the Crown, fortune hunters, gamblers, cutthroats, Spaniards, Creoles, Negroes, Indians. They all come to life at Palma's magic touch.

He created a whole world for his own and his reader's enjoyment when he rescued it from the oblivion in which it lay forgotten. And he infused his creations with his own rollicking humor and that sly, tongue-in-cheek wit which is so characteristic of the sons of Lima. He has had many imitators, but none has possessed his inimitable style and his sense of language. He was thoroughly versed in the Spanish classics and he was familiar with the French, German, and English literature of his day, but his ear was ever attuned to the living language, of the streets, the market place—the tales he had heard as a child. His style is a mosaic of all these elements, embellished with the inventions of his own puckish fancy.

Palma's was a long and happy life. After brief service in the consular career, he was appointed director of the National Library of Lima, and he devoted himself to it, his writings, and his family. The founders of Lima are said to have been thirteen. The number should be increased to fourteen, for what they created, Palma perpetuated. His memory is venerated, not only in his own country, but by all those who are in his debt for the pleasant hours they owe him.

The two following selections exemplify various facets of his work.

The Goblins of Cuzco*

[RICARDO PALMA]

THE only basis in fact for this tradition is the tale told by the people. Everybody in Cuzco knows it as I relate it here. No chronicler makes

* Reprinted from *The Knights of the Cape, and thirty-seven other selections from the Tradiciones Peruanas,* by Ricardo Palma, translated by Harriet de Onís, by permission of Alfred A. Knopf, Inc. Copyright 1945 by Alfred A. Knopf, Inc.

mention of it, and only in one manuscript of brief notes dealing with the time from the viceroyalty of the Marquis of Salinas to that of the Duke of La Palata did I find the following lines:

"During this time of the rule of the Prince of Squillace, the Admiral of Castile, known as the Excommunicated, met a bad end in Cuzco at the hands of the Devil."

As is evident, these lines throw little light on the affair, and I have been told that in the unpublished "Annals of Cuzco," belonging to Bishop Ochoa, there is no further information, except that the mysterious event is assigned to a different epoch than that I have given.

My reasons for preferring the time of Don Francisco de Borja and Aragón is not only the reference quoted above, but the telling circumstance that, in view of the character of the poet Viceroy, the pious words with which the tale ends are typical of him.

Having set my chronicler's conscience at rest with the foregoing reservations, I shall now get on with the story.

I

Don Francisco de Borja and Aragón, Prince of Esquilache and Count of Mayalde, a native of Madrid and Knight of the Orders of Santiago and Montesa, was thirty-two years old when Philip III, who esteemed him highly, named him Viceroy of Peru. The members of the court criticized the appointment, because until this time Don Francisco had devoted himself only to writing verse, making love, and dueling. But when, contrary to custom, this gossip reached the monarch's royal ears, he said: "It is a fact that he is the youngest of the viceroys that have yet been sent out to the Indies, but Esquilache has a head on his shoulders, and he has a stout arm besides."

The King was not mistaken. Peru was threatened by fleets of freebooters; and though Juan de Mendoza y Luna was a good Governor, he lacked the vigor of a younger man. Jorge Spitberg, with a Dutch fleet, after laying waste the coasts of Chile, turned to Callao. The Spanish fleet went out to meet him on July 22, 1615, and after a fierce, bitterly contested five-hour struggle off Cerro Azul or Cañete, the flagship was set afire, several ships were sunk, and the victorious pirates put the prisoners to the sword.

The Viceroy, the Marquis of Montesclaros, came to Callao to direct the resistance, more out of a sense of duty than because he had any hope of being able to prevent the landing of the pirates and the consequent sack of Lima with the scanty and poor forces at his command. The City of the Kings was in a state of veritable panic, and the churches were thronged, not only with frightened women, but with men, who, instead of stoutly preparing to defend their homes, were appealing for divine aid against the Dutch heretics. The old but doughty Viceroy had less than a thousand men under arms in Callao, despite the fact that, according to the census of 1614, Lima had a population of 25,454.

But all Spitberg did was to fire a few rounds from his cannon, which were dispiritedly returned, and then set sail for Paita. Peralta, in his *Lima fundada*, and the Count of La Granja, in his poem on Santa Rosa, describe those days of tribulation. It was the belief of the pious that the withdrawal of the pirates was due to a miracle wrought by the Saint of Lima, who died two years later, on August 24, 1617.

According to some, on the 18th, and, to others, the 23rd of December, 1615, the Prince of Esquilache entered Lima, having been saved by Providence from falling into the hands of the pirates on his voyage from Panama to Callao.

The Viceroy was accorded a sumptuous reception, the city authorities sparing no expense to enhance its splendor.

The first thing to which he turned his attention was the organization of a fleet and the fortification of the port, which checked the boldness of the pirates until the reign of his successor, when the Dutch corsair Jacob L'Heremite made his great assault.

The Prince of Esquilache, who was descended from Pope Alexander VI (Rodrigo Borgia) and from St. Francis Borgia, Duke of Gandia, governed Peru under the influence of the Jesuits, as did his successor and relative the Count of Lemos.

When the fears aroused by the threats of the freebooters had been allayed, Don Francisco set about putting the public treasury in order, promulgated wise laws dealing with the mines of Potosí and Huanacavelica, and on December 20, 1619, created the court of commerce.

Being a man of letters, he established the famous Prince's school for the education of the sons of noble Indians, and no comedies or miracle plays could be shown without having first been censored by him. It is the duty of a ruler—he said—to make sure that good taste is not perverted.

The Prince of Esquilache's censorship was purely literary, and certainly no judge could have had more authority. In that galaxy of poets of the seventeenth century, the century that produced Cervantes, Calderón, Lope, Quevedo, Tirso de Molina, Alarcón, and Moreto, the Prince of Esquilache holds an outstanding position, if not for the grandeur of his ideas, for the freshness and correctness of his verse. His shorter compositions and his historical poem *Nápoles recuperada* assure him a deserved place in the Spanish Parnassus.

Among the witticisms attributed to the Prince of Esquilache is the remark he made to a man of scant intelligence who read a great deal but derived no profit from what he read: "Forget about books, my friend, and convince yourself that the longer you cook an egg, the harder it gets."

When Esquilache returned to Spain in 1622 he was honored by the new King, Philip IV. He died in the crowned city of the bear and the madroña in 1658.

The arms of the house of Borgia were a red bull on a field of gold, green bordure, and eight golden heather.

With this introduction to the poet Viceroy, let us go on to the folk tale.

II

There stands in the city of Cuzco a magnificent house known as the "house of the admiral." It seems that the admiral in question was as much of a sailor as some I can think of who have seen only pictures of the sea. The fact is that the title was hereditary and was handed down from father to son.

The house was a striking edifice. Two of its most notable features were the water drains and the sculptured beams of the roof, on one of which was carved the head of the admiral who built the house.

That four admirals lived in Cuzco is borne out by the family tree that in 1861 was presented to the Congress of Peru by Don Sixto Laza in a petition to have himself declared the sole and legitimate heir of the Inca Huascar and thus entitled to an income from the guano beds, the duchy of Medina de Rioseco, the marquisate of Oropesa, and several other tidbits. We were going to have to pay dear for the honor of having a prince of our own! But it is on record, against the day we tire of the Republic, theoretical or factual, and for a change decide to install the monarchy, absolute or constitutional, for anything can happen, by the grace of God and at the pace we are going.

According to this genealogy, the first admiral was Don Manuel de Castilla, the second, Don Cristobal de Castilla Espinosa y Lugo, who was succeeded by his son, Don Gabriel de Castilla Vázquez de Vargas, and the fourth and last was Don Juan de Castilla y González, whose descendants were all female.

It is told of the Castillas, to show how proud they were of their lineage, that when they recited the Hail Mary they employed this wording: "Holy Mary, mother of God, our relative and lady, pray for us. . . ."

The arms of the Castillas were a trouçonné shield, the dexter quarter in gules with a castle of gold on azure, the sinister in silver, with a lion rampant on a field of gules and a sinople bend with two dragons also in sinople.

It would be difficult to decide which of the four admirals is the hero of this tradition, and in view of this doubt the reader can make any one of them the scapegoat in the assurance that he will not come back to complain if there has been a mistake.

The admiral in question was prouder than Lucifer, vainer of his pedigree than a peacock, and stiffer than his starched ruff. In the courtyard of the house stood a magnificent stone fountain to which the people of the neighborhood used to come for water, taking at its face value the saying that nobody was ever refused water or fire.

But one morning His Excellency got up in a devil of a bad humor and gave his servants orders to beat to a jelly any of the trash that ventured to cross his threshold in search of the liquid that cools but not intoxicates.

One of the first to receive this punishment was a poor old woman, and the news of the outrage caused general indignation.

The next day the woman's son, a young priest attached to the parish of San Jerónimo, a few leagues distant from Cuzco, came to the city and learned of the affront his old mother had suffered. He went immediately to the house of the admiral; and the owner of the bearings and quarterings called him a son of a goat and a *vela verde*, and that aristocratic mouth spewed forth verbs and gerunds, toads and snakes, and he wound up by giving the priest a terrific beating.

The excitement the attack gave rise to was tremendous. The authorities were afraid openly to take a stand against a person of the admiral's rank, and they let time go by, hoping it would take care of things, as it generally does. But the clergy and the populace declared the haughty admiral excommunicate.

The insulted priest, a few hours after the outrage, made his way to the Cathedral and knelt in prayer before an image of Christ, a gift to the city from Charles V. When his prayer was finished he left at the feet of the Supreme Judge a petition stating his complaint and demanding divine justice, for he was sure he would not receive it at human hands. It is said that he returned to the temple the next day and picked up his complaint, on which there had been written in the margin: "Petition noted. Justice will be done."

And so three months went by, when one morning a gallows was seen standing before the house of the admiral and dangling from it the body of the excommunicate. Nobody was ever able to discover the authors of the crime, in spite of the fact that suspicion naturally fell upon the priest. But he had many witnesses to testify to his whereabouts and was able to establish an alibi.

At the inquest that followed, two women of the neighborhood stated that they had seen a group of "little men with big heads," generally known as goblins, setting up the gallows, and that when it was ready they had knocked three times at the door of the house, and at the third knock it opened. In a little while the admiral, in ceremonial dress, came out surrounded by the goblins, who without further ado strung him up like a bunch of grapes.

With testimony of this sort, justice was left completely in the dark, and since it was impossible to lay hands on the goblins, it was decided that the best thing to do was to bring in a verdict of "death at the hand of person or persons unknown."

If the people accept as an article of faith that it was the goblins who brought the excommunicated admiral to his end, it is not a poor chronicler's place to wear himself out trying to find another explanation, no matter how much the incredulous folk of the time whispered that it was all the work of the Jesuits, to insure that those of the sacerdotal order were treated with the respect that was their due.

III

The Mayor and the magistrates of Cuzco reported what had happened to the Viceroy, who after reading the lengthy report said to his secretary:

"A nice theme for a ballad! What is your opinion of this, my good Estuñiga?"

"That Your Excellency ought to give those stupid magistrates a piece of your mind for not being able to discover those guilty of the crime."

"But then the affair would lose its poetry," answered Esquilache, smiling.

"That is true, sir; but justice would have been done."

The Viceroy remained pensive a few seconds; then, getting up from his chair, he laid his hand on his secretary's shoulder.

"My friend, what has been done has been well done; and the world would be better off if, in certain cases, instead of sly, tricky lawyers and other ravens of Themis, it were goblins who meted out justice. And now good night and may God and the Virgin Mary watch over us and keep us from goblins and remorse."

*Where and How the Devil Lost His Poncho**
[RICARDO PALMA]

"So there you are, my dear fellow. I lost my head, and went about riding a wild mule with the stirrups dangling, over a girl that came from the country where the Devil lost his poncho."

* Reprinted from *The Knights of the Cape, and thirty-seven other selections from the Tradiciones Peruanas*, by Ricardo Palma, translated by Harriet de Onís, by permission of Alfred A. Knopf, Inc. Copyright 1945 by Alfred A. Knopf, Inc.

This was the way my friend Don Adeodato de la Mentirola concluded the account of one of the adventures of his youth. Don Adeodato is an old fellow who took up arms in the royalist cause with Colonel Sanjuanena, and who even today prefers the paternal rule of Fernando VII to all the republican forms of government, theoretical and practical, there ever have been or ever will be. Aside from this weakness or peculiarity, my friend Don Adeodato is a jewel of great price. There is no one who is better informed on the subject of Bolívar's philanderings with the ladies of Lima, or who can quote, chapter and verse, from the history of all the old scandals that have taken place in this City of the Kings. He relates the things with a frankness and familiarity that is amazing; and as I have an insatiable curiosity about the life and doings, not of the living, but of those who have turned to dust and are pushing up the daisies, I stick to him like a button to a shirt, and I wind him up, and Don Adeodato unlimbers his tongue.

"Now how and where was it that the Devil lost his poncho?" I asked him.

"What! You who write verses, and pretend to be a historian or story-teller and have things printed in the public newspapers, and have been a congressman, don't know what in my days even the two-year-olds knew? That's what literary fame has become since 'the birth of a nation.' Dry leaves and chaff! Tinsel, nothing but tinsel!"

"I'm sorry, Don Adeodato. But I confess my ignorance and beg you to enlighten me; to teach those who do not know is a precept of the Christian doctrine."

Apparently my humility flattered this last leaf upon the tree from the times of Pezuela and La Serna, for after lighting a cigarette and settling himself comfortably in an armchair, he began with the story that follows. Of course, as you all know, neither Christ nor His disciples dreamed of crossing the Andes (although there are learned historians who affirm that the apostle Thomas preached the gospel in America), nor was there such a thing as the telegraph in those days, or steamboats or printing presses. But just overlook these and other anachronisms, and here is the story, *ad pedem litteræ.*

I

Well, sir, when Jesus Christ Our Lord was traveling about the world, riding a gentle little donkey, restoring sight to the blind and the use and abuse of their limbs to the paralyzed, He came to a region where there was nothing but sand as far as the eye could see. Here and there a slender, rustling palm raised itself aloft, and under its shade the Divine Teacher would stop with His favorite disciples who, seemingly absent-mindedly, would fill their knapsacks with dates.

That stretch of sand seemed eternal, sort of like God, without beginning or end. Night was falling, and the travelers were heavy-hearted at the idea of having to spend the night with only the starry sky for a canopy, when with the last ray of the setting sun the silhouette of a belfry appeared upon the horizon.

The Lord, raising His hand to His eyes like a visor to see better, said:

"There's a town there. Peter, you know about navigation and geography, could you tell me what that city is?"

St. Peter licked his chops at the compliment and answered:

"Master, that city is Ica."

"Get along, then, get along."

And all the apostles fetched their donkeys a kick with their heels, and off the cortege trotted toward the town.

When they were just outside the city they all got off to slick themselves up a bit. They perfumed their whiskers with balm of Judea, tightened the straps of their sandals, brushed off their tunics and cloaks, and then continued on their way, not without a word of advice from the gentle Jesus to His favorite apostle:

"Remember, Peter, you're not to go losing your temper and cutting off people's ears. Your hotheadedness is always getting us into trouble."

The apostle blushed to the whites of his eyes, and nobody would have said, to see him so kindly and contrite, that he had ever been so handy with a knife.

The people of Ica rolled out the red carpet, so to speak, for the distinguished visitors; and although they were anxious to be on their journey, the inhabitants found so many ways to detain them and they were the object of such attentions and celebrations that a week had gone by before you could say scat.

Wine of the finest brands, Elías, Boza y Falconi, flowed like water. During those eight days Ica was like a foretaste of paradise. The doctors sat idle, the druggists sold no medicines; there wasn't even a toothache or the mildest case of measles.

The notaries' pens got all rusty, because not once did they have a complaint to draw up. Not a cross word was heard between man and wife, and even those rattlesnakes known as mothers-in-law and sisters-in-law—and this really was a miracle!—lost their venom.

How apparent it was that the Supreme Good was dwelling in Ica! The city breathed peace, joy, happiness.

The kindness, charm, and beauty of the ladies of Ica inspired St. John to write a sonnet with an envoi which was published on the same day in *El Comercio*, *Nacional*, and *Patria*. The Icans, between drink and drink, made the apostle poet promise to write the Apocalypse,

A Pindaric poem, a work immortal,
If lacking in sense, with genius glowing,

as a poet friend of mine says.

So with one thing and another, the eighth day had come to an end when Our Lord received a telegram urging Him to return to Jerusalem at once to keep the Samaritan woman from pulling out Mary Magdalene's hair; and fearing that the people in their affection might put obstacles in His way, He sent for the patriarch of the apostles, closed the door, and said to him:

"Peter, you handle this any way you think best, but we have to leave here tomorrow without a soul knowing it. There are circumstances under which one has no choice but to take French leave."

St. Peter drew up his plans, informed the others, and the next morning the guests had disappeared from the house where they had slept.

The city council had prepared a surprise serenade for that morning, but they were left all dressed up and no place to go. The travelers had already crossed Huacachina Lake and had disappeared beyond the horizon.

Ever since then the waters of Huacachina have the property of curing all ailments except the bite of wild monkeys.

When they had put several miles between themselves and the city, the Lord turned back for a last look and said:

"You say this place is called Ica, Peter?"

"Yes, sir, Ica."

"My, what a fine place!"

And raising His right hand, He blessed it in the name of the Father, the Son, and the Holy Ghost.

II

As the correspondents of the newspapers had written to Lima describing at length, in detail, and with flowery phrases the celebrations and banquets with which the visitors had been honored, the Devil received the news by the first European mail boat.

They say that *Cachano* bit his lips with envy, the rascally old snout-nose, and exclaimed:

"What the devil! I'm just as good as He. The very idea! Nobody is going to get ahead of me!"

And calling up straightway twelve of his courtiers, he disguised them to look like the apostles. For that is true, *Cucufo* knows more about the art of make-up and fixing over faces than an actor and a coquette put together.

But as the journalists had forgotten to describe the attire of Christ and His disciples, the *Maldito* decided that he could get around the difficulty by looking at the pictures in some travel book. And so, without further ado, he and his comrades dressed themselves up in high boots and threw over their shoulders a four-cornered cape, the poncho.

The people of Ica, when they saw the group coming, thought the Lord was coming back with His elect, and rushed out to meet Him, prepared to throw the house out of the window this time, so that the Man-God should have no cause for complaint and would decide to establish Himself for good in their city.

Until then the Icans had been happy, very happy, superlatively happy. They never mixed in politics, paid their taxes without a word, and did not give a hoot whether Prester John or the Moor Muza was in power. There was no gossip or talebearing from one neighborhood to another or from house to house. All they thought about was cultivating their vineyards and doing as much good as they could to one another. It was a land so flowing with happiness and well-being that it made the other regions jealous.

But *Carrampempe*, whose teeth begin to chatter with rage when he sees anybody happy, made up his mind the minute he arrived to stick his tail in the pie and ruin the whole thing.

El Cornudo reached Ica just as a marriage was about to take place between a young man like the flower of the flock and a girl like a ewe lamb. They were a couple that seemed made for each other, they were so well suited in disposition and character, and they gave promise of living out their lives in peace and in the grace of God.

"I couldn't have come more opportunely if they had sent for me," said the devil to himself. "By St. Tecla, the patroness of out-of-tune pianos!"

But unfortunately for him, the couple had been to confession and had taken communion that morning, so the snares and temptations of *El Patudo* could not prevail against them.

With the first toasts drunk to the happy couple, the wine went to everyone's head, producing not that fine, genial, harmless exhilaration of the spirit that reigned at the banquets Our Lord honored with His presence, but a gross, sensual, indecent frenzy.

One young fellow, a Don Juan in his salad days, began to make insinuating remarks to the bride; and a middle-aged woman, with service stripes, started making eyes at the groom. That old girl was pure gasoline, and with one spark of willingness from the young man a blaze would have started that the Garibaldi fire-engine and all the fire companies would have been unable to put out. And things did not stop here.

The lawyers and notaries got together to drum up trade; the doctors and druggists went into cahoots to raise the price of *aqua fontis;* the mothers-in-law decided to scratch out their sons-in-law's eyes; the wives began to whine and beg for jewelry and velvet dresses; the upright citizens began to talk about larks and hot times; and, to put the whole thing in a nutshell, even the town council began to shout that they would have to tax people ten cents for each sneeze.

That was anarchy with all its horrors. It was as plain as the nose on your face that *El Rabudo* was at the bottom of the business.

And the hours went by, and drinking was no longer by the glass but by the bottle, and people who used to get mildly mellow went on such a bender that night as had never been seen before.

The poor bride, who, as I have said, was in a state of grace, was in complete distress, and was doing her best to get people to separate two groups of rowdies who, armed with cudgels, were tanning each other's hide.

"The Devil has got into them; that's what it is," the poor girl kept saying to herself, and her guess was not far off. Going over to *Uñas Largas*, she took him by the poncho, saying:

"But, Lord, don't you see that they're going to kill one another?"

"And what's that to me?" answered *El Tiñoso* coolly. "I'm not from this parish—more power to them. Let them. So much the better for the priest and for me. I'll act as sexton."

The girl, who of course could not take in the full implication of these gross remarks, answered him:

"Jesus! What a hard heart Your Excellency has! By the sign of this cross you must be the Devil!"

El Maligno had no sooner seen the girl's fingers forming the cross than he tried to rush off like a dog with a firecracker tied to its tail; but as she had hold of his poncho, *El Tunante* had to slip his head through the opening, leaving the four-cornered cape in the bride's hands.

El Patón and his acolytes evaporated, but it said that since then, every once in a while, His Satanic Majesty comes back to the city of Ica looking for his poncho. When this happens the elbow-benders go on a proper spree and. . . .

TOMÁS CARRASQUILLA

(1858–1941)

WITH THE EXCEPTION of Ricardo Palma, it would be impossible to find another writer of the period in the entire Hispanic world who can compare with the Colombian Tomás Carrasquilla, in wit, riotous humor, and a skill that is nothing short of genius in the use of language. Yet, curiously enough, he is hardly known outside his own frontiers, and even there, praise is doled out with certain reservations. He was born in the province of Antioquia, a region that has a distinct character of its own and is noted, among other things, for its hard-headed, practical approach to life. Medellín, the capital, is one of the great industrial and mining centers of the country, and a certain rivalry has always existed between it and Bogotá, where literary history is made, and this may be responsible in part for the indifference with which Carrasquilla's work has been treated.

In a series of short stories and novels Carrasquilla has painted the life of his region. Despite his keen sense of the ridiculous his characters are never caricatures, but living flesh-and-blood *antioqueños*. In the portrait gallery of his creations every class of society is included, from highest to lowest, and through them we see the life of Antioquia and the mentality of its inhabitants, all written in a style that is a source of sheer delight.

The story that follows—one of his most famous—was the first he ever wrote, in 1896. He wrote it for the entertainment of a small literary group of friends, and one of them had it published without his knowledge. In view of its success he decided to follow his natural inclination, in spite of the fact that he had prepared himself for teaching and the law, and practiced both from time to time in a somewhat desultory fashion. There is no doubt that as time goes by, Carrasquilla will come to be recognized for what he was, one of the greatest writers of regional literature of his day.

Simon Magus

[TOMÁS CARRASQUILLA]

AMONG my critical, literal-minded fellow citizens it is accepted as an article of faith that my parents, by their sternness and their firm belief in the maxim "Spare the rod and spoil the child," managed to curb the terrible temper of our family to a degree. Whether this opinion has any foundation or is mere speculation, the fact is that if the authors of my days did not manage to bring up their offspring in the way they should go, it was not for lack of trying. They certainly put their hearts into it.

There is no end to the tales my sisters tell about being shut up all day in that dark pantry closet, where they nearly died of fright. My brothers still wince as they recall the smart of a three-thonged rawhide or my father's riding whip against their bare skin. They tell of my mother that she always carried at her waist, in the manner of a sword, a cat-o'-nine-tails, and not as an ornament. When it was least expected, and without warning, she laid it about her, and let the chips fall where they would. Not to mention those small, excruciatingly painful pinches with which she drove home the point of every reprimand.

Thanks be to God, this parental severity did not extend to me. Only once in my life did I taste the bitterness of the lash. The fact that I was the youngest of the children, and small and puny in the bargain, explains this forbearance.

Everybody in the house adored me; I was the idol and the family treasure, but it was hard for me to reciprocate this general affection when all mine was devoted to Frutos.

When I came of an age to realize that I was a person like anybody else who could love and be loved, there at my side I found Frutos, who, more than all the others, and as her sole occupation, seemed to me to have only one purpose in life: to like what I liked and to do everything I wanted.

Frutos was in charge of the cleanliness and care of my person; and so deft and gentle were her hands that neither the rubbings of the damp cloth, as she washed "that face like a sun," bothered me, nor did I go into a tantrum when she combed my hair, nor did she hurt me when, with a needle and without shedding a drop of blood she dug out of my feet things . . . that I am ashamed to speak of.

Frutos taught me to pray, put me to bed, and watched over me while I slept. In the morning she woke me up with my cup of chocolate. What else did she do? When I came home from school for lunch, there was Frutos waiting for me with my corn cake, my meat, my fried plantain. The best of those delicate dishes in whose preparation Frutos had a hand was for me. These were generally chocolate ground without the addition of even a pinch of flour, fig preserves, sausages.

And the tricks she knew! Dear Lord! She would sprinkle bran around the foot of the orange tree; then she would prop a little trough over the bran with a stick; to this she would tie a long string and, holding the other end, hide behind a clump of cane to wait until the sparrow came down to eat. The poor thing had no more than taken its first peck when Frutos pulled the string, and bang! Under the trough was a bird for me.

Out of a broomstick, a piece of rag, some thread, with a stitch here, a bit of stuffing there, she would make me a horse with fiery white eye, long mane, reins and all, which made the other boys turn green with envy. Any bit of board, with a few horsehairs or wires, in her hands became a guitar that tinkled faintly, and I strummed away on it all day long.

And the drums out of old tin cans! And the kites with fancy tails!

With a wit and grace I found incomparable, she told me the famous adventures of Pedro Rimales—Urde, they call him now—making me laugh until I was weak. She transported me to the "Land where you go and don't come back," following the mysterious bird of "the seven-colored feather," and enchanted me with the marvelous feats of "Pato-jito," which I took to be the gospel truth, as I did the tale of "Sebastian de las Gracias," a romantic folk hero who with equal ease intoned a ballad to the accompaniment of his guitar or dispatched a sinner to the other world with a knife thrust. Half the charm consisted in not having the verses or the music to which they were sung vary in the least from one time to the other, or the effect was spoiled.

In her cracked voice, and solely for my pleasure, Frutos sang me certain native airs—they were called *corozales*, she said—which transported me out of this world, so beautiful and melodious did they seem to me.

My "most-favored-nation" status was respected by everyone in the family. To have attempted anything different with Frutos around would have been like running head-on into a stone wall. To my mother's complaint: "That boy is spoiled to death," Frutos's answer was: "Everyone is picking at the poor lamb." "What he needs is a whipping," growled my father, to which Frutos's reply was: "Not as long as I live," and taking me by the hand, she went off with me. And when this happened, she sulked all day; and everyone kept out of her way.

And when I told her that I had been punished at school! Holy Mother! The things that mouth spewed forth against that Jew, that hangman of a schoolteacher; against Mamma, who had no more backbone than a snail, and was foolish, in the bargain, to tolerate such things; against my father, who wasn't man enough to go and give that old devil a couple of good punches. On the occasion of one of these punishments, Frutos got so hot under the collar that she waited at the house door for the teacher to come by, and as soon as she set eyes on him, she ran up to him, and shaking her fist under his nose, shouted at him furiously: "Oh, you devil! What you did to that child! Like Our Redeemer on the road to Calvary! If only he were mine, I would pull out every one of your goat whiskers." The teacher, who outside the classroom was a summer zephyr, took no notice of her; and I played up my sufferings for all they were worth, for on the days when there had been strap or rod, I was repaid with usury. Frutos gave me every tidbit she could lay her hands on, and cosseted me in every way she could think of. I was not "the child," but her "grain of gold," her "little king," and other things in the same vein.

Nobody in the family had as many clothes as I, because Frutos was always bemoaning the fact that "the child" was naked, and she worried my mother and sisters until, whether they wanted to or not, they had to buy or make me new clothes. And not just any kind, but to suit Frutos's taste.

The result of all this was that I wallowed in that love, till I needed nothing in the world but Frutos. Frutos was my life, my all, and the other members of the family, even my parents, meant absolutely nothing to me.

What could Frutos have seen in a snot-nose of eight years to idolize in that fashion? I don't know. All I can say is that Frutos seemed to me an extraordinary being, a kind of guardian angel, something that could not be defined or explained, but superior to anybody else.

And now let's see what Frutos was.

She—her name was Fructuosa Rua—at that time must have been in her sixties. She had been a slave of my maternal grandparents. When slavery was abolished she left the house, to enjoy, no doubt, those fine and entertaining privileges of the free. But either she did not feel sure of herself or she had a bad time of it, for some years later she came back somewhat disillusioned. Though she did say that she had known the world and, according to her, had had a wonderful time.

Finding my mother, whom she had raised, married and the mother of several children, she came to work for us in the care and upbringing of the small fry. For many years she held this post, with certain attributes in the kitchen in the preparation of special dishes. She kept my mother severely in her place, though in her own way she was very fond of all the family and had a great respect for my father, whom she called "my master."

My mother liked her and overlooked her temper and bad humor. Frutos had had children of her own, but at the time I was in her charge they were not with her, and she did not seem to care much for them and paid little attention to them when they happened by to visit her. As a result of the gout that afflicted her, she had practically retired when I was born, and in taking charge of the Benjamin of the household, she was really assuming a heavier load than she could carry. If it had not been for the way she set her heart on me, she could never have stood all the trouble I gave her.

Frutos was pure Negro by race. I never knew anyone so black, of a soft, shimmering blackness, with lips that stuck out a mile, especially on the days she was in a bad humor, which was most of the time. I don't know if women in those days used, as they do now, that thing that sticks way out behind. I think they must have, and of course Frutos did too; and the size of her was such that her skirt of purple percale, which touched the ground in front and got entangled in her splay toes, was so short in the back that her white petticoats showed through.

A low-necked, ruffled shirt comprised her bodice, and her rough, thick arms were completely bare. She covered her woolly hair with a brilliant bandanna, which she tied in front like an Oriental turban. Only when she went to church did she wrap herself in a shawl that time had turned green. When out for a walk or on any everyday occupation, she used no wrap. But tidy and neat as a new pin, for no one was cleaner about her person than Frutos.

Very black and very ugly, wouldn't you say? Nevertheless, she had the most aristocratic prejudices and was class conscious to a far greater degree than many whites. She would not let me play with colored children, because she said they would not respect me as they should when I was a man. She would never let me stay in her room, even when she was suffering from gout, "because a white child that stays in colored folks' rooms gets silly and turns into a ninny." She alleged similar reasons for not letting me go to the kitchen, and that was a spot that fascinated me. Only on Christmas Eve was I allowed to stay there as long as I liked, and even to stick my dirty little paw into everything. But this was because on such days the whole family went into the kitchen. My father and my older brothers, with the solemn air of persons of consequence, made their appearance there, to lift out of the boiling kettle with the skimmer a golden doughnut, a cake of crisp, feathery puff paste, or take a turn at stirring the caldron of custard, which as it bubbled and popped made craters the size of thimbles.

The time that I was in school, which was Frutos's hours of leisure, she spent weaving, an art at which she was very deft; but as soon as the scholar appeared on the scene, spindle, cotton, and thread went into a corner. "The child" came ahead of everything else; only "the child" put her in a good humor; only "the child" brought a laugh to those lips that were the normal abode of angry words and growls.

My mother, amazed at this phenomenon, used to say: "The Lord must intend this boy for a saint, to let him perform such miracles as a child."

With a wall like this at my back, I developed such a touchy disposition, such a temper, that nobody could come near me with a four-foot pole. If I did not get my own way, I threw myself on the floor, hitting my head against everything around me; or I let out howls to raise the dead, accompanied by tears and sobs, not to mention breaking anything I could get my hands on and biting.

Aunt Cruz, a very timid and circumspect person, took the liberty of saying one day in front of Frutos when I was having one of my tantrums that "the child" was spoiling for a whipping. It would have been better if she had been struck dumb. Frutos called her everything she could lay her tongue to, and took such a dislike to her that every time she laid eyes on her she snorted with rage.

My father, seeing the turn things were taking, complained and went so far as to mention a thrashing. But Mamma quieted him down, saying, as she clapped her hand to her brow: "Don't touch him! For Heaven's sake, don't touch him! There'll be no living with Frutos."

And as I had a rare facility for grasping everything bad, I realized that I had them in a forked stick and I worked my advantage to the limit. Whenever the storm began to seem really menacing I took to my heels and sought refuge in Frutos's arms. Out to the garden we went, the site of our conversations, and, once there, we might have been in the moon.

As I grew, Frutos's tales and narrations grew to match. Frutos's specialty was the lives and miracles of the saints, the doings of the souls of the departed, and this so entranced me that I could have listened forever. The gift of gab she had! My faith and admiration were boundless; I came to believe that Frutos represented the sum of the wisdom of the universe. Every word that fell from her lips was gospel to me.

In the course of her narrations we finally got around to tales of witchcraft and goblins, and here I reached my seventh heaven. Everything I had heard before, which had so enchanted me, now seemed trumpery. Witches! That was the real thing. Here was something worth while to which one could devote oneself body and soul for all one's life!

Until then my ambition had been to be a clown or the chief of police. But from then on I said to myself: "Clown, nothing! I'm going to be a witch."

Everything daring, stupendous, useful seemed to me comprehended in witchcraft. I was feverish with enthusiasm.

By making Frutos tell her stories over and over again, I managed to engrave them in my memory to the last trivial detail.

From the stories we went on to the commentary.

"Catching witches?" she said to me once. "The easiest thing in the world! All you have to do is take a handful of mustard and sprinkle it around the room, and at night when the good-for-nothings comes into the room, they start to scrape up the mustard. And while they are bent over doing this, all you have to do is throw St. Augustine's girdle over them, and there you have them lassoed hand and foot. A priest of Tunja used to catch a lot of them like that, and he tied them to the leg of the table; but his cook was so silly that she gave them soft-boiled eggs, and they sailed away in the shell. The foolish thing! Why, you can't even speak about an eggshell in front of witches, because the next minute they have shrunk to the size of an ant's eye, and off they go."

"Oh-ho. And how can they fit in an eggshell?"

"Heavens," answered Frutos, "that's nothing. They make themselves any size they want to in the eggshell."

"Can't you kill them?" I inquired.

"You can, but it's not so easy. If you give them a good stab they die; but as they are so smart, they give themselves another stab, and that way it's a tie and they're even and they get well again."

"And what happens when you do kill them?"

"Silly boy. They only die of the stab once in a great while. You have to run the knife right through them at the start to kill them. But with our Father Saint Augustine's girdle, their tricks are no good to them."

"Where do you get that?" I interrupted.

"The girdle?" replied my interlocutor, with the air of one speaking of the well-nigh impossible. "That's very hard to get. The bishop sometimes lends it to the real good priests."

"Maybe Mamma could borrow it from him," I exclaimed excitedly.

"Ave Maria, child! What are you going to do with the girdle?"

"What am I going to do? Catch witches and tie them to the trees!"

In spite of the difficulties in the way of getting hold of the girdle, I went to my mother with my plan. She was very much engrossed in a card game she was playing with some of her friends.

"Mamma," I said to her, "I want to talk to you just a minute."

And putting my mouth against her ear, I made my request in that high-pitched whisper children use.

The ladies, who were not deaf, let out a peal of laughter.

"Get away, you nuisance," exclaimed my mother. "Where in the world does this child get such crazy notions."

I slunk away, red with embarrassment and grumbling to myself.

For days I thought of nothing but how I could get hold of the girdle. My "witch mania" had taken such a hold on me that I wanted to talk of nothing else.

"Who has stuffed you full of all this nonsense?" my sister Mariana, the learned member of the family, once asked me. "There's no such thing as witches. That's old Frutos's humbug! And you believe it!"

"You're a liar! You're a liar!" I raged at her. "There are too. Frutos told me so!"

"And if Frutos said it, it must be so—as though Frutos were the Mother of God! You big fool!"

"Freckle-face, freckle-face!" and I rushed at her with every intention of biting her.

She caught me by the shoulders and gave me a good shaking.

"I'm going to tell Papa on you, so he'll give you a good hiding, for that's what you need, you spoiled brat. Nobody can stand you any more."

I rushed off to find Frutos, and choked with sobs, I cried:

"What do you think, Frutos! That stupid Mariana told me that there weren't any witches and that you were just telling me stories."

With a horrified expression on her face, she dried my tears, and taking me gently by the hand, led me in silence to a bench beside the kitchen door.

"Look, my child," she began, "there is no doubt that there are witches. What an idea! Certainly there are. But—you mustn't believe in them."

My eyes, dry by this time, must have opened to the size of saucers. I couldn't understand, but Frutos had said it, and it must be so.

We discussed the topic at length, and as I let no opportunity go by to delve deeper into the matter, I asked her:

"Tell me, Frutos, are witches people that become witches, or is it God that makes them that way?"

"Don't be foolish. My God makes nobody but Christians. The ones who want to become witches."

"And are there men witches too?"

"Of course there are. Don't you remember I told you about it. But as they don't have long hair, they can't go way up in the air and have to fly low."

"And how do you learn to be a witch?"

She was quiet for a little while, and then with the air of one who bares his innermost heart, she said to me in a low voice:

"People can turn themselves into witches very easily. The way they do it is like this: you rub all your joints real good with oil; you take off everything but your undershirt, and then go up to some high place; when you're way high up, you spread your arms wide, as though you were going to fly, and then you say, but really meaning it: 'I don't believe in God or the Blessed Virgin!' three times, one right after the other, without breathing, and then you take off into the air and fly through space."

"Don't you fall?"

"Of course not. That is if the oil is the right kind, and you say things right."

A shiver ran through me. I must not have known that kneeling was a sign of adoration, for if I had, I would have been at Frutos's feet. She had made me the happiest soul in the world.

That night after I had said my prayers I got into bed and said in a very low voice: "I don't believe in God or the Blessed Virgin! I don't believe in God or the Blessed Virgin! I don't believe in God or the Blessed Virgin!" I had a little trouble getting to sleep after this declaration of atheism.

Early the next morning I was running down the hall with arms spread wide as though flying, and repeating the prescribed formula. Mariana heard me and called out: "Mamma, just come here and see what this good-for-nothing is saying." But my mother did not manage to "see" my words, because before she got there, I was out in the street on my way to school. I couldn't say why, but I was not anxious to have my mother see me doing such things.

When I got home Frutos was not waiting to meet me. I had to go to look for her, and for the first time I found her in a rage with me. Mamma had practically eaten her alive on account of the things she was telling and teaching me, and it was all my fault for being a tattle-tale, and I had better not come around bothering her any more, asking her to tell me stories, because with a blabbermouth like me—

At lunch my father scowled at me as he said: "Young man, any more nonsense out of you like this morning, and you'll be sorry!"

I was dumfounded. My father threatening me! Frutos refusing to have anything to do with me! And just when there were so many things I had to ask her! I did not know what to do about the long hair, or what kind of oil to use!

For three days I implored Frutos to tell me just those two little things, and gave her my word of honor that I wouldn't open my mouth. I might have been talking to the wall. Not a word could I get out of her.

And the worst of it was that what had begun as a fancy, a whim, in the face of difficulties and opposition was becoming an obsession, an irresistible desire.

To be a witch! To be able to fly at night over the housetops, over the church-spire, "into the blue"! Was there anything in the world to compare with it? What would they say at home when I said to them: "Anything you want from Bogotá? I'm going there tonight"? And Mamma would answer: "Bring me some apples." And before you knew it, I would be back with a beautiful branch loaded with them which I had just broken off. Or just to start soaring like a hawk, up, up—

I had to be a witch. There were no two ways about it. I felt smothered down on the ground. I needed air. "I don't care," I thought to myself, "let them scold me. Even if Frutos won't talk, I'll know what to do. Who taught the first person that became a witch? I can always get hold of oil, even if I have to use castor oil. But that long hair, like a woman's—where do I get that?"

I scratched my head.

I, who from the last amen of evening prayers until six in the morning slept like a log, began to lie awake at night. In the nervous excitement of my insomnia I saw marvels that seemed entirely feasible: twice I saw myself gently flying around, higher, higher, and below I saw the towns, the fields like a picture on paper.

Pepe Ríos, the son of a neighbor, was my bosom friend; and I finally decided to take him into my confidence and tell him my plans. At first he did not seem to share my enthusiasm, and he came out with that same nonsense about there being witches, but one must not believe in them, which served to strengthen my conviction, seeing that he was in complete agreement with Frutos. But I painted the plan in such glowing colors that he finally caught my enthusiasm.

Pepe was not one of those who drown in a spoonful of water. His inventive mind found a solution for everything.

"Look," he said to me. "Tomorrow there is going to be a *Salve* at church, and I'm one of the altar boys. I know where the sexton keeps the oil, and when I go in to get dressed I'll steal some. You get a good bottle, and we'll fill it up."

"And what do we do for hair?" I asked. "Because we want to fly good and high. It's no fun just flying above the ground like the goblins."

"That's as easy as pie," answered Pepe. "My sisters and my mother have false hair, and we'll steal it. What difference does it make if it isn't our own hair? Just so it's long and plenty of it, that's enough."

"What a boy!" I thought to myself as I stood there gaping-mouthed. "What a team he and Frutos would make!"

The next day, pretending we were looking for a parrot that had got lost, Pepe and I invaded the bedrooms of the Ríos girls. Poking about here, looking there, we finally came upon a big box with a mirror on it, and in it a trove of hair of every color, some in coils, some in curls, some in braids covered with a net, some straight and smooth, some wavy, and all mixed with snaggle-toothed combs and hairpins. A little bottle of red liquid attracted my eye, and as I was about to lay covetous hands on it, Pepe said:

"Don't touch that. It's for Mamma's cheeks. Why, she might even kill us!"

Very little hair was left in the box after we had made our selection.

"Now, listen," he warned, as he handed it over to me, "you hide this carefully in your house. Don't let them smell a rat. If they catch us. . . . And don't say one word about what we're going to do. You talk so much."

"That's what you think," I answered him with great solemnity. "Don't you worry about me saying anything."

From that day we were inseparable. To be sure, Frutos was not in the least pleased at this sudden intimacy with "that Caiphas," the name she applied to Pepe.

That night I informed the family that I didn't intend to go to bed until the grownups did, because I was almost ten years old. And I didn't. To pass the time, I fluttered about the candles like a moth, lighting papers or trimming the wick, with which I greatly annoyed Mariana, who was the only one in the family that stood up to me.

"You pest," she grumbled, "not even at night are we to have a little peace. Go on to bed, nuisance!"

But I was so pleasantly employed that I did not even bother to answer her, just sticking my tongue out, or crossing my eyes at her.

"Devil!" shouted Mariana. "If Papa doesn't give you a thrashing— I'm going to get hold of you, and I'll pound you to a jelly!"

I crossed my eyes still more.

Doña Rita, Pepe's mother, and her daughters used to come over to play lotto occasionally in the evening, and Pepe always came along; but after the formation of our alliance, he sacrificed the pleasure of calling the numbers to go off with me. In this way we were free to discuss our plans at length, and the "elevation" was set for the following Sunday night.

Two days to go! What excitement! I even lost my appetite; I even forgot about Frutos, who was having an attack of gout.

"Now, what devilment are they up to?" she would mutter gloomily as we went by her room.

Finally the eagerly awaited Sunday dawned. From noon on, we were out in the back yard getting the hair ready. We had got hold of an old umbrella, and out of the cover, as best we could, we made ourselves wigs, with the help of God, some black sealing wax, and string.

When we had finished the complicated job we tried them on in front of Mariana's mirror, which we had sneaked out of her room. They looked wonderful! How beautifully the long locks snaked down!

We hid everything carefully away and went out in the street to play so nobody would suspect anything. But we were seething inside.

After a day that seemed as though it never would end, evening came and Pepe appeared with his mother. As soon as the lotto game was under way we slipped off to the back yard.

A violent argument broke out between us as to which was the best spot from which to take off in flight. Pepe was in favor of the oven which was on the back porch; I insisted that the stone fence was the best place, because the oven was not very high, and besides it was under the eaves, and we would have to fly at an angle and could not mount high enough. We finally settled on the pigpen, which seemed to have everything. From there we would fly to the Alto de las Piedras, which overlooked the town to the south, and once there, we would launch ourselves into the blue. We would take off simultaneously.

Although there was a moon, we had taken along a piece of candle, and by its light we began our "witching" toilette in the dining-room. We hung our linen suits on a chair, rolled up our shirts, and each provided with a chicken feather, we began our anointing. Dear Heaven, the smell of that oil!

When the bottle was empty and our joints were as sticky as taffy, we adjusted our wigs, securing them with a chin strap of rope.

Tremulous with emotion, we slipped into the back yard, with the air of circus acrobats coming out to greet their public.

At the farthest end of the yard, behind the rustling foliage of the banana grove, where the ground sloped down, was the pigpen, built of stout logs, with a fern-thatched roof. The water drained down that slope to form a black, malarial pool that fertilized the volunteer tomatoes and mullein weeds that had sprung up around it.

The outraged grunts of the pig, protesting at having her privacy invaded at such hours, were frightening, but they did not daunt us. We simply ignored them.

Pushing ahead of Pepe, I did not stop until I had my foot on the top rail. Holding fast to one of the uprights on which the roof rested, like another Girardot with his flag, I paused for a second. My eyes were filled with the immensity of space.

I expended all my pent-up faith in that instant, and almost choking with fear of failing to observe the inviolable rule by an inopportune breath, I repeated:

"I don't believe in God or the Blessed Virgin, I don't believe in God or the Blessed Virgin, I don't believe in God or the Blessed Virgin," and took off.

Something strange was happening. I did not seem to be flying upwards as I had planned. I was cold, my head felt funny, and—that was all.

I opened my eyes. Someone was laying me down on a floor. I felt something like blood on my face; I looked at myself: I was almost naked and covered with mud. From the disorder of the furniture, from the lotto cards and numbers scattered about the floor, from the general atmosphere of alarm, I suspected what had happened. A chill as of ice congealed my heart; I closed my eyes not to see myself, not to look upon something dreadful that I was sure was going to happen.

"Toñito! Antoñito! Did you fall? Are you hurt?" Everyone was talking at the same time.

They were feeling me, bringing a candle close to my face.

"It's nothing. He's all right."

"It's nothing. He's just stunned."

"He's opening his eyes. Antonio! Antoñito!"

"Calm yourself, calm yourself, Miss Anita! Nothing has happened!"

The sound of teeth grinding together struck me to the heart. I opened my eyes, and saw my mother stretched out in a chair, her arms rigid, her hands clenched, her face livid and twisted to one side, her eyes rolled up in her head, her nostrils dilated as though she could not breathe. She was trying to scream, but no sound came out of her throat, as she shuddered in the throes of a convulsion. Some of the women were holding her down, sprinkling water on her, rubbing her hands, holding smelling salts under her nose. My sisters were crying.

I jumped up off the floor screaming: "Mamma, mamita!"

"He's all right," they all began to shout, "he's all right. He's not even hurt."

"What happened, for Heaven's sake? How did you get yourself into such a mess?"

"He has hurt his face. Toñito, keep away. Just look at him."

In horror of myself I tried to run away, but they cut me off at the door with a tub of warm water. The cook lifted me into the middle of the steaming bath, and I offered no resistance. She stripped off my filthy shirt, and as I stood there, naked as our first father, she began scrubbing me with the help of some of the ladies.

"But what has this child got into? It won't come off," said one.

"What a stench!" answered another, covering her nose with her handkerchief.

"Give me the soap and let's see if I can get it off."

I was soon a mass of lather. "My dears," observed the soaper, "this is palm oil, and not dirt from the pigsty."

"So it is! So it is!" the others answered in chorus.

"But where on earth did it come from?"

I was lifted out of the tub onto the floor, and wrapped in a bath towel. Mariana, herself again, brought a nightshirt, and was about to put it on me when a crowd of people burst into the room. My father was one of them.

"Is he dead?" he asked in a voice I had never heard before.

Without waiting for an answer, he went out. Hardly a second had elapsed till he was back with a strap.

"Don't whip him," came a chorus of feminine voices.

"Poor lamb," said the soaper. "It's not his fault."

"Papa, it's not fair. Look, he's hurt," lamented the members of the family.

Papa paid no attention to any of them. Taking me by the arm with one hand, he raised the doubled strap in the other and said in an unsteady voice:

"I have put up with your nonsense for a long time, but this is one too many. Take that, you good-for-nothing, and see if it teaches you a lesson." The strap cracked across my bare skin.

A cry like the howl of an animal filled the room: it was Frutos.

"Master, master!" she sobbed, trying to pull the strap out of his hand and putting herself between him and me. "Master, in the name of God, don't whip him, for the sake of our Redeemer who died on the Cross!" and she knelt before him, clasping his knees, almost making him fall. "It's not his fault, it's not his fault!"

My father pushed her aside, but Frutos got to her feet, and, standing in front of me, she wrapped her skirts about me.

"You old witch!" shouted my father, pulling off her bandanna and grabbing her by the hair, "Get away from here or I'll kill you." With one hand he pushed her aside, while with the other he pulled me out of the protecting wrapper.

"Take her away from me before I kill her," he shouted in fury.

Raising the strap again and counting one—two—up to twelve, he brought it down on my bare body, which jerked from side to side like a dummy.

Frutos straightened up and then like a lifeless bundle fell back on the floor uttering strange noises.

Not one cry did I let out—I, who used to raise the roof off the house if a fly settled on me.

Frutos lay writhing on the floor; suddenly she raised herself up and then fell back again, flinging herself about in shameless disorder, pushing aside people, and knocking against the furniture. Some of the people tried to take hold of her, but she drove them back with blows, kicks, and bites. Finally she managed to bring out with a voice that was dreadful to hear:

"Let me out of this damned house right away."

All the men grabbed her, and after a struggle punctuated by groans and blows, they managed to get her out in the hall. In the confusion I caught a glimpse of her, and in spite of my love for her, she struck me as a diabolical being. Her hair was standing out around her head, her eyes were staring and bloodshot, and foam was coming from her mouth.

The doctor came in and examined me. He said I had no broken or dislocated bones, not even a sprain. He looked at the scratch on my cheek, took out an instrument, and without hurting me extracted a splinter from the scratch. He gave me something to drink that had brandy in it; took a cup, held a lighted paper in it, and applied the cup to different places on my back, raising up the flesh in painful tension. Feminine hands, wet with camphorated brandy, rubbed me all over, and finally they tied bits of rag dipped in a yellowish liquid on me at various spots.

While they were in the midst of these operations, there came the sound of hurrying steps accompanied by the rustle of starched skirts. Doña Rita appeared in the door with one of the wigs in her hand.

"I can't tell you how sorry I am," she exclaimed, all out of breath and her face working. "I have just made de Ríos give Pepe such a thrashing. Look what those devils were doing"—here she held up the wig for all to see—"they were being witches. That is where they got the idea of flying. What do you think of that? And this is the hair we had for the wig of Jesus!"

Everybody gathered around to examine it and exclaim over it. The doctor took it in his hands and laughed until the tears ran down his cheeks.

"Ave Maria, doctor!" went on Doña Rita. "Don't you see? It was a miracle, nothing but a miracle, that these fiends didn't break their necks. Did you ever hear the like, doctor? Jumping off that high pig-pen! And a fall like that! Fortunately he fell in the mud, and that bush broke the fall. Otherwise he would have been dead when they picked him up. We were in here having such a nice game of lotto; I had just filled three rows, doctor, when—we heard mine call out: 'Hurry, hurry, Antonio has killed himself.' Doctor, I thought I was going to drop dead right where I was. They all ran out with candles, and in a few minutes they carried him in with nothing on but his undershirt, covered with pig filth up to his eyes, and gushing blood. Just as though he had been killed, exactly. Mine was saved, because as he is so lazy, he wouldn't jump first. But, would you believe it, doctor, the scamps had covered themselves all over with palm oil that they had stolen from the sexton. They say you have to use it to be a witch. But, believe me, he got a first-class hiding. I tell you I think these children today learn from the Old Nick himself."

"It's not Old Nick," interrupted my father, coming in from the adjoining room. "It's that devil of a Frutos whom Anita has put up with all these years that put that stuff in their heads. And don't think this boy has gotten off so easy. He may die of the effects. He's had a bad fall."

"The danger is remote, and there are no alarming symptoms about the case," the doctor answered. "I haven't even had to give him any special treatment."

"I hope you're right," said my father. "It's all that damned Frutos's fault. From the minute they called me and told me he'd fallen off the top of the pigpen, I knew just what had happened. Well, he's had a lesson he won't forget."

He went on to tell about my attempts to fly through the hall, and my blasphemous incantations.

When the mystery was cleared up, everybody broke into comments and questions.

Their talk brought me out of my somnambulistic state. I felt myself the unhappiest person in the world. "What do I care if I die," I said to myself, "now that Frutos had fooled me with lies, and is so bad, and a person can't fly? And now Mamma is dead"—for I firmly believed she had died—"and Papa has whipped me in front of all these people—and they all saw me with my clothes off—and Pepe has gone and told everything—"

I felt as though all the springs of my soul had been broken, and I was left without faith, without illusions. I closed my eyes tight, the quicker to die and rest, but it was no good. Terrible visions kept going through my head, and sigh after sigh escaped my breast.

Very late that night, after everyone had left, I finally went to sleep.

It would have been better to stay awake. I saw Frutos flying about, laughing at me, making faces at me. I heard the bells tolling sadly, so sadly, and I caught the smell of cypress and burning wax, and saw my mother in a black coffin—so black. Then I was in a swamp, buried up to my neck, and I tried to get out, I tried to scream, but I couldn't.

Finally with one supreme effort I managed to free myself. I gave a scream and woke up, trembling from head to foot, my hair standing on end, and drenched in cold sweat. There was a light in the room, and my mother had me by the hands and was shaking me.

"Toñito—Toñito," she called. "Don't be afraid, darling. It's just a bad dream."

"Is Mamma alive," I thought to myself, "or am I still dreaming?"

She picked me up as though I were a baby, and, hugging me to her breast, she kissed me on the forehead, and her tears wet my face:

"See what you did, my child, to make Papa punish you! And what if you had killed yourself? What would I have done?" And the tears kept rolling down her cheeks.

"Mamita dear! You're not dead, are you?"

"No, my lamb. Don't you see that I am here with you? I just fainted with fright. But I'm all right now. Take another sip of this medicine the doctor left. It's good!"

She was alive! I sat up to take the glass, and saw my father sitting at the foot of the bed. He was crying too. He put his hand on my forehead, felt my pulse, and then said in a very sad voice:

"He's got a high fever. Awfully high."

And he went to call the doctor, who was sleeping in the next room. They gave me some drops in sugar water.

I calmed down, and cried and cried, but they were tears of happiness.

I was in bed for six days, listening to the comments of Doña Rita and other callers, some funny, some lugubrious, on my adventure. I learned from them that Frutos had left the house and had sent for her belongings. Days before, this would have driven me out of my mind, but now it had no effect on me.

Don Calixto Muñetón, the luminary of our town, who always spoke on Independence Day and when the bishop paid us a visit, who read a great deal, and who had composed a novena for the Holy Child, was among those who came to call. Without its being the 20th of July, he unleashed his eloquence on the subject of my fall. He held forth on human frailities, excoriating the sin of ambition. And when he was ready to leave, with his bamboo cane in his left hand, and holding up his right like a signpost, he turned to me with a pitying glance and summed up his remarks in these words:

"And so, my young friend, remember: anyone who tries to fly too high generally lands in the pigpen!"

JAVIER DE VIANA

(1872–1926)

EXCEPT FOR HIS fellow countryman, the playwright Florencio Sánchez, no writer of his period has left us more vivid, unforgettable paintings of the gaucho than the Uruguayan Javier de Viana. Like Estanislao del Campo, José Hernández, and William Henry Hudson, the author, though a man of position and culture, has managed to give expression to the thoughts, the emotions, and the psychology of the gaucho as though they were his own. And in a sense they were. Although a member of one of the most distinguished families in Uruguay—his great-grandfather was the first governor of Montevideo—Javier de Viana was raised on a ranch. He received his first education from nature and from the gaucho peons who were his closest friends. It was in their language that he first learned to express himself, and his whole life was shaped by these early associations. He never lost his sympathy and understanding for them, despite his subsequent active life in politics, journalism, and literature. He is the author of a number of novels and plays, but it is as a writer of short stories that he is unexcelled.

The following selection is from his best known short story. With consummate pity and tenderness it depicts the tragedy of the young gaucho who falls a victim to his own superstitous belief in the spell a woman has cast upon him.

Gurí

[JAVIER DE VIANA]

SIX weeks went by, and Juan Francisco, Gurí, back on his own stamping grounds, completely taken up with the training of the race horse a rich rancher of Rincón de Ramírez had entrusted to his skill, dismissed from his mind all thought of Clara and the spells she might be trying to put on him. There in his familiar surroundings, leading an active life, his fears gradually faded away until they were no more than the memory of a bad nightmare.

His every thought was concentrated on the roan, a crossbreed of great promise that was to be matched against another crossbreed, a bay that belonged to a horse fancier of Yaguarón. The news of the race had spread far and wide, and excitement was running high. It was the topic of conversation around the fireplace in the ranch kitchens and at the roadside taverns. To the high stakes and the reputation of the two horses there was added the circumstance that one was from Uruguay and the other from Brazil, which gave the race something of an international character and piqued the pride of the spectators. And to further heighten interest, the two most skillful and best known trainers were meeting too—Gurí, who was handling Núñez's roan, and the Indian Luis Pedro, who was handling Silveira Pintos's bay. Naturally neither of them spared any effort to have his horse in the best possible shape, spurred on by a rivalry of long standing, the desire to win, and the recompense that awaited the winner.

All these circumstances restored calm to Juan Francisco's spirit; and this calm in itself became his most effective cure, for it was clear that if a spell had been put on him, he would have felt the effects by this time. Having rid himself of his gloomy thoughts, he could take satisfaction in the fact that he had broken off his relations with Clara for good, a thought that raised him in his own estimation. Sometimes as he exercised the roan early in the morning, the oxygen-laden air from the hills produced in him a kind of gentle intoxication, an overflowing vitality, a great joy at being alive. When he remembered the terror he had felt at that hoot of an owl, which echoed for a moment and then was lost in space, he smiled, feeling that it had been a silly, childish thing to be so frightened by such a feeble portent. He still believed in ghosts, souls in torment, charms, spells, all manifestations of supernatural powers, divine and infernal; but he felt no fear, looking upon them as a remote danger, as one fears the lightning only when it storms. His peace of spirit made it possible for him to sort out his thoughts, put his mind in order. It gave him a chance to know Clara for what she was: depraved, overbearing, false, unreliable, incapable of loving anybody; but without enough determination or actual viciousness to commit a crime. In one of her frequent explosions of temper she might threaten to put a spell on him, but she would not have the purposefulness to carry it out. And that visit of Paula's and her story might very well have been a scheme, a lie invented by Clara to make him come back to her out of fear. To be sure, there was that question of the neckerchief that he could not get back from her; but was it not probable that it really was lost, or that she had given it away or thrown it out? He could not recall having seen her wear it for a long time, nor did he think she would have held out when he had her by the throat on the point of strangling her— The whole thing had been a farce, and he had been such a fool as to swallow it and torment himself the way he had done. He had been seeing things, that was all; and although he was rather ashamed of his weakness, he smiled, forgot, and devoted all his attention and his time to the care of the roan that he was bringing into prime condition.

And the days slipped by, luminous, placid, like the blue firmament overhead, that incomparable autumn sky, beneath which nature, its laborious tasks at an end, takes on the calm, serene, almost august beauty of a proud matron.

This was Gurí's frame of mind that Sunday, the fifth of June, which had been set for the race. For a whole week people had been gathering: some from far off, those chronic vagabonds who can smell a good time miles away, like crows carrion; peddlers; owners of race horses; owners of bowling alleys, of knucklebones, of ninepins games; and, above all, the army of refreshment venders. Around Benito Cardoso's tavern a village seemed to have sprung up over night; more than thirty tents had been pitched near the big stone buildings and in the big clumps of mataojo, without counting the near-by willow grove and the various ombús, all of which had been invaded by the crowd.

In the whole vicinity the only ones who had stayed home were the sick and the dogs: the first, because they could not go, the second, because by police ordinance no dogs were allowed. There were large crowds of strangers. The rich Brazilian ranchers of Yaguarón, of Cerro Largo, and Treinta y Tres came in a group, and were showing off their horses with their silver-trimmed saddle gear, their thick money belts full of gold. In their frank, gay, boisterous manner they rode about, laying heavy bets and taunting the backers of the roan: "It's got creeping paralysis and couldn't beat anything."

Along both sides of the track, a good track six hundred meters long, with a well-kept, roped-off grass border, eight or ten carriages and surreys were parked—which in the country is a huge collection of vehicles—and in each there were crowded eight, ten, a dozen stout women, squeezed into corsets and the silk dresses used only for special occasions, and girls decked out with all the ribbons they could find in their trunks. Each carriage was surrounded by a group of young men, relatives, acquaintances, suitors, or sweethearts.

At two in the afternoon the horses were brought out on the track and the interminable heats began. It was not until an hour and a half later that the starter's flag dropped. The bay took the lead, and the Brazilian visitors broke into howls of delight. But as the contest between the two rivals grew more intense, for a few seconds not a sound was heard. Then like a human avalanche the whole crowd rushed toward the goal. The race had been very close. The judges deliberated for a long time, and when order had finally been re-established, the chief of police pronounced the ritual phrase:

"Gentlemen! Attention! The roan is the winner by a nose."

Gurí, avoiding the congratulations of those who had bet on the roan, lost himself in the crowd and went into one of the tents where there were not so many people. It was run by an old woman and a young girl. It was poorly patronized, because the girl was known to be a flirt who led men on and then laughed at them, and her victims and those who knew her by reputation were giving her a severe letting alone. Vain, full of life, she was feeling the offense keenly. Her almond-shaped black eyes glittered hotly, and her sun-browned cheeks had a deep-red glow, like the fruit of the haw. Her Creole pride ran hot in her blood, and her young flesh was tormented by indomitable desires, and her mind, by voluptuous dreams. Her eighteen years imperiously demanded homage and caresses. Juan Francisco had approached her on more than one occasion, but she had laughed at his shyness and offended him with her disdain. But that afternoon she received him with great cordiality. The indifference of the others and the aureole of triumph that surrounded Gurí brought her down from her high horse, and she was affable and ingratiating. As she served him the coffee he had ordered, she asked him about the particulars of the race, smiling at him with a sweetness to which the boy was not accustomed.

"Have you seen the way the *macacos* are buzzing around like a stirred-up hornets' nest? They came here as though they owned the place, and now that they've had to eat their brags and lost their money, they're as savage as a snake that's lost its poison."

And she laughed, happy over the local triumph and the defeat of the foreigners.

The entrance of some customers drew Rosa away. She went over to wait on them, friendly, chaffing, answering their teasing in kind, and looking over from time to time and winking at Juan Francisco, who sat quietly in the corner sipping his coffee.

The noise outside was deafening. Other races had been run, and people were arguing at the top of their lungs as to why this one had lost and the poor showing the other had made, there was an exchange of challenges and bets and jokes that were more like insults. There was the sound of singing, the strumming of a guitar, the wheezing of an accordion, the calls of boys selling pasties and fried cakes, drunken shouts, the laughter of women, the neighing of horses. And all this under a lowering sky, in an atmosphere heavy and foul with the sweat of so many people and horses, the reek of frying fat, of roasting meat, of simmering stews.

The tent was empty once more. Rosa selected from a tin platter the best custard-filled cake and handed it to Gurí.

"A poor person's gift," she said, "but each gives what he has."

Flattered at the attention, he took it, blushed, and stammered:

"If you wanted to give all you have, it would be a rich person's gift—"

"Just listen to him!" she answered with an amused gesture as she turned her back.

It was getting dark. Juan Francisco got up to say good-bye. As he took Rosa's hand he drew her to him with the intention of giving her a kiss, but she ducked away.

"Not here, silly! They'll see us."

"Afterwards?"

"Maybe—"

"Honestly?"

"Get along with you," said the girl, giving him an affectionate shove. And when Juan Francisco looked back he met a look and a smile that were the equivalent of a formal promise. With his face on fire and his legs unsteady, he left the tent and went out into the crowd.

Night had fallen, dark and threatening rain. It was hard to see anything but the vague outline of people and horses, but in the tents the braziers and the kerosene lamps glowed, and the din continued. In the tavern there was gambling for heavy stakes at the green baize table surrounded by rich ranchers and presided over by the chief of police, a giant with Indian cast of features who had committed a number of crimes himself, very fine in his cavalry lieutenant's uniform, and who was acting as croupier and playing at the same time.

About nine o'clock Gurí set out for Rosa's tent. Waiting for him at the entrance was the Indian Martiniano, an old Paraguayan with whom Gurí had an understanding.

"Where is she?" he asked in a low voice.

"*Acoi hecomí*," the old man answered in Guarani, to which Juan Francisco replied impatiently:

"Talk in Christian."

"She's there behind the tent."

Juan Francisco slipped away without another word, swore at a peg he stumbled over, and came upon Rosa, who, wrapped in a heavy poncho, was waiting for him.

The gaucho slipped his arm around the girl's waist under the blanket, at the same time pressing a long kiss on her cheek. Without moving, she said:

"Be still; don't make any noise; the old woman hasn't gone to sleep yet, and she's as wary as a stray dog."

Gurí kept quiet, but his muscular arms tightened around the girl's plump waist, and his hot mouth, drunk with desire, kissed her feverishly on the mouth, the eyes, with all the ardor of his blood and his nature. She offered no resistance, yielding with delight, trembling from time to time in eager expectation.

About a quarter of a hour went by in this delightful dalliance. Then she freed herself.

"Wait a minute," she whispered, slipping noiselessly around the tent to the entrance. She came back quickly.

"The old woman is snoring," she said smiling, with a warm throb in her voice. "Where shall we go?"

Gurí stood perplexed. Where should they go? He hadn't even thought of that. But he settled it quickly in his primitive way:

"Right over there, under that big ombú behind the tavern."

She laughed:

"What a pig! Like the dogs—"

"Just for tonight. Tomorrow I'll set you behind me on my horse and take you to a l'ttle house that's as warm as an oriole's nest."

"Easy, boy! Don't sell the hide before you've skinned the sheep. And after—"

He did not let her finish; he drew her toward him, held her tightly in his arms, and kissed her mouth. She said nothing and, clinging closely to him, followed him submissively to the enormous ombú whose spreading top rose majestically behind the white tavern.

The darkness was increasing, the noises were dying down. From inside the tents came faint flickers of light and muted snatches of sound.

Juan Francisco spread his poncho over the thick exposed roots of the ombú; then he drew her down beside him on the rough seat, and their mutual caresses fed the flames of their desire.

Suddenly a shiver ran down Gurí's spine. He recalled the threat, that terrible threat that he would lose his virility, that he would be a man only for Clara, and a cloud came over his spirit as when a flock of crows flies over a narrow valley. What if it was so? And with his spirit caught in this torturing doubt, he began to be afraid. His judgment became helpless, his will collapsed in the face of this mysterious spell to which distance was nothing and which was as irresistible and cruel as a malediction.

The first effect of a spell, the first harm from which all the others come, is the destruction of a man's sexual potency, of the supreme vital energy, and the end of his love life. This was solemnly vouched for by all familiar with witchcraft, and it must be true. Juan Francisco was gripped by fear, and the effects of his autosuggestion filled him with panic. For a time he had thought he was saved. Why? Had he had occasion to put it to the test? Why could the implacable enemy not have been lurking beside him, invisible, just waiting for the moment to deal him the mortal blow? When it begins to thunder is when one fears the lightning—

Rosa stirred impatiently, and he threw himself upon her in a frenzy, biting her as he kissed her, trying to forget and to forget himself, to cast away the black thought that was scratching at his mind with its spider's feet. But all his efforts were in vain. In the thick, cold blackness of the night he saw Clara's hovel, he saw the mulatto Gumersinda preparing her diabolical spells, he saw little Paula running away with eyes wide with fright, and he saw his former mistress smiling a devilish smile, her face set in a ferocious desire for revenge. A terrible struggle began in him between his will and the force of suggestion, a desperate combat of heroic charges and maddened retreats, of violent attacks and impotent onslaughts. It was like a man buried alive in a coffin of iron, wearing down his nails, bursting his muscles in his infinite desperation to save himself.

But every attempt met with defeat. His desperate efforts to cast out of his mind the memory of the fatal mischief were useless. And more frenzied, more enraged with every passing moment, unable to reason, moved only by animal impulses, his desire grew with his impotence. A jaguar held fast by two lassos could not have threshed about more wildly or roared in madder despair than that unhappy lover.

Rosa, humiliated and exasperated, pushed him away with both hands and got to her feet. And with a voice trembling with hate and contempt, she threw these words at him:

"You should have let me know you were gelded!"

Juan Francisco lay stretched face downward on his poncho, which was torn to shreds. He was motionless, like a steer that has been poleaxed. Around him everything was like thick, black crepe against which winked glimmers of light, like the glow of fireflies in the canopied summer nights. Past, present, future, all lay motionless in his benumbed mind. This calm lasted for a long time, that profound calm which follows a great spiritual shock. Then the ideas began to move again, milling about, like a herd being sucked down by the waters of a heavy-running stream. Without anything to cling to, his mind went under. He tried to reconstruct what had happened, but he sank in a mire of disjointed memories. All he could grasp, all that was real, was his abasement, his moral death. His helpless soul floated on the torrent of his misfortune, as mute and somber as a mountain lion caught by flood waters on an island of wild hyacinths that the river drags along in its roaring tide.

A long time went by. A blazing streak of lightning made Gurí blink. A long, hoarse roll of thunder made his numb body shiver. With a great effort, he managed to pull himself into a sitting position on the roots of the ombú.

He opened his eyes wide and looked all around him, like a man rousing himself from a nightmare. It had grown colder and was raining hard. There was no longer any light in the tents, and no sound of voices. Inside the tavern the game was probably still going on around the green table, but the steady beat of the rain and the rumble of the thunder drowned out every other noise. In that dark loneliness only he kept vigil in the refuge of the giant ombú, impenetrable to water and to sun. And among that multitude which he sensed sleeping about him, unperturbed, dreaming of happiness, he alone was accursed, a being unworthy of living among other men, a miserable creature bowed down by the unbearable weight of a curse.

With another effort the gaucho got to his feet, weaving about as though drunk. He took two or three meaningless steps, and stopped to rub his eyes hard. He stood thus for a few moments, not knowing what to do. Then he tried to get his bearings, and, stumbling at each step, paying no attention to the rain or the mud, he managed to reach the place where he had tethered his horse. He slowly rolled up the tie rope, took his horse by the bridle, and returned to the ombú, where he had left his saddle. One by one, calmly and with his usual care, he arranged the different pieces. He cinched the girth tight, spread out the saddle pads evenly, taking care to put the oldest on top so the good ones would not get wet, unfastened his quirt from the saddle straps, slipped the bit in the horse's mouth, and mounted.

Where was he going? He did not know himself. He had become an automaton with no other guide than his instinct. When in danger the mountain lion makes a stand against a tree, the capybara plunges into the water, and the gaucho mounts his horse.

Gurí mounted, brought down the quirt, set spurs to the horse, and took off at a gallop, fleeing in terror from an enemy that was in his own soul and that he could not shake off, no matter how far he rode or where he tried to hide.

As he had forgotten to pick up his poncho, and the rain had turned into a downpour, in a little while he was soaked through. His baggy pants were sticking to his thighs, his boots were full of water; but none of this mattered to him, for he was not aware of it.

He had slackened the reins, and the horse was trotting uneasily, frightened by the thunder and the lightning. They were riding against a howling southwester, which tore at the horse's mane and buffeted the rider's face. The ground was oozing water, the brooks were overflowing, the fords were deep and slippery, but nothing could detain the wild, pathless flight of the young gaucho.

Neither the steady roll of the thunder aroused his mind, nor could the incessant flicker of the lightning bring light to his broken spirit. In his imagination he could see everything: the village, Clara, the hovel of their degrading love, the brutal scene of their breaking off. Then those tranquil months on the ranch when he affectionately and conscientiously trained the roan; the race, the pride of winning, the tent of the Paraguayans, the cup of coffee, the cake, and finally, Rosa, with her graceful body, her gay, young face, her hot eyes, and her caressing smile—the night, the ombú, his despairing impotence. Everything was present, clear, with a profusion of details, as vivid as a picture just seen. But this agglomeration of images did not produce any feeling; only his eyes saw them. As it was impossible for him to make any effort, he did nothing to drive them away, and besides they were not painful. The destruction of his personality had been complete, organically and emotionally; both feeling and will had disappeared, and all that remained was memory. His spirit was as insensible as his body; nothing, internal or external, left the slightest impress upon either. If he had come upon a lake in his path, he would have plunged into it, just as he would have advanced against a dagger held to his breast.

It was a long ride. For hours the young gaucho wandered aimlessly through the water-logged fields. The next morning a gaucho who had spent the night gambling in Benito Cardoso's tavern was amazed, as he went to get his horse, to see a dun, saddled and grazing loose. He looked all round him for the rider and, not seeing him, went over to the horse and recognized it.

"Why, it's Gurí's! Wonder where the Indian is?"

As he observed it more closely, he noticed that the saddle was soaking wet, in spite of the fact that it was not raining any more; and this and the look of the horse, which told of a long trip, made him think its owner must have spent the night riding.

"Nobody but a man in love or a drunkard would have been riding around the country last night. And Gurí— But in any case that Indian would never turn a horse out saddled. Maybe he got into a fight."

He took the dun by the bridle and looked about in the grass, and it was not long before he saw an object that he quickly identified as Juan Francisco. At first the gaucho stood back, without venturing to touch him, thinking he might be wounded or dead, for the lad was stretched out full length in the mud, face down and motionless.

"Maybe he was hit by lightning," he muttered, and was about to cross himself when he looked up at the sky and, seeing that it was clear and serene, decided that the precaution was unnecessary. He drew closer and, bending over the boy, touched him on the shoulder.

"Friend Gurí," he shouted, "it's not such a good bed as to sleep in it all day."

As Gurí neither answered nor moved, the man drew back cautiously.

"Maybe he really is dead. But for my money—"

Prudence got the better of curiosity and, shrugging his shoulders, he observed philosophically:

"Dead or soused, let the law handle it," and he headed for the tavern to report what he had found.

The first person he met was old Sosa, who, as soon as he heard the first words, rushed out toward the field. The gaucho followed close behind him.

"It's my opinion that he's pickled."

"That's impossible. I know Gurí like I know my own brand, and he never gets drunk. It must be something else. What if those—"

His guide understood what was in Sosa's mind and completed the phrase for him:

"You think they might have beaten him up out of spite?"

They walked on until they found Juan Francisco lying in the same place and in the same position. The rancher bent over him, spoke to him without getting any answer, felt him, and, finding him alive, knelt down beside him and lifted his head. The lad was breathing slowly without opening his eyes or moving his lips. On his face, covered with mud, there was an expression of intense suffering. All Sosa's solicitous questions fell upon deaf ears. Finally he decided to carry him to the tavern with the help of the kindly gaucho.

They put him to bed on a cot in a little room in the back, where he lay all day completely immobile. It was impossible to get a word out of him or to make him take the different home remedies that were suggested. By evening Sosa, who was deeply worried by the lad's state, talked of sending for a doctor.

"A doctor! It's a long way from here to town, and before he got here the patient would have time to die or get well. Now if there was a good healer—"

Benito Cardoso felt it his duty to speak up:

"If a healer is wanted there's one near here who knows as much medicine as any doctor and who has performed cures plenty of doctors would be proud of—"

"Who's that?"

"Don't you know who it is? It's the mulatto Luna. Take my word for it, the mulatto Luna knows more than all the doctors who've gone to school."

"The mulatto Luna," said Sosa thoughtfully. "I've heard of him. They say he knows his stuff. Does he live near here?"

"Oh, sure. Right over there, only six leagues away."

The mulatto Luna got there that evening and said after examining Gurí that his condition was serious. A high fever had set in, and the healer could not tell what was causing it. The day had been bad, and toward night he got much worse. The sick man was completely delirious, muttering words no one could make out and shuddering; at times his face would become contorted in a grimace of fear, as though he were seeing a legion of demons. He was seized by frequent convulsions that sent up his already high temperature. After great efforts he was finally made to swallow a brew the healer considered infallible; but it was two o'clock in the morning before the patient began to grow calmer and was able to sleep a little. The fever gradually dropped, the delirium calmed, and he seemed to be on the mend. But shortly after noon the fever came back following the same pattern.

Four days of anxious waiting went by like this, with momentary improvements followed by a complete relapse, to the despair of the healer and the deep sorrow of Gurí's kindly protector. In all this time it had been impossible to get a word out of the sick man which would throw any light on his state. In his delirium he would mutter strange words and phrases that made no sense; but when that disappeared he would sink into a brooding silence, against which all the attempts of the mulatto Luna and the affectionate efforts of the rancher to draw him out were useless. He spoke only once, and that was when the latter talked of sending to town for a doctor. No, it would be useless; he would not take any medicine. He only drank the healer's brews because they gave him momentary relief, but as for curing him, neither he nor anybody else could do that. He knew that he was going to die, and he was not afraid of death; he wanted to get it over with as soon as possible. Taking advantage of this opening, Sosa tried to get him to tell what he could about the cause of his ailment.

"Son," he said to him in a fatherly tone, "why won't you tell me what happened to you? Why don't you tell me, who has been like a father to you, who saw you come into the world, who raised you, and has always treated you like a son?"

Tears came into the black eyes of the kindly, venerable, gray-bearded rancher, noble and virile of countenance, as he pronounced these words.

Gurí, moved too by the suffering of the man for whom he felt the greatest affection and respect, murmured, closing his eyes as though to shut out a nagging vision:

"I can't; don't ask me. Just let me die."

The rancher rebelled at the answer.

"That's not acting like a man," he said firmly.

Juan Francisco sat quickly up in the bed and, with eyes dilated, lips drawn back, and hands clenched, exclaimed in a hoarse, fierce voice:

"I'm not a man any more!"

And as though the effort had finished him off, he fell back, as rigid and pale as a corpse.

"Gurí! Gurí! My son!" groaned the rancher, bending over the sick lad and shaking him to bring him back to consciousness. Unable to do so, he rushed out to find the healer, who was drinking maté in the kitchen. As the games were still going on and there were a number of people in the house, in a second the room was full of curious onlookers.

After long, anxious waiting the boy regained consciousness; but he did not say another word, and he seemed to be much worse.

Sosa and the healer grew more worried every day. Rosa had been indiscreet enough to make some remarks about what had happened under the ombú; remarks that spread through the neighborhood and changed with every telling, gathering many and fantastic details, arousing the curiosity of the country folk as they fell upon the fertile soil of their lush imagination, always prone to accept the supernatural.

By the eleventh day the fever had disappeared, but the illness was worse. Of that vigorous lad, overflowing with life, "with two cedar trunks for arms, and two ñandubays for legs," all that remained was a shadow, a pitiful creature consumed, crushed, devoured by a terrible moral malady. During the day he lay in a state of complete immobility, like a jacent statue; but as night came on, he began to writhe like one possessed. His hallucinations started with the twilight and lasted until dawn. Every twenty-four hours marked a steady decline; death was approaching rapidly.

While in the next room the chief of police and ten or twelve inveterate gamblers kept up their game night after night, in the little room where Gurí was guttering out, the rancher Sosa and the mulatto Luna kept solicitous watch, both at their wits' end.

"What is your opinion?" the rancher once asked.

And the old mulatto shook his head, where all his knowledge was in a muddle.

"I don't know, Don Sosa," he answered; "all I know is that poor Gurí is dying."

"But what is he dying of? You said the fever had left him, and if it isn't the fever any more, then what is killing him?"

The healer shook his head once more.

"I don't know. I don't know anything. I do what I can and help all I can, but when I don't know, I don't know, and I come right out and say so, because I am not a doctor who can cure all kinds of sickness—or God, to undo witchcraft—"

Sosa looked at him steadily.

"Do you believe . . . ?" he asked.

"In what?"

"In witchcraft."

"Of course I do! I have seen more cases of it in my life than all the kisses my mother gave me."

"You think that Gurí . . . ?"

"I don't think anything. But if it isn't that a spell has been put on him— He's just exactly like others I have seen—and he's going the way they did."

"And don't you know anything for a spell?"

"I do—Sometimes it works, sometimes it doesn't. In things having to do with the devil there are no rules, and it's nearly always useless— Besides, to do anything, you have to know where it comes from, who put it on him, how it happened— And the lad has a padlock on his mouth, like a barn door."

"And you can't try anything? Do we have to let him die, like a dog, like an animal with the plague?"

"That's the way it is, Don Sosa. Life is just loaned to us, and we have to hand it over when the owner calls for it."

With this philosophical observation the old mulatto took up his bottle of rum, which he always had by him, and tilting it high, drank off a good share of the contents.

Juan Francisco kept getting worse; he saw his end approaching, and he awaited it calmly, with the proud, innate indifference of his race.

On the twenty-first day of his sickness, on an overcast, close afternoon that foretold a storm, his limbs began to grow numb and a sticky sweat beaded his brow. He no longer had strength to move. Those legs with muscles of steel that once clamped like a vise over the flanks of an unbroken colt were now only bone and skin; those arms that could check the rush of the wildest bull lay beside his body, inert, incapable of the slightest movement. Sosa, speaking to his companion and struggling to keep back the tears, summed it up in a beautiful figure of rustic rhetoric:

"He's like a tree that's been blasted by lightning."

The early hours of the night went by quietly. Sosa, crushed with sorrow, sat by the head of the cot smoking one cigarette of black tobacco after another, and drinking the matés the mulatto Luna handed him. A tallow candle stuck in a bottle stood on the floor at the foot of the bed. The charred wick was twisted around itself, and the feeble light barely picked out the dark face of the healer, leaving the room in a sad penumbra.

Juan Francisco continued in a state of sopor; his breathing grew slow and wheezy; his body and face were damp with a cold, viscous sweat. About midnight he awoke and with staring eyes in which the pupils glittered he cast a languid glance about the poor room.

Sosa drew near him and asked solicitously:

"How are you, Gurí? How is it going?"

The lad smiled sadly with fleshless lips on which the smile was like a grimace of pain and whispered:

"All right. This is it."

Then, still motionless, he fixed his glance on the ceiling, where he seemed to see reflected all the scenes of his life, all the images, all the recollections. His mind had acquired the lucidity that so often precedes death, and took satisfaction in passing a last review over the years lived, from which it was taking final leave. The certainty of his end had wiped out all his suffering, and he was savoring the pleasant state of well-being of his last moments. He recalled his childhood; he saw himself happy and strong along the banks of the Tacuarí; he saw himself as a boy, enjoying the skill of his muscles in his hard, dangerous tasks; he saw himself free, master of his acts, in the land he loved; and then he saw his fatal meeting with Clara and the beginning of his undoing. With a kind of idle curiosity he wondered how the spell had been put on him. He remembered how it had been done in a case he

had heard about: first, four daggers stuck to form a cross in the door
of the house; then, an old woman—old Gumersinda—running a new
needle threaded with red thread, which had to be new too, through the
eyes of a green toad, and then sewing seven crosses with the thread in
a neckerchief—his white neckerchief—which was then burned at midnight in a bonfire of green herbs having spell-binding powers. In this
way the piece of clothing disappeared, and there was no way to undo
the spell. That must have been the way it was put on him; he was sure
as he recalled Paula's words. Old Gumersinda had asked: "To make
him come back?" and Clara had answered: "No, to kill him!" And
she was getting her wish; he was dying and in a miserable, miserable
way after suffering the tortures of the damned. As though all the elements of his personality had come harmoniously together before his
final passing, he recalled and evaluated everything. So much wretched-
ness in such a short time. That fateful night of the race was stamped on
his mind: the old ombú with its wide-spreading branches seemed like a
vicious monster; its thick, twisting surface roots, huge, cold snakes that
had buried their venomous fangs in his body. When he left the place
he was no longer a man. Rosa's stinging phrase still echoed in his ears
and seared his soul as with quirt lashes. He had had that supreme
insult thrown in his face and had not killed the person who dared to
say it. He had not killed her because he had neither the courage nor
the strength, because what she said was true: he was not a man any
more. He, the last scion of an indomitable race, the last twig of the
luxuriant tree that crowned the hills, he, the untamed gaucho, the
gray fox, the fierce jaguar, lord of the open plains, had fled through
the darkness, had spent the night cowering in the fields, seeking refuge
like some cowardly varmint pursued by a pack of dogs. And with
pistol and dagger in his belt, he had not thought of killing himself, he
would not have been able to kill himself, because he was not a man any
more. He, the pattern of the strong male, the breaker of mustangs, the
herder who could cut out the wildest bull, the gaucho cast in the
ancient mold, whose native intelligence disdained all teaching as an
insult to his strength and bravery, was no longer a man. Degraded,
humiliated, abased, he was dying shamefully in a bed, cut down by
the curse of a vile woman, like an old dog wasting away in a corner,
like a tree withering on the hillside. And leaving behind so many
mustangs' backs, so many young bulls' horns! And above all, the
country, the green, austere country, the unbounded open spaces and
the pathless hills, the roaring rivers and the smiling sky, the diaphanous
days and the nights of magnificent blackness; his country—land, nature, mother. Oh mother, in whose arms he would soon be at rest!

His face had taken on the waxy pallor of the dying; his nose grew sharper, his temples sank, his ears stood away from his head, and his lips hung pendulous.

Beside the bed the rancher, pale as a ghost at the approach of that doubly mysterious death, kept his eyes fixed on the candle that was almost burned down and cast barely a glimmer of light.

Outside the wind whistled and the heavy rain beat on the tin roof of the little room. There came a clap of thunder, so dry and sharp that it was like the explosion of a mine. Juan Francisco trembled. One last gleam came into his eyes, his lips parted, and in a horrible cry, voicing a superhuman despair, he roared:

"Clara! Clara! Clara!"

And that was all. There was the choking sound of the death rattle in his throat, and his lids fell halfway over his lightless eyes.

MANUEL BERNÁRDEZ

(1867–1936)

MANUEL BERNÁRDEZ is another Uruguayan who achieved great distinction as a short-story writer. He, too, depicts the people and the life of the Uruguayan countryside, but instead of the River Plate region, it is the northern part of the country bordering on Brazil that most of his work deals with. He was a man of humble origin who achieved high rank in public life and in literature, thanks to his exceptional gifts and ability to overcome all obstacles. He served his country as congressman, as consul and minister in different countries, and although his output was limited, he won deserved honors as poet, essayist, and especially for his stories dealing with the life of his own country people. His narrations are characterized by a singular felicity in portraying the rural types he knew so well, and by his restrained yet dramatic style.

The selection that follows is a masterly account of a man hunt in which the police officer, having failed to track down the outlaw he is after by the methods he usually employs, has recourse to the supernatural.

Paid in Full

[MANUEL BERNÁRDEZ]

I

THE shearing went steadily on through the heavy heat of the afternoon. In the big mud-walled shed the hobbled sheep gasped for air, bleating fretfully now and then.

Above the steel click of the heavy shears the shouts of the clippers crackled like rifle fire: "Doctor"—someone had cut too deep—and the veterinarian came with his pot of tar and gave the wounded animal a couple of smears. "*Lata*," shouted another who had finished a sheep, rolling up the fleece and releasing the animal, who staggered off bewildered, bare, clean, yellow as a new-laid ostrich egg. The shearers, wearing only a shirt and *chiripá* and some a handkerchief tied around their head, worked bent over the sheep without exchanging a word, stifled by the heat and their uncomfortable posture. In a corner of the shed one of them stood up—a bearded countryman with a hard face— and released a sheep. The shearing of a sheep was paid at the rate of two *latas*—about four cents. To the shout of "Sheep, *lata*" the foreman came over and gave him his two coins. Putting one in his belt, he handed the other to a thin young fellow working beside him, drenched with sweat and pale with the heat:

"Here's your *lata*."

They were shearing on shares. The lad straightened up a little, took the coin, and stood there looking at his partner. "Look here," he said, "you're holding out on me. We've been shearing all morning, and this is the first money you've given me. I saw you when you made out like you was getting a drink and you took over four fleeces at two *latas* apiece.

The other held his glance, and the heavy frown that darkened his brow gave his hard face an even fiercer look. Standing up over the sheep he had turned on its back, he asked hoarsely, holding the shears in his hand: "What's that you're saying, you mangy whelp? I've had about enough out of you." "Mangy—your mother," answered the young Indian. And that was all he said. The other threw himself upon him, grabbed him by the neck, flung him down on top of the sheep, and, raising the open scissors, buried them in his back. The boy jerked two or three times, then straightened out and lay still. One of the blades had gone through his ribs, and the other into his breast through his heart. The blood began to gush out, staining the struggling, half-sheared sheep.

The whole thing had happened with the swiftness of a dream. Before anyone fully realized what had taken place, the killer had bounded out of the shed, into the yard, leaped on the only horse in the stable at that time, and set out across the fields. The galloping hoofs echoed against the sun-baked ground.

II

Sandes—the famous Sandes—chief of police for that district, was in his office when an excited young Indian, riding a spavined pony, came with the news of the crime. The rancher had told him to say that the killer was an ugly customer and that they had better send good men if they wanted to take him. Sandes, who had a deep hatred for anyone who killed without fighting, wanted to go himself. But the sergeant, José Difunto, saluted and said:

"You stay here, captain; let me go."

"All right, but you know: don't come back without him."

"I know, I know. Don't you worry. Just give me the paper."

Sandes gave him the signed warrant to arrest the criminal and to kill him if he resisted. Sergeant Difunto could not read, but he never set out to arrest anyone without a warrant, just in case. He liked it when they resisted, and he had brought more than one out of the hills lying crosswise on his mount. As a result of these inclinations he had received a number of cuts, but they had healed over by themselves, like ax slashes on the trunk of a ceiba. He was Sandes's right arm, and in Paysandú and in Mercedes the old timers must still recall that vigorous Indian, with face as boneless and smooth as an old country-woman's and without any vice worth mentioning except that of fighting, a vice that his police duties, in those days dangerous and arduous, gave him many opportunities to satisfy. By temperament Difunto was unsociable and uncommunicative. When he was out of earshot the men under him used to say that the sergeant's tongue was stiff because he never unlimbered it.

III

He selected one soldier, and, both riding good horses, Difunto set out on the hunt for the fugitive. He left his machete behind because it rattled, and went armed only with his knife, which he could always depend on, and a police pistol, which he carried mostly for show. As his first move he went to the scene of the crime to pick up the trail. When he arrived the shearing had been resumed; the shears clicked as though more eager than ever to cut, in the midst of a vast silence charged with conjectures.

The dogs began to bark, and an old Negro, Uncle Adrian, came out to drive them back and see who it was. When he saw the sergeant he hurried forward. "Get out, Chicolate. You, Gaviota! Damn these hounds! Get down, Don Dijunto, get down. There he is in the shed. God be merciful to sinners! What a thing! What a thing! It was a dreadful thing, that's what I told them— Come this way, sergeant. There's the poor soul over there, stiff as a poker."

When the sergeant walked into the shed there was a momentary pause in the metallic song of the scissors. Some of the shearers quietly turned their heads away, judging it better for the "law" not to see their faces, and kept busily at their work. When Difunto came in, an old bagger, who was tramping down the wool in a long sack hung from the roof, jumped to the floor and with a grave, dignified air came over to shake hands with the sergeant who may have thought he was the grandfather of the dead lad. But it was just old Fantasía. He had received the name in tribute to his imagination, which enabled him always to find a story to fit every case. Aside from this, Fantasía,— Don Fantasía, the women called him—was a good soul, one of those gaffers who love to recall their past at every opportunity and have always taken part or seen everything out of the ordinary that has happened anywhere.

"Let's have a look," said Difunto, moving over toward the dead man, who was still lying face down. They had removed the sheep, but he was still in the same position, his body drawn up and his arms outspread. "Let's see how this happened."

Some of those present, including Misia Silveria, who was going around with maté when the thing happened, tried to talk, but old Fantasía would not let them; with a solemn gesture he silenced them and took the floor. He told everything he had heard all of them say, making a long, involved story of it, full of contradictions. He wound up by asking the sergeant for a word with him alone. He led him out to the water barrel and said to him confidentially:

"When the dead man fell—God save and preserve us!—he fell face down. They wanted to turn him over, but I wouldn't let them. That way the killer can't get away."

Difunto stared at him.

"Don't you believe me? Don't you know?" asked the old man in astonishment.

"I'd heard it said—but I think it's just nonsense."

"Nonsense, man? I guarantee you that he can't get away."

"Sure he won't get away—because I don't go to sleep on the job."

At this old Fantasía smiled with an air of one to whom there are no hidden secrets. Laying his hand on the sergeant's shoulder, he said:

"Look, partner, I don't believe in the devil, but when it lightens I cross myself; I don't believe in werewolves, but when I am out at night and I hear a pig grunt far from the houses, I take out my knife and kiss the cross of the hilt. What I am telling you is the God's honest truth. I am older than you and I've seen a lot of things. When a man kills another, you listen to me: if the dead man falls face up, the killer can go and there's no policeman that can catch him; but if he falls face down, you can take it from me, bad luck will follow him, and trick him, and bring him to justice. I've seen it happen time and again. I'll tell you about a case: once in a saloon over by Arapeises a fellow I worked with killed a man, a gringo everybody hated. He let him have the knife right in the breast, and the man fell on his face. Well, sir, there was no way to get that fellow to clear out. He started off, we saw him ride into the locust grove, and in an hour he was back, looking at the dead man: "I can't go because I left my poncho—" We said to him: 'Good God, man, get out of here before they catch you.' " He went, and in a little while there he was again. Then an old Negro who was there and saw it said: 'But how is he going to go? Don't you see that the dead man is lying face down. Turn him over!' And that was what we did. We turned the gringo over, and the other fellow never came back—"

"Does that mean you think this fellow is coming back here?"

"Of course, man! It couldn't be otherwise. Look, listen to me: he's intimate with Martina, the one they call the Mustang, who lives in that cabin on the hill. He left without clothes or money, and I'll bet my bottom dollar that if you leave the dead man the way he is, tonight the killer will come to get his belongings and tell his girl good-bye. It never fails. Look, once—I can remember it as if it was yesterday—a fellow by the name of Amansio, a wrangler—"

He was prepared to begin another story, but José Difunto cut him off by the simple method of turning his back on him. But half convinced by the old man's superstitious eloquence, he ordered the body not to be touched until he came back. The foreman said to throw a horsehide over it and to leave it alone. The dogs got the scent of the dried blood and howled that night until dawn. The women were so nervous they could not sleep, and one dreamed that she had seen the dead man dancing, and that the two wounds in his back had turned into mouths, and he talked with one and laughed with the other.

IV

As Difunto galloped along on the killer's trail he kept thinking about what the old man had said. The supernatural aspect penetrated and made an impression on the dense shadows of his ignorant mind. But, nevertheless, he put more confidence in his sense of scent. By blood and by training he possessed that exquisite lucidness that constitutes the science of tracking, and he could spend days without eating or sleeping following a trail.

He decided to use the help of occult forces, "the help of the dead man," as he put it, as a last resort. He would call upon this if he lost the killer. As he left the ranch he made a mental note of the Mustang's cabin so he could find it at night if need be. That strange and terrible expedient of calling on a dead man for help seemed to him in a class with using a pistol, a thing he did only when an enemy fired on him and he could not reach him with his knife.

From the route the fugitive was taking he drew his conclusions: he must be heading north, planning to cross the Queguay, to keep on past the palm groves. The horse he was riding would not last many miles, especially at the pace he was going. It would probably give out around Ramírez's ranch, there on the banks of the Queguay. This was the way he figured it out, and he decided to play his hunch, galloping with his companion over the fields, through one ford and another, over ditches, keeping his eye fixed on the trail half obliterated by the high grass. The fugitive had come this way, this way! The Indian nervously chewed at his chin strap in a frenzy to catch up with the criminal. He had been through this canebrake, along this trail, through this mud flat. By the side of a path through the woods there was a twig of a briar bush recently broken off: it had probably caught on the fugitive's clothing, and he had broken it off rather than take the time to free himself. The trail kept on. There was no doubt about it: he was going to change horses at Ramírez's.

V

And so it was. The killer, after a break-neck flight in which he got everything he could out of the poor horse, reached the Ramírez ranch. He knew the foreman. He had worked there in brandings and sheep shearings. He had even taken part in the last roundup. They would not refuse him a horse, he figured, because in those days nobody ever refused a man in trouble a horse.

Vague fears troubled the killer. What if they suspected something, what if they were already waiting there to take him? Oh, but he would fight. He touched his knife as he ascended the long slope on whose cleared crest the ranch stood out. He looked carefully—nothing, all was quiet. The dogs did not even bark at him. Three came out leisurely to sniff at him, and only a yellow bitch, one of those that bite without barking, grabbed the tail of his horse, which was too tired even to kick at her. The killer rode up, greeting first one, then another, and dismounted under an arbor, now completely at ease. To a hand who knew him and seemed surprised at the way he was dressed, he explained that he had lost everything he had gambling at the shearing and was going home to get money to pay up.

He was weary, his body felt limp, and after the tension of his flight, in place of the fear of being captured that tormented him in the first moments, a reaction set in, a kind of boldness, confidence in himself, and satisfaction at having evaded the police. Reactions of this sort are frequent, and they are almost always the undoing of killers. That tale of Poe's, in which the man who murdered his wife gives himself away by his stupid overconfidence when he was out of danger, is very sound psychologically. The killer José Difunto had been trailing so carefully had that reckless quarter of an hour, which old Fantasía would undoubtedly have attributed to the fact that the dead man was face down.

The foreman was not at the ranch, but he came shortly after the killer arrived. The latter greeted him heartily: "How are you, Don Panta? You don't change a bit."

The foreman was surprised to see him. He had no idea he was in the neighborhood. "What are you doing here, *Abrilojo*? What brings you up this way?"

The killer's name was Santos Muñíz, but he was known there as *Abrilojo*, "keep your eye skinned," because once when he was playing cards with an easy mark from whom he won even his saddle, Muñíz, who knew all the tricks of the sharper, kept saying to his adversary, laughing: "Keep your eye skinned," as he dealt himself the ace of spades, or a trump, or any card he needed. Everybody was amused by the trick, and the name *Abrilojo* stuck.

Muñíz repeated to the foreman the same story about his gambling losses. Don Panta looked at him out of the corner of his eye, laughing at his getup. "Quite a player you must have run into, because to clean you out—"

But if he had any suspicions, he kept them to himself. There was a kind of tacit complicity among country folk to cover up for each other in certain kinds of trouble. Don Panta liked Muñíz because he was a good hand. He worked from sunup to sundown and did not talk. He knew that he had been in trouble with the law and that he was brave. If he suspected that there was some other reason than the one he was giving for turning up there, it never crossed his mind that it involved murder. He believed him capable of killing in a fight, but not treacherously. If he had thought that, he would have refused him a horse. Fighting bravely and killing was something those men understood and admired; they had nothing but contempt for the coward who strikes from behind. Don Panta turned to a hand who was just riding up.

"Hey, Juansito, have you turned the horses out? Look, drive them in again, this man needs a change—"

Now completely at ease, the killer realized that his mouth was very dry and that he was hungry. The sun was going down, and it seemed to him that in the cool of evening and with a good horse under him, his flight would be almost pleasant. He told the foreman he was hungry.

"If you wait a little while, we're going to eat right away. Go on over to the kitchen and have a maté. I'll get your horse saddled."

"Look, Don Panta, if you've got a horse that's a swimmer—"

"What are you going to do? You going to try catching catfish by hand?" asked the foreman with a great guffaw that shook his big, well-fed country body. "All right, you go ahead—I'll give you a gray that swims like a *tararira*. But don't you go playing him, for with the kind of luck you're having today—"

VI

The sun had slipped completely down the unclouded, copper-tinged sky. The light was still clear on the hills but thickening in the hollows where it seemed that the shadows had spent the day lurking in the high grass and now came creeping up the slopes to see if the sun had gone yet.

The hands were still eating in the kitchen as Muñíz came out with one of them who was going to get a half-broken horse that he had fastened in the barn. He was breaking him to the bit and he was going to leave him in the barn all night with the bit in his mouth, because he was stubborn and kept trying to slip the bit. They walked out to the arbor, talking the matter over. Muñíz, who had the reputation of being a good wrangler, told the other that he had made a mistake breaking the horse to the bit in the light of the moon, because it was going to be a slobberer.

"It doesn't matter," said the hand, "I'm not going to make a riding horse out of him. I'm breaking him to work, and it's a good thing for him to slobber a little, so his mouth won't get too dry with the heat."

Muñíz untied the gray, which was eager to be off. It was a fine, proud animal, with a short back and a flat rump, the sign of a fast horse. Its eyes and muzzle were black, its nostrils broad, and its hoofs small, high and round like a goblet turned upside down. Muñíz, who was a good judge of horse flesh, sized it up at a glance and smiled with satisfaction. The hand told him good-bye and went off to get his own horse. Muñíz examined the girth, as any cautious countryman does when he has not saddled himself.

The foreman had given him an old straw hat. He put it on, adjusting the chin strap, fastened the tie rope to the headstall, lit up a cigarette, and mounted. Only then did he notice that the stirrups were short for him. He let them out and then, holding the gray in, rode out of the grove. He called out: "Be seeing you," to the hand who was going down the hill after his horse, whistling an *estilo* as he went. Dusk had set in completely, and things were visible only to country eyes. It was a wonderfully quiet evening; not even the cows were lowing, as though they had been overawed by the solemn twilight silence. When Muñíz saw himself out on the vast open range with a good horse under him, he heaved a sigh of relief and looked defiantly about him—but his blood froze in him, and he reined in the gray with a cruel jerk as he saw on his left, almost upon him, a rider wearing a military cap, coming at a dead gallop, and another rider behind him.

The full awareness of his danger came over the killer once more, but his daring, his desire to live, quickly restored his presence of mind. For a second he thought of giving the gray his head, but he checked his impulse. The others were well mounted too, and they would probably *bolear*[1] his horse. Quickly he thought of a plan. If the sergeant did not know him, it might work out; if he did, he would fight them. Without any outward trace of emotion he turned his gray toward sergeant Difunto, who was in the lead. He did not know him; that was a blessing. If he had a description of him the straw hat might throw him off. He did not realize that his plan was more feasible than he would have believed, for the sergeant, calculating the time well, assumed that the killer would have left an hour earlier. The sergeant reined in his horse:

"Good evening."

"Good evening. Where the devil are you going in such a hurry, sergeant? Looking for a deserter?"

"No," answered the sergeant, coming up at a trot. "Nobody has deserted. Are you from these parts?"

"Yes, sir, a hand here."

"Have you been here today?"

"All day. We've been loading wool, for the shearing is over. I'm going out to bring in the blooded flock now. Didn't you meet up with the wool carts? They were going to Paysandú."

---

[1] *bolear:* Bolear is the use of *bolas*, three leather-encased stones, fastened together by leather thongs. The Indians and gauchos, who learned their use from them, employed them to entangle the feet of a running animal and throw it or bring it to a halt.

The killer had met them and assumed that the sergeant had seen them too.

"Yes, I saw them. Tell me, has anybody been here trying to borrow a horse?"

"Yes, sir, a fellow did come by, but they wouldn't lend him one. The foreman suspected that he was in trouble. His horse was winded, and he staked him out—"

"Has he been gone long?"

"Not very; he was here just a little while ago. Hey, look down there; there he is, down in that hollow, pulling up the stake—"

Difunto didn't wait to hear any more. He had him dismounted! What a piece of luck! He dug his spurs into his horse and, followed by the soldier, he raced down the slope to where the hand was whistling his *estilo*, putting his whole soul into it and adding certain modulations he had invented himself, as he rolled up his pony's rope. Muñíz smiled for a second, muttering between his teeth: "Swallowed the bait, you damned fool," and then decided to change his course. "The sergeant is a tracker"—he said to himself—"and he certainly has trailed me. He guessed that I was making for Brazil. But he's so eager he's going to outsmart himself."

And he set out at a gallop toward the Queguay, whose rolling green banks were close by. He rode into the water when he got there, selecting a spot where the trail would show plainly in the young grass. Then, instead of crossing over to the other side, he kept to the bank, with the water up to his girth. He went along for about a quarter of a mile, and then came out on a gravel-covered spit where the horse would leave no hoofprints.

Only then did he throw away his cigarette so the glow would not give him away. "Now, let's see which is the smartest. Try to pick up my trail in the water."

He settled his feet in the stirrups and listened for a moment. The only sound was the monotonous murmur of the flowing water and the hoot of an owl that flew back and forth over the killer's head. "Son-of-a-bitching bird, get out of here with your bad luck!" he exclaimed angrily, lashing at it with his quirt. He rode up the slope and broke into a gallop again. He was soon up to the ranch again, and he detoured without coming near it until he was back on the road he had traveled that afternoon. The ranch lay in silence. "I'll bet he's trying to pick up my trail again," he said to himself. "Go ahead; I'm scared to death of you. While you go that way I'll go this way, and we won't bump into each other. Gray, don't you go back on me. Don Panta is a hell of a good guy; what a horse this is! I'll tell my girl good-bye and then shake off that dung. Wonder what he did to the poor hand."

VII

The poor hand was tied up. As soon as the sergeant and the soldier got within range of him, the latter covered him with his rifle and the sergeant shouted:

"You're under arrest!"

The hand cut short the *estilo* he was whistling and shied with fright.

"Give yourself up," ordered Difunto in his hoarse voice, which rang full in the placid evening. "Give yourself up, or I'll have to take care of you."

"But wait a minute, sergeant. What's the trouble?"

Without further explanation he had his hands tied behind his back by Difunto himself, who was a past master at the job. The poor hand shrieked, shouted, called the police every name he could lay his tongue to, but it did him no good. "Come on, move," and they gave him several shoves to tame him down, making him roll on the ground like a sack of maté leaves. The prisoner, pale with fury, shouted to them to untie him and he'd show them who he was. At this point José Difunto grew very solemn. He pulled out of his belt the warrant signed by the chief of police, and while the soldier shoved the boy ahead, Difunto, on horseback, showed him the paper, saying in a soothing voice:

"Look here, boy, look here, and stop your carrying-on. This is not my doing: here is the paper. This is the order for your arrest. And don't try to get tough, or I'll have to take care of you, like I told you."

They took him to the ranch. The men there had seen what was taking place, and everybody was excited. The arrested hand was a boy who had been raised on the place. Everybody liked him and they were determined not to let him be taken. The foreman stepped forward, saying:

"Why, sergeant, why have you got this man tied up?"

"Because he killed a fellow over at the Rodríguez place, and here is the order for his arrest."

"But when was this, sergeant?"

"When was it? Today."

There was a general guffaw. The foreman understood at once.

"But, friend, that's not possible. This man hasn't been off the ranch for two weeks. The one who did the killing must have been Santos Muñíz, who came by here riding hard and asked me for a horse, telling me he had lost everything in a card game."

"Oh, sure. And you think I'm going to swallow that. You mean to tell me this isn't Muñíz?"

"What's the matter with you, man. Muñíz is that great big fellow with a beard you were just talking to. The one with a straw hat, riding a gray horse. He played you for a sucker—if you will excuse my saying so! Why you were talking to the man you wanted and you go and arrest another poor devil!"

The hands, like a trained chorus, burst into laughter, astounded and pleased at the way the sergeant had been tricked. "What a devil that Muñíz is! Did he pull a fast one!" They made no attempt to hide their satisfaction.

Difunto finally understood, and, trembling with rage, he made a lunge forward as though to fight all the hands at once. They scattered, some of them with their hand on the hilt of their knife. The sergeant wheeled around, shouting at the soldier:

"Get on your horse!"

"I was just going to untie—"

"Let him alone. Let them untie him if they want to. Come on."

And they galloped off, followed by the derisive whistles and the merry hand clapping of all the hands.

At the foot of the hill Difunto pulled up his horse a little. His anger did not blind him. He frankly admitted to himself that he had been fooled. And in that darkness, in that mysterious silence of the night that hung over the silence of the sleeping country—caught between those two great silences—Difunto felt defeated. A superstitious impotence took possession of his wild, ignorant soul, and with a deep sigh he said, as though settling the matter with himself:

"All right!—I see I couldn't do it— Now let's see if it's true that the dead man is going to help me."

He crossed himself, and, without even attempting to pick up the trail of the killer, he frantically urged his horse toward the road they had come by that afternoon.

The soldier, who had listened in astonishment to the enigmatic words of the sergeant, drew abreast of him and asked:

"Excuse me, sergeant. Where are we going?"

The other made no answer, sunk in his usual brooding silence, merely spurring his horse ahead. But he may have repented, or perhaps he felt the need of justifying, if possible, this waiving of his almost infallible skill as a tracker, because, without easing up on his horse, which was leaping over the tussocks of high grass, he said hoarsely to his Indian aide:

"Don't you see that now it's the dead man who's going to catch him? And is he going to pay me back if we get him! We're heading for the girl's house."

In the starry calm of the night the two men galloped steadily ahead over the road traveled shortly before by the gray that was carrying Muñíz, blinded by his arrogance, to meet his fate.

VIII

Martina was a pretty girl, sun-browned, fiery-eyed, light-footed. Her curly, rebellious hair hung about her shoulders like the mane of a young colt. She would tie it back with a red ribbon, and this gave her a sharp, inciting seductiveness, which was counterbalanced by her masculine air. She had been born in a soldiers' camp, dropped one chill night, and had been seasoned by the hardships of her wandering childhood. She had grown up strong, and hated men, perhaps recalling as a woman the brutality she had suffered as a girl. For this reason they had given her the nickname Chúcara, the Mustang. Muñíz had defended her in a difficult moment and then had carried her off with him. From then on, their lives were joined. She would be alone at times when he went off to make a living for them. He never hired out except by the day; he would bring home his earnings, rounded out with his gambling gains, and they would spend a month together, doing nothing, loving each other, joined in long embraces, feeling that life outside that straw-thatched cabin, covered over with vines that he had brought in from the neighboring woods was their enemy. In the eave a pair of ovenbirds had made a nest. They would come down for mud beside the water barrel, without the least fear of the girl, and she enjoyed the company of these industrious little birds on the days her man was away working for both of them.

Chúcara had been asleep for a long time. To save candles she went to bed early, unchaining Tacombú, her zealous protector, a huge mastiff, who adored her and watched over her.

Suddenly she awoke with a start. A horse was coming at a gallop, then slowed down to a trot, a walk, and stopped in front of the cabin. But the dog did not bark. Could it be—?

"Open up, girl, it's me."

She opened the door, surprised and delighted. The gray, startled by the blackness of the door, the noises of the night, moved a few paces as though to go, but then stepped on one of the reins and stood still, while his rider, followed by Tacombú, whining with pleasure, lifted up the girl in his arms and put her back in the rawhide bed. They sat there on the bed in the dark.

"How you smell of sheep! What's the matter?"

Muñíz pressed her close to him. "Nothing is the matter, girl—I just wanted to see you—I have to be leaving."

With an uneasy feeling that something was wrong, she tried to question him further, but he put his hand over her mouth. "Be still!" His keen ear had caught the sound of a dull vibration—unquestionably the gallop of a horse. The dog, taken up with his welcome, had heard nothing. But in the silence that followed, he, too, caught the approaching noise and rushed outside barking. From the pounding of the hoofs Muñíz understood that there were two riders; through the cracks of the cabin he could make out two masses in the darkness coming quickly nearer, and he got up from the bed:

"Don't be scared, girl. I'm going to have to fight them—I killed someone, and they are coming for me—but they're no good!"

Without saying a word, Chúcara kissed his mouth and slipped into a corner. Muñíz tightened his belt and unsheathed his short, stout dagger, made for fighting and to hamstring a bull. He caught up a blanket from the bed, rolled it around his left arm, and took his place beside the door. Martina, armed with a butcher knife, waited tensely at the other side, her nightgown a faint whiteness in the dark, and her eyes glowing like a cat's.

Difunto and the soldier had dismounted. The dog rushed at them furiously. Difunto parried the animal with his left arm, about which he had wrapped his poncho. The dog sank his teeth into it, rising up on his hind legs, and Difunto, steadying himself to withstand the rush, slit the animal open with one slash.

The soldier was cautiously hanging back. They came forward, crouched over, trying to make things out in the darkness. Though the stars were shining the night was very black. Difunto gave Muñíz's gray a whack, and it trotted off, stumbling on the reins.

"Be careful, sergeant; he's waiting inside, and he's kinda dangerous. He's in the dark, and he can see us—"

"Don't you suppose I know that."

Difunto advanced slowly, looking around him, plumbing the darkness, as though searching for something. Suddenly he stumbled over a wash trough of ceiba wood about a yard long, the kind to be found around all farmhouses, which Muñíz had made the girl for scrubbing and cleaning. Difunto emptied out the water and put the trough over his breast like a shield, choking with repressed laughter at his diabolical idea. Covered with that breastplate, which was as light as cork and almost impenetrable to the knife because of its pithy texture, Difunto made a rush at the door, still laughing, his knife raised high to protect his head. Muñíz steadied himself as he saw him charge and, shouting: "God help you!" brought down his knife with all the strength of his arm. But the weapon buried itself in the trough, and Difunto's peal of raucous laughter accompanied the sound of his knife against the straw hat of the killer, who dropped to the floor with his head split in two.

Not frightened, but stunned, mad, unable to understand what had happened, Martina rushed forward just as the lagging soldier approached, stretching out his neck to see what was going on. As he caught sight of the girl he started back, and Chúcara, with the knife in her hand and a wild fury in her breast, leaped at him and slashed him across the face.

"Oh, you bitch, you've cut me!" howled the Indian, and, blind with fury, he whirled his gun and brought the stock down on the head of the girl, who fell across the doorstep of her cabin, her mass of curly hair spread out like little black snakes. José Difunto was still laughing as he came out holding the trough in which Muñíz's dagger was still stuck. He stepped across Chúcara, muttering with satisfaction:

"The bastard! He fooled me—but I paid him back."

ROBERTO J. PAYRÓ

(1867–1928)

A DISTINGUISHED ARGENTINE critic, Enrique Anderson Imbert, says of Payró: "Posterity will remember him first of all for his character, upright, brave, generous, with nothing base or mean. And then, when many a beautifully written but empty page has been forgotten . . . Payró's books, fashioned from basic, human elements and reflecting a decisive period of Argentina's existence, will continue to offer the greatness of that which endures changes of fashion and taste, of that which men find useful because it teaches them they are a part of history."

Payró has become a classic of Argentine literature. More than any other author of his day he found his inspiration and themes in the reality of the moment and the surrounding scene. He not only described with vividness, accuracy, and wit what he saw; he grasped its significance.

A native of Buenos Aires, connected with the old colonial families of the province, as a young man Payró went to Bahía Blanca, since grown to be an important city but then little more than a village, where he founded and directed a newspaper. Here he came to know the life, the people, the politics that make up the subject matter of his best known books, *Divertidas aventuras del nieto de Juan Moreira* and *Cuentos de Pago Chico*. The middle class was elbowing its way to the top. Bahía Blanca, which is the Pago Chico of his books, was a microcosm of Argentina. There as everywhere existed the same parochial outlook, the same corrupt politics, back scratching, complete indifference to public interest, and a determination to get ahead at all costs. Payró's weapon of attack was not indignation or invective, but satire and humor. All his life, in his journalism, his books, his political activities—he was one of the founders of the Socialist party in Argentina—he worked to develop a sense of civic responsibility on the part of his countrymen; yet he had a humorist's benevolence toward their shortcomings. He saw in their dynamic vitality, their very ruthlessness, a strength that he hoped might be a promise for the future. Like Dickens he manages to make even his scoundrels amusing, engaging in their frank, unabashed humanness.

In the following selection, *The Devil at Pago Chico*, one of his best-known stories, he paints with great skill and a profound knowledge of the psychology of the country folk a tragicomic episode that reveals how deeply ingrained their superstitions lie.

The Devil at Pago Chico

[ROBERTO J. PAYRÓ]

VIACABA, that bluff, kind-hearted countryman whom so many have been acquainted with, at that time had a farm a few leagues from Pago Chico on the backwater of a little stream. After reflecting the sheer cliff, bare of all vegetation, the puny willows, clinging by a precarious foothold to the rock, and the sheepfold, it made an almost right-angled turn and ran slowly along to empty its meager current into Rio Chico, which, if the truth be told, never really became a river even with that help, except in time of flood or freshets. Viacaba had lived there for many years with his wife Panchita, his two sons Pancho and Joaquin, who were grown by this time, his daughter Isabel, a homely but bright dark little thing, and a couple of hands, Serapio and Matilde. Between them, the boys and the old man were more than enough to look after the regular work on the little *estancia*.

This work was far from heavy, although Viacaba owned a good many cattle and mares, and a few hundred sheep he kept for food, as he did not care about sheep raising.

The house was large and had several rooms. It could be seen from a distance on the bluff cut in two by the brook, which, like the wilful, flighty thing it was, had preferred this path to the easy way. It may be that when it dug its channel the lay of the land was very different.

And just as the house could be seen from the distance, so from the house one had an unbroken view of the curving horizon, bare, utterly flat, a stretch of pampa covered in this season with dry, dreary, grayish-yellow grass, making a dusty carpet, against which the twisting green line of the banks of the stream stood out like a border of bright new velvet on a broad, frayed cloak.

That afternoon the heat was stifling. The fields shimmered, as though they were covered with thin, vibrating plates of steel, and the blinding gleam they gave off made the head swim. The sky was almost white, without a single cloud, covered with a dense, invisible haze. The locusts kept up their incessant, strident shrilling, and the air hummed with a monotonous buzz of insects whose source it was impossible to locate, but which deafened and stupefied with its insistence.

So it was not strange that, worn-out with the morning's work and the suffocating heat, everybody at the Viacaba place was asleep, the men in the shadow of the eaves on the east side of the house where the sun no longer shone, and the women inside the house where the darkness feigned an illusion of coolness.

The air hung motionless, as it had at this time of day during the whole period of drought, which had lasted so long and was becoming so severe that the cattle were losing weight and looking out of condition, signs of a probable epidemic. The sleeping men were breathing stertorously, and heavy drops of sweat poured off them, running in trickles down their brown skin. They slept uneasily, harassed by the heat and the buzzing, persistent flies that returned despite the men's unconscious attempts to drive them off. They would have continued in their heavy stupor had not the gallop of a horse pulled up short at the hitching rail, and the furious barking of the dogs, which a moment before had been lying in the shade, their tongues hanging out, panting like a locomotive engine, aroused them from their nap.

Matilde, a peon from Santiago del Estero, a huge, surly fellow whose woman's name suited him "like a brace of pistols on an image of Christ," sat up grumbling, lazily got to his feet, and shuffled off to see who the importunate visitor might be. The others, peering toward the hitching rail, got a glimpse of a gray horse, black with sweat and covered with dust, that was breathing like a bellows, shaking head, ears, and tail to rid himself of the swarm of flies that had settled on him. The traveler followed Matilde, who walked ahead to inform Viacaba.

"It's a 'frog' who's asking for water," he said. "Shall I give him some?"

"Of course. Tell him to come over here in the shade."

By the time the man reached the shadow of the eaves, all the men were on their feet, and Panchita and Isabel, who had been awakened by the noise, were moving about inside the house.

"Good afternoon, friend. Come in and sit down. Get him a drink of cold water, Serapio. Afterwards perhaps you'd like a maté. What are you doing out in this sun when not even the snakes come out of their holes?"

The Frenchman explained that he had to get to town without fail that afternoon so he could take the stagecoach early the next morning.

He was a tall, lanky young fellow, very blond, with pale eyes, a narrow forehead, and a long, colorless hook nose, like the beak of a bird of prey. In spite of the fact that his face was long and thin, there was something of the vulture about him, and his exaggerated politeness was powerless to efface the disagreeable impression he had made on those simple, rude men from the moment he entered. It was as though some repellent effluvium emanated from his body, and the five countrymen, so different in their appearance and manners, could not help eying him uneasily.

He avidly drank the water that was drawn for him from the well, and sat down on a bench under the eave against the rough, whitewashed wall, blinking his eyes to keep from falling asleep. And when Isabel came out, followed by her mother, carrying the maté she had just brewed in the kitchen, he got up ceremoniously though somewhat awkwardly, making them a deep bow and offering his compliments to the charming *señoguita* and the pleasant *señoga*.

It was with a rather wry face that he sipped the bitter beverage to which he was not accustomed, and with another bow handed the maté gourd back to the girl. As she turned back to the kitchen, her starched petticoats rustling as she moved, with a grimace and a sidelong glance she made plain to Pancho how little she, too, cared for the stranger. Her mother stole covert glances at him when he was not looking. The men struggled to keep up the languishing conversation.

The visit lasted for over an hour. Matilde watered the gray and tightened his girth, as though in that way to hasten the rider's departure.

While he rolled a cigarette with the makings Viacaba had offered him, the Frenchman talked of the drought and the harm it was doing the livestock. He had come a long distance, and all the country he had traveled through was in the same sorry state: the pastures were as dry as chips, not a drop of water in the water holes, the swamps as smooth and dry as stones, the brooks so low you could step across nearly all of them, and you could count every rib on the cattle; the sheep were in bad shape and mangier than ever before; the mares were nothing but skin and bone.

"We've been lucky that things haven't been too bad here yet," said Viacaba with a certain pride.

But he looked up quickly in alarm when the stranger said that in

many places he had seen big whorls of dust the wind was blowing up
from the land bare of vegetation.

"Dust storms," he said, in a foreboding tone. "They must be starting."

And he sat brooding. There had not been a calamity of this sort in
years, but the last time it had happened, it had sown ruin and havoc
in its wake, destroying the herds and leaving the pampa itself as though
dead and buried under an ashlike, shifting cloak of dust.

The high-pitched, rasping voice of the stranger, with its discordant
sounds, heightened the unpleasant recollection and increased the dislike and suspicion he had aroused in all of them.

As the sun began to sink a little, the Frenchman took his leave with
much bowing and scraping and protestations of gratitude. Viacaba
accompanied him to the hitching rail, while the others, in a row under
the eave, stood watching him ride off. The gray, rested now, started
off at a brisker pace, and just as it was about to break into a gallop,
Viacaba called out to the rider from the hitching rail:

"Be careful with that cigarette stub."

"*Oui! Oui!*" answered the other, without understanding what he
had said.

A moment later Isabel, coming back with another round of the interminable bitter matés, put into words what everyone was thinking:

"I don't like that man one bit."

"That goes for me, too," growled Matilde, picking up his saddle.

"He seems kind of dumb," added Pancho, the most tolerant of them
all, after Viacaba.

They sat in silence for some time, the visitor still on their minds,
for when Serapio finally spoke, he did not have to mention to whom he
was referring:

"There he goes across the swamp."

Barely visible now, the mass of man and horse was disappearing into
the high grass that covered a broad belt of land in the direction of
Pago Chico.

"Dumb, you say," put in Joaquin, who had been turning Pancho's
words over in his mind. "Well, to me he looks like a bird of ill omen,
with that beak of his and that head like a plucked owl. Please God he
hasn't put some kind of a spell on us——"

"Stop borrowing trouble, Joaquin," Viacaba cut him short. "You
know the funny faces gringos nearly always have. But what of it? You
think that makes them witches?"

Not that Viacaba was not superstitious, but age and experience had
attenuated it somewhat in him.

The hands went out in the fields, heading westward, where the bulk of the herds was, Joaquin following after them. To the east, across the brook, there were only a few mares and the string of grays.

The two women and Viacaba and Pancho sat on under the eave without any desire to move in that stifling atmosphere. The sun was about to set, and the sky was getting redder by the moment.

At twilight, when the others came back, at dinner time, the sky to the west was an immense expanse of purple, and in the east, like a tenuous veil, was the same purple reflection. In front of this veil a straight column of dun-colored mist rose above the swale, like a column spinning on its own axis.

"Didn't I tell you! This is the beginning of the dust storms," remarked Viacaba when he saw it, as he followed the others into the kitchen.

How had that man, raised in the country, born in the middle of the pampa, knowing its every aspect, all its secrets, come to make such a mistake? Hadn't he taken a good look? Or was it that the grim recollection of the dust storms, the obsession with the possibility of such a calamity, paralyzed his mind?

It was not a whorl of dust raised and twisted in the air, like a Solomon's column by the wind from the dry fields, and then carried from side to side in a capricious dance like some fantastic creation of a nightmare. No. The column remained stationary in the same spot and rose and widened in the calm heated air, which was gilded and reddened by the last flickering radiance of the sun.

The disk of the sun finally disappeared from sight. The waves of purple that followed it, covering the western sky, slowly ebbed away, like water slipping over a declivity. And like harbingers of the coming night, faint breezes sprang up, growing and multiplying from moment to moment.

It was now dark, and yet the column in the hay field was still visible, vaguely luminous, like the one that guided the people of Israel in the desert.

Meantime the Viacaba family was having supper in the kitchen, gathered around the fireplace. Everybody was more cheerful and talkative, reacting from the afternoon's enervation, because the air, though still warm, was getting stronger and beating its wings more vigorously.

The conversation, though diverted for a moment, always came back to the event of the day: the Frenchman's visit. Nobody had a kindly ' word for him.

"Devil take that owl! Never in my life did I see an uglier bird,"

Joaquin kept harping superstitiously. "And the way he looked at you with those washed-out eyes, in spite of all his *"vulevús.*" He looked to me like—"

"The devil, didn't he?" interrupted Matilde. "That's just what I thought. They say that's the way he looks: blond, like that, with light eyes and a nose like a parrot's beak. I couldn't see his feet because he was wearing shoes, but I'll bet anything they were hoofs."

Like the sinister echo of these words came the terrified voice of Panchita who had just gone to the well for water, and which rang through the patio like a call of alarm and terror:

"Fire! Fire! The swamp's on fire!"

"What did I say?" growled Joaquin, rushing out after the others.

The menacing column had begun to grow higher, spreading and giving off a pale radiance. It looked like a huge tree with a small top, round and whitish. Then, as the wind began to blow more strongly, it suddenly disappeared, and immediately afterward it was as though the tree, blazing from one end to the other, had fallen, for, starting at the same spot, a crackling line of fire, sparks, and small, hungry flames appeared, which were reflected in the night mist hanging above the ground. In an instant the glowing red line ran along the ground, growing, spreading eastward, the direction from which the wind was coming, as though trying to cover the whole horizon. And the wind, whispering to itself, laughing like a child playing some mischievous trick, swept gaily through the tall, dry, rustling grass. From the high ground beside the buildings, overlooking the fields, Panchita and Isabel stared in horror at the threatening, terrible spectacle of the fire. The men had saddled quickly and had set off at full gallop toward the swamp, taking in only the most visible aspect of the peril, too confused to think clearly.

The wind, tired of laughing, was now amusing itself making strange and devastating fireworks. It swirled above the blaze, raising clouds of smoke and showers of sparks; it wreathed the smoke around the near-by shrubs, illuminated by the fire, making it seem that they, too, were burning, and sent out sparks like those of a Roman candle, or turned them into golden "flowerpots," finally allowing them to burn themselves out or fall on the grass in a fine, destructive shower. Or in a swift gust it suddenly quenched the immense red line, and then, as though repentant at having so quickly forsaken its amusement, with another gust blew it into a blaze again, until it seemed as though the very sky had taken fire. Waves of heat as from a blast furnace or a forge, a muted crackling as from a distant volley of artillery fire, reached to where the women stood, along with the acrid smell of burning straw from the heavy clouds of smoke rolling along the ground.

Seemingly slow because of the distance, but in reality with great swiftness, the line of fire was spreading. It was forming the arc of a circle, whose center was the higher land, and it was closing in on the buildings as though besieging them with marvelous strategy. Between the house and the fire the fields were lit up, and huge blurred shadows moved and advanced and withdrew across them; these were the squat, broad tussocks of straw and the elongated silhouettes of the riders who were crossing back and forth near the blaze.

A tumult, a drumbeat of alarm, suddenly exploded in the sound-filled silence, making the ground shake; it was the herds, the droves stampeding madly westward, hammering the dry, hard earth with their hoofs. Like a shapeless shadow they passed, wrapped in clouds of dust, through which emerged only an occasional glimpse of flanks or heads with manes disheveled by the wind. The frenzied hoofbeats died away until they were lost in the night . . .

"The horses!" moaned Isabel, shaking off her numbness for a moment.

"Blessed Virgin! Will we ever see them again?" murmured her mother.

Behind them remained other sounds, muted, confused, indecipherable, filling the pampa and borne to the women's ears by the burning wind, dense with smoke and bearing ash that was still hot.

Viacaba, his sons, and the peons had thought to arrive in time to extinguish the fire. But when they were about a block from it their hearts sank within them: the tall, thick dry hay, the thorny, interlaced bushes, the pampas grass, yellow now and tall enough to hide a man, were blazing as far as the eye could see, amidst crackling tongues of flame, popping like successive series of bombs. Waves of heat, hot as the fire itself, rolled over them; when they looked at one another they saw their sweaty faces black as soot, in which only the eyes gleamed. The horses, their ears laid forward, almost flat toward the fire, snorted and tossed their heads, refusing to advance further.

As they pushed a little nearer they were enveloped in smoke and sparks, and it was as though they were advancing through clouds amidst a shower of shooting stars. The burning bits of straw swirled about their heads for an instant and then sped on to spread disaster, abetted by the wind. It was almost impossible to hear for the crackling of the dry grass, and they had to communicate by shouts.

"—fireguard," they heard Viacaba bellow as he dismounted. The beginning of the phrase had been lost in the uproar.

Through the veil of flames the vast blaze hung before the men's eyes, the night took on an unwonted darkness. It was as though the moonless sky were descending, descending, blacker and blacker, until it seemed that it would reach the very fire.

When they heard Viacaba call out they all got off their horses. At a gesture from him they drew near to hear him shout:

"But not here. That would only make it worse. At the edge of the swamp—"

They turned back a way, leading their frightened horses, who kept turning their blazing eyes back toward the fire, snorting, blowing, jerking to get free and run away. Though covered with sweat they were shivering, and their flanks quivered like water riffled by a breeze.

And thus, enveloped in lurid Bengal lights, men and beasts drew back to the edge of the swamp, where the low grass began, withered and dry, too. Serapio hobbled the horses and tied them to some bushes a fair distance away. Then he rejoined the others.

Viacaba and Pancho quickly set fire to the low grass along a strip about a yard wide running more or less parallel to the blaze. Joaquin and Matilde went behind them, and after the grass was well ignited they beat out the fire with bunches of greener grass until these caught fire, or with their saddle blankets. They were unable to wet them because the water was too far away.

They looked like smelters working beside a river of molten metal. They were panting, sweating; their dark faces, hot and shining, swollen, puffed up, had lost their contours; their eyes glittered feverishly, and down their cheeks and forehead ran rivulets of ink.

Their sacrifice was idle. The fire mocked at the obstacle of the burned-off stretch they had attempted to lay in its path. It laughed with its accomplice the wind, on whose wings it sent its spies and its propagandists at the men and their Herculean, vain efforts.

The noise of the stampede, which had terrified the women, suddenly reached their ears like a distant tremolo of drums heard through the crackle of the fire. Viacaba raised his bewildered head, and his eyes bulging, crazed, yelled:

"The herds, Serapio, Matilde, the herds! The herds!"

As they grasped the enormity of the disaster they abandoned their efforts to check the fire and rushed toward the horses.

They were gone. Roweled by fear, they had managed to pull up the bushes, and, snorting, maddened, fettered by the hobbles, in wild, terrified leaps, dripping sweat, they were making their way west, toward safety, toward life—

They finally overtook them, mounted, and set out on a dead run in different directions, as though in accordance with a previously agreed upon plan. However, they had none. Where could they take the stock, even if it was not scattered and lost in the shadows of the pampa? Where could they find a safe refuge for it? Where could they guard it from this boundless disaster?

The women, as though turned to stone by fear and anxiety, stood in the same place, like sleepwalkers, their eyes fixed on the fire, which continued to advance every minute with greater swiftness and intensity, and not only toward the buildings, but to right, to left, north, south, cutting them completely off on each side, and then turning back, to block their retreat, throwing an insurmountable barrier around them. The heat was so intense that every minute the unhappy creatures felt they were on the point of being asphyxiated.

The fire had reached the brook. Hope sprang up for a moment in their breasts. But the fire laughed at the insignificant channel, which was already covered over with flying straw by its accomplice the wind. It leaped across it to the other bank and advanced to lick at the hitching rail and the willows that shaded it and, roaring with delight, ran toward the west. Behind it the night seemed blacker than ever, and the shock-benumbed woman watched how the shooting stars of the fire rose and died in the abysmal night the fire left in its wake.

Further off to the south, where the Southern Cross gleamed, there, too, the dried grass served as a bridgehead for the invasion. In a moment the whole channel of the brook was ablaze. And on the other bank, from the bushes of the higher ground, the wind wrenched loose shoals of sparks, which came to rest at the women's feet. Some of them landed on the house and died out in the thatch of the roof. The women were so paralyzed with anxiety that they failed to notice the new danger. And sparks and burning bits of straw flew about more and more thickly.

"Mamma! Mamma!"

Isabel's heart-rending cry gave word of the crowning disaster: the main roof was burning, giving off a great cloud of smoke, in a circle about a yard across.

"Water! Bring water!" shouted the mother, aroused from her stupor. Both ran toward the watering trough beside the well. One filled a bucket, the other a pitcher. They rushed back, but they lacked the strength to throw the water that high.

"You bring the water!" stammered the mother. And standing on a stool, lacerating hands and knees, hampered by her skirts, she managed to climb on to the roof, screaming wildly—as though anybody could hear her!

"Viacaba—Pancho—Joaquin!"

Isabel brought pitchers and buckets of water, running, panting, the sweat pouring off her. The mother, hardly knowing what she was doing, lay face down on the roof, automatically reaching back for the water, and pouring it into the spreading blaze. And while she was carrying out this slow, toilsome operation, the wind went on shooting its burning arrows into the house. In a minute the house was ablaze at a number of different places.

"Get down, Mamma, get down. You'll be burned alive . . ."

The poor soul climbed down at last. Like a merry bonfire the house was burning from end to end, lighting up the patio from the hitching post under the disheveled willows, blown back and forth by the wind, to the pen where the sheep milled about, crowded, climbed over each other, bleating pitifully, and trying to break through the stout fence. That sinister glow effaced, blotted out the other, which now was part of the horizon.

In the distance the men saw that burning beacon and turned back, one after the other, in utter despair.

There was nothing to do. At the risk of their lives they barely managed to get a few things out of the blazing oven. The rafters fell in with a great crash, the eave disappeared, and all that could be seen by the red light was the blackened walls. Sitting on the ground, overcome by their helplessness and rage, from time to time they gave vent to their lamentations. And the visit of the foreigner that afternoon kept returning to their feverish imaginations with terrifying, diabolical associations.

"That gringo, that gringo!"

"This is all his fault."

"He put the evil eye on us."

"He must have thrown his cigarette stub in the swamp, the bastard!"

"No, *patrón!* It wasn't that. He was the Devil, he was Mandinga! As sure as we're sitting here!"

Matilde's childish superstition became an incontrovertible fact the next day when in Pago Chico, where they had gone to seek refuge in their desolation, people told them that no Frenchman had come through there. It then spread by word of mouth until it assumed the quality of a historic event, even though the chief of police did find out and stated that a man answering the description of the presumed firebug had been in the neighboring town of Sauce that evening where, at dawn, he took the stagecoach for Azul.

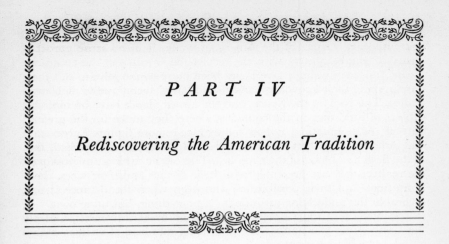

PART IV

Rediscovering the American Tradition

AT FIRST GLANCE it seems a paradox to say that the writers who made up the movement known in Spain and Latin America as *modernismo*, which began at the turn of the century, were the true discoverers of the American tradition. For the most part they were poets or essayists, subjective and lyrical, and for this reason they are not included in this anthology, even though among them were some of the greatest figures in Spanish American literature, men like José Martí, José Asunción Silva, Rubén Darío, Amado Nervo, José Enrique Rodó. To further heighten the paradox, although they were powerfully influenced by Europe—most of them had lived there, some the greater part of their lives—they mark the independence of Latin American literature. The folk and traditional elements are not visibly present in their work, but in all there is an acute awareness of America and its problems. Time had given them a century of perspective, and their knowledge of Europe enabled them to evaluate America, to discern and appraise all that was typical and unique in it. The essential concern of most of them was to define their America, to see what it really was in comparison with Europe and the United States, and this was their legacy to those who followed them.

In the nineteenth century the history of America, from the conquest through the independence, had been a series of patriotic myths, each country exalting its own heroes, who seemed to float above reality. Reality, however, was not these great figures alone, but the people whom they led and directed, without whom they would have been nothing. It is the people, with their problems, their aspirations, their day-to-day life, who have become the new heroes. The affirmation by contemporary writers of the American values is in no sense parochialism or lack of contact with the rest of the world. On the contrary, Latin American writers have never been more cosmopolitan. But they are applying their knowledge and their literary technique to their own reality. The Indian, the Negro, and the mixed bloods have become the subject of literature in the countries where they make up the greater part of the population, not as the exotic, remote figures Europeans, and Americans not yet emancipated from Europe, had depicted, but as the flesh and blood of their nations. There is no attempt to gloss over the reality; they are presented with their virtues and their vices, their limitations and their possibilities, and even when the balance is unfavorable the underlying attitude is "a poor thing, but mine own."

The novel and short story have taken on great increment, and all the Latin American nations are producing numbers of writers, many gifted, some of very great talent. In their search for an interpretation of their America they have turned to their past, viewing it with unprejudiced eyes, taking into account their European and their autochthonous heritages, the native civilizations, the colony, the independence, the civil wars, all colored with that wealth of folk materials typical of peoples that have clung so tenaciously to their traditions. Progress and education will soon bring uniformity to all these countries, and present-day writers are endeavoring to set down the traditional and the regional aspects, with their speech and local idiosyncracies, before radio, newspaper, and ease of communication sweep them away. As everywhere, the work of contemporary Latin American writers is characterized by concern over the social problems that confront the whole world today in the particular form these problems have taken among them: the revolution and its aftermath in Mexico, the agrarian problem, and the problem of incorporating the Indian into the life of the nation. And, as is the case in our own country, these writers know that the hour of America has come. There is an affirmative tone to their work, a belief in themselves, an ironical tenderness toward aspects of their own reality about which they would have been apologetic or despondent a generation or two ago. They have achieved maturity.

RICARDO ROJAS

(1882–   )

Historian, dramatist, poet, short-story writer, professor, Ricardo Rojas is recognized as the dean of Argentine letters. He has been president of the University of Buenos Aires, dean of the Faculty of Philosophy and Letters, and his life has been wholly devoted to his writing and teaching. His historical works, such as *Literatura argentina* and *La argentinidad*, deal with the history of Argentine literature and civilization; they throw new light, not only on Argentina's formation and development, but are of significance for all of Spanish America. One of his best-known works is *El santo de la espada*, a biography of General San Martín, liberator of the Argentine, for whom Rojas has an admiration verging on reverence. He is also the author of a biography of Sarmiento, *El profeta de la pampa*. Like Sarmiento, Rojas is from the provinces, not a native of Buenos Aires, and it may be that this gives him that ability to encompass the whole of Argentina in his vision, a faculty the *porteños*, as the inhabitants of Buenos Aires are known, sometimes lack.

Rojas is the author of several volumes of short stories, a number of which deal with the folklore of his country. In the following selection, from the volume *El país de la selva*, Rojas describes in his pleasantly erudite fashion the European origins of the widespread belief that the devil can assume human shape to achieve his designs, and the process of adaptation of this superstition to the American scene.

The Incubus *

[RICARDO ROJAS]

Zupay, the demon of the forest, has assumed animal form in the region about the Saladillo, and human shape in the tale I am about to recount.

The faithful of the Middle Ages believed in all these metamorphoses. To them the sylvans and fauns of pagan Greece were devils, and to many theologians men of the stature of Albertus Magnus and the rebel

* Translated with the author's permission from *El país de la selva* by Ricardo Rojas.

Luther were the spawn of Satan. It was from this time that the legends of incubi, who tempted virgins carnally, and succubi, who put the abstinence of the devout to the acid test, flourished. Both incarnated the mystery of a lascivious Devil who assumed sexual form on earth to satisfy his appetite of love. Physiologists of the period went so far as to study the nature of incubi and the creatures engendered by them. At the same time theologians devoted special treatises to the question of whether the penitentiary canons should consider *copula cum demone* a sin against piety or a sin of lust. And inasmuch as their bodies are of "a thin, vaporous substance that emanates like an effluvium," according to Father Sinistrari, they could take on forms as beautiful as they were deceiving, and filter through the cracks of doors and keyholes. When the devil attempts a seduction he does not show himself as a lustful, violent satyr, but in the guise of a handsome youth, elegantly garbed. This sinister side of ancient Catholicism migrated, too, to the American scene. Such superstitions spread through the wild new land, and in adapting themselves to this strange setting, as in the case of so many others, not only did the subtleties of scholasticism disappear, but the plot took on a new coloring and the players new attitudes.

A legend I came upon in the heart of the jungle stems from these remote traditions. In it Satan does not appear to the adulterous woman in the same fashion as to that Hyeronima of another medieval tale. Nor did the imagination of our people conceive him as wearing the billowing Spanish cape, as is the case in tales of Flemish or Italian origin. Here the house is a rustic cabin; the seducer, a gaucho dressed in his best finery; the victim, a guileless countrywoman who never suspected she was falling into a snare laid by an incubus; the scene, the forest with its ambient of mystery.

The woman and her man lived in a remote spot of the forest they knew so well. Far from the neighboring villages, the crags and brambles constituted their happiness. The wilderness presented no obstacles to his strength and bravery. Bird and animal fell victim to his skill. She, young and beautiful, sometimes accompanied him or waited for him in their cabin until he returned at night with his bag of the day. They were happy in their remote retreat, living on the honey and game that sufficed for their simple meals. Some afternoons the man came home, ax in one hand and in the other a white "flower of the air," the silken glory that hangs from the gnarled quebrachos; the woman repaid the flower with her kisses; the days rolled by, and the couple lived a life of love in the lap of fecund nature. A son was born to them, and the new being brought still more joy to their lives. Seated under the eave of the cabin, the father would ride him on his knee, pointing out to him, when he was old enough to understand, the *tucu-tucu* that passed

overhead slashing the blue of the rustling night, or entertaining him
with the heavenly bodies:

"See the moon, little one?"

"I thee it."

"And you see the donkey?"

"I thee it."

"And the Virgin with the God-child in her arms?"

"Yeth." Then the father would point to a star, a constellation, the
Milky Way—*Cielu-mayu*—river of the sea, in whose silvery waters flowing between banks of shadow he showed him the little yellow ducks,
like those the child was already throwing stones at in a near-by brook.

This happiness was to end, and the day it happened, the woman saw
a stranger coming down the narrow gorge that led to the rustic dwelling. She wanted to turn away but was unable to; the stranger advanced
toward her as she stood motionless, held there by a fascination against
which she was powerless. The rider's strong breast gave her a foretaste
of his embraces, a wanton breeze came laden with intoxicating wild
perfumes, sensations of pleasure fluttered along her spine. At the same
time the image of her husband, off gathering honey, rose up before
her.

"Cross, Cross, Devil." Her lips would have formed the words of the
exorcism if she had suspected that she was in the presence of Zupay,
or she would have held before him a knife, its hilt forming a cross, but
she did nothing. The stranger was standing beside her; she was swoon-
ing from the poison of the lying visions; the sun disappeared behind
the clouds, as though hastening to hide the scene in darkness; the dog
slunk along on its belly, unable to bark. And the stranger, as he moved
away, murmured in the ear of the woman that was already his:

"I shall be waiting for you; when the night bird calls, follow it.
It will guide your steps through the darkness—"

When night descended, the man, wearied with his day's work, fell
into a heavy sleep. She lay awake, watching through the open window
the twinkling of the distant stars. Suddenly an owl on the ridgepole of
the house hooted, and then the flapping of its wings could be heard in
the vast silence. The woman slipped from the bed and, crawling on
hands and knees, left the house. The eyes of the bird were shining
overhead and led her down paths she had never trod to a spring of
transparent waters, where the lover was waiting who had dragged her
from her house in pursuit of a chimera.

"Let us go further into the woods," he undoubtedly said to her. They
would make their way to some hidden nook, where happiness, wealth,
delight awaited them; the grass would be their bridal bed, the leaves
their canopy. But before they went she must leave her eyes in a gleam-

ing magic caldron, where, when they returned, she would find them more beautiful and shining than before.

They set out. She followed blindly, the sockets of her eyes empty. On both sides of the path the thick forest stretched, invisible to the unhappy creature, although she could hear, like the sound of distant crowds, the echo of the whispering foliage. In the heavens all was peace; the world was drenched in moonlight. And beside her went not the handsome youth she had known, but Zupay in his pristine satyr's shape.

Hours later the gaucho awoke and noticed anxiously that his beloved wife was gone. He got up quickly, and, distracted, not knowing where to look, unable to understand the mystery of what had happened, set out through the darkness of the wood. Wandering about, he came by chance on the fountain. He sensed that something horrible had happened there. And to his horror, as he looked into it he saw his wife's eyes gleaming in the magic caldron. He picked them up, looked at them, and clasping them to his breast as though defending a priceless treasure, he kept on through the forest, beside himself with fear and anger, suspecting a crime, and waiting for the dawn to reveal some bloody tragedy.

Before the day began to break, the adulterous couple returned to the fountain. When Zupay saw that the eyes were gone he fled like a frightened coward, as though to escape the coming light. The woman, deserted and blind, ran wildly about the forest. Later a party of honey gatherers found her body crumpled at the foot of a clump of huge quebrachos. Meanwhile the gaucho had returned to his cabin, crushed with sorrow, still holding the pupils in his hand, his happiness gone forever, for in the mirror of the eye's dark pupils he had seen the imprisoned visions of lust and death.

Up to this point the tale is a legend. Nothing is left here of the theological traditions.

In the popular lore, when the Devil tempted a virgin, a believer, a wife, he could be conjured, not only by the sign of the cross, but by the name of the saints, holy relics, lustrations, and fumigations, in accordance with formulas prescribed by confessors. Sometimes amulets of verbena, castor beans, jasper, or coral were used. On other occasions mixtures of azedarach bark, cinnamon, aloes, nutmeg, and benzoin were burned in a new pot, depending on whether the devil partook of the nature of fire, air, earth, water— But why go on? The scholastic imagination lost itself in a labyrinth of special cases, a maze of precautions. The Catholic missionaries taught this to the people of the jungle, but nothing of it remains now. For this reason, in the legend we have set forth there is hardly a trace of a moral lesson. But in those primitive regions the faithfulness of woman is a cult that has been preserved in all its vigor, and the minds that forged it and the lips that perpetuated it in the simple homes of the region have severely punished its infraction.

ALBERTO GERCHUNOFF

(1883–   )

A TRAIT common to every American nation is the ability to turn its immigrants into hundred per cent Americans, frequently in the first generation, and without fail in the second. These are often the best Americans, for the fact of being an American, with all this implies, is still in the nature of a miracle to them. No country has this ability to a greater degree than Argentina. (It may even be that certain manifestations of an exaggerated nationalism stem from the large immigrant population it has absorbed in the last fifty years.) A typical case in point is Alberto Gerchunoff. He is of Russian-Jewish parentage, and Argentine to the marrow of his bones. He has been one of the editorial staff of *La Nación*, Argentina's most important newspaper, for many years. Though primarily a journalist, he is the author of an excellent volume of essays on Don Quixote, *La jofaina maravillosa*, and a collection of short stories dealing with the Jews who settled an agricultural colony in Argentina, *Los gauchos judíos*. With great tenderness, simplicity, and a quality that is almost Biblical, he describes their new pastoral life and the process of their transformation into *gauchos*, which he uses in the sense of Argentinians, for he realizes that the gaucho is the matrix of the Argentine.

In the following selection from *Los gauchos judíos* he recounts an old legend the Jews had brought with them from their Russian homeland, and sets it against the new American background.

The Owl *

[ALBERTO GERCHUNOFF]

MOUNTED on his pony, Jacob rode past the Reiner place, greeting them in Spanish. The old woman answered in Yiddish, and the girl asked him if, as he came back from the fields, he had seen Moses, who had left that morning to look for the gray.

"Moses?" asked the boy. "Was he riding the white horse?"

"The white one."

"Did he take the road to Las Moscas?"

"No," answered Pearl. "He was headed toward San Miguel."

"San Miguel? No, I didn't see him."

The mournful tone of the old woman's voice revealed her anxiety.

"It's getting late, and my son went off without eating anything except a couple of matés. He's not carrying a revolver—"

"There's nothing to worry about, ma'am. You can ride all around these parts and never meet a soul—"

"May God hear you," replied Doña Eva. "They say there's a gang of outlaws near Ornstein's place."

The conversation came to a close with an encouraging word from Jacob. He gave his pony a touch of the spur to make it buck a little so Pearl would appreciate his skill as a rider.

The sun was going down, and the autumn afternoon was sinking to rest in a blur of haze. The sky was streaked with red. The yellowish tone of the stubble fields, the pale green of the pasture, furrowed by the narrow gray slit of a brook, gave the landscape a melancholy sweetness, like that described by the Hebrew bards, when the shepherdesses drove home their patient flocks under the skies of Canaan.

Darkness was swallowing up the humble houses of the colony, and the last glimmer of light broke in gleaming reflections on the fence wires.

"It is late, my daughter, and Moses has not returned."

"There's nothing to worry about, Mother. It's not the first time it's happened. Don't you remember last year just before the Passover when he went with the wagon to the woods at San Gregorio? He didn't come back till the next day."

"I remember, but he was carrying a revolver, and there's a settlement near San Gregorio."

An uneasy silence followed. The chirping of the crickets and the croaking of the frogs broke the twilight hush. From the pond came the noisy cry of the *teros*, and from the near-by grove, small muted noises.

* Translated with the author's permission from *Los gauchos judíos*, by Alberto Gerchunoff.

An owl flew over the barnyard, hooting mournfully, and came to rest on a fence post.

"What an ugly bird that is!" observed the girl.

The owl gave another hoot and stared at the two women, filling them both with a sense of foreboding.

"They say they're bad luck."

"That's what they say, but I don't believe it. What do these country-folks know."

"Don't we Jews say that the raven announces a death?"

"Oh, that's different—"

The owl flew low to the ground as far as the eave of the house, where it gave another hoot and then flew back to the post, looking at the women all the time.

Down the shadow-choked road the hoofbeats of a horse sounded. The girl screwed up her eyes, raising her hand like a visor, and then shook her head.

"No, it isn't white."

From the row of houses across the road the wind brought the echo of a song, one of those monotonous lamentations in which the Hebrew poets mourn for the loss of Jerusalem and exhort the daughters of Zion, "the magnificent and only Zion," to weep in the night that their tears may arouse the clemency of the Lord. Mechanically Pearl murmured:

"Weep and lament, oh daughters of Zion."

Then in a louder voice she sang the song of the Jews of Spain which David Ben-Azam, the schoolmaster, had taught her:

We have lost Zion
We have lost Toledo
Where shall we find consolation. . . .

Her mother's anxiety continued, and the girl, to take her mind from her worry, resumed the conversation they had left off.

"Do you believe in dreams, Mother? The other day Doña Raquel told us something that frightened us so."

In reply the old woman related another fearsome tale. A cousin of hers, "as beautiful as a star," had been betrothed to a man of her village. He was a carter, very poor, very upright and God fearing. But the girl did not like him because he was humpbacked. The night of their betrothal the wife of the rabbi—a saintly woman, indeed—saw a raven.

The carter sold one of his horses and with the money bought his betrothed a prayer book for a present. Two days before the marriage was to take place, the engagement was broken, and the next year the girl married a rich man of the village.

The mere memory of the incident affected Doña Eva deeply. Her face in the shadows grew longer, and in a doleful voice she continued her uncanny tale. The girl married, and one after another her children died, making of that home the abode of sorrow. Her first sweetheart? The poor man had died.

The family decided to consult an eminent rabbi about the matter. He carefully examined the holy texts and found a similar case among the old traditions. He advised the woman to return the beautiful prayer book to the dead man. In this way she would recover her peace of mind and happiness.

"Carry it," he told her, "under your right arm and return it to him tomorrow night."

The poor woman did not answer a word. The next night she took the prayer book under her arm and set out. A steady rain beat against her face, and her feet, weak with fear, could hardly find the road through the hard snow. When she reached the outskirts of the town she huddled against a wall, weary and heartsick. She thought of her dead children and of that first sweetheart whose memory had disappeared from her recollection long years since. Slowly she turned the pages of the prayer book, with its ornamented, colored initials that she liked to look at as she intoned the prayers in chorus in the synagogue.

Suddenly a darkness came over her eyes, and when she came to herself again, the carter stood before her, with his patient, withdrawn face, his twisted body, his hump.

"This is your prayer book, and I am returning it to you," she said to him.

The phantom, whose eyes were filled with earth, put out his hand of bone and took the book.

Then the woman, recalling the advice of the rabbi, added:

"And may peace be with you and pray for me. I shall pray to God for your salvation."

Pearl sighed. The night closed in, gentle and diaphanous. In the distance the fireflies moved about like tiny sparks and brought to the spirits of the old woman and the girl a vague fear of ghosts. And there upon the hitching post, behind which the cattle lay, the owl sat, its eyes fixed upon them as though magnetized, gleaming, unwavering.

A thought she was reluctant to voice kept nagging at the girl:

"But if the gauchos say those things about that bird, it might be—"

Doña Eva looked at the hitching post and then buried her gaze in the blackness of the road. In a quavering, almost imperceptible voice she murmured:

"It might be, my daughter—"

She shuddered as she said it, and Pearl, her throat gripped by the chill hand of the same anxiety, huddled close beside her. Just then they heard the echo of a horse galloping. The two leaned forward to hear it better, trying to see through the thick darkness. They hardly breathed, and the moments rolled over their hearts with painful slowness. The dogs of the neighborhood began to bark. The gallop sounded faster and nearer, and a second later they saw the white horse rushing up in headlong career. Mother and daughter leaped up in terror, and a long cry like a howl came from their mouths. The sweating horse had stopped at the gate. It was riderless, and the saddle was covered with blood.

RICARDO GÜIRALDES

(1886–1927)

THE UNTIMELY DEATH of Ricardo Güiraldes in 1927 at the age of forty-one brought to an end the career of the greatest South American writer of our times. It was untimely in the sense that much could still have been expected from one who had just reached his prime, and that men who possess his gifts and his generosity are all too rare; but not because he had not left behind him a work that will live as long as Spanish is read, the book he published the year before his death, *Don Segundo Sombra*. His short stories that make up the volume *Cuentos de amor y de muerte* are of the same high order, and his earlier novels *Raucho* and *Xaimaca*, though they falter at times, foreshadow the work that was to come. Güiraldes was also a consummate poet.

He belonged to the landowning aristocracy of Argentina and had traveled and studied abroad from boyhood. He knew English literature well and was as familiar with French as with Spanish. He was one of the initiators of the contemporary literary movement in Argentina. The early work of most of the young—now not so young, alas!—writers who have since achieved distinction first appeared in the pages of the entertaining though short-lived small literary reviews he helped to found, *Martín Fierro* and *Proa*.

A rare synthesis of Europe and America had been effected in him. He was not a mere tourist or traveler in Europe. He spent much of his time in France and had a host of friends there. But always the memory of his ranch on the pampa was uppermost in his mind, and when he wrote, it was the scenes, the people, the emotions of that life he loved that filled his pages. *Don Segundo Sombra* is dedicated to "the gaucho I bear within me as the monstrance bears the holy wafer."

In *Don Segundo Sombra* he has distilled the essence of the pampa and the gaucho. Perhaps there never was a gaucho like Don Segundo, "so compleat and parfait," but that is of no consequence. In spite of the fact that the reader lives the life of the pampa, endures its heat, its dust, its wind, shares in the work and excitement of the roundups, the brandings, the horse breaking, this is not a realistic work. Like W H. Hudson, Güiraldes has captured the poetic truth, the eternal quality of the scenes he describes—which is the highest form of reality.

Don Segundo Sombra contains the gaucho in his totality, his beliefs, his customs, his ethos, and yet the book is essentially a fairy tale. As n many of his short stories, Güiraldes has taken an old, trite plot— here the Cinderella story—as though to show how unimportant plot is. An orphan boy runs away from home, attaches himself to a wandering gaucho, learns from him how to live in the fullest sense of the word, and in the end discovers that he is the heir to a rich estate. Within this simple framework is packed all the beauty of the land, of work, of the companionship of men, of freedom, of adventure, told in a language that is a blend of the precise, sober, yet colorful speech of the gaucho and Güiraldes's sensitive, scintillating prose, in which classic and modern influence have been tempered by his genius into an instrument having the beauty and power of a Toledo blade. It is a man's book, to be set alongside *Robinson Crusoe* and *Huckleberry Finn*.

The selection from *Don Segundo Sombra* that follows is a well-known folk tale that also served Tomás Carrasquilla as the theme of one of his finest short stories.

Misery and the Devil *
[RICARDO GÜIRALDES]

THE day had died to a bank of luminous cloud on the horizon when from a hilltop we saw the old bead trees of an abandoned farm. Don Segundo studied the fence; there was a place where the wires had been cut—perhaps some convoy of wagons had spent the night there and sneaked forage for their animals—and we could get through. Without

* Reprinted from *Don Segundo Sombra, Shadows on the Pampa*, by Ricardo Güiraldes, translated by Harriet de Onís, by permission of Rinehart & Co., Inc. Copyright 1935 by Rinehart & Co., Inc.

sight of a town anywhere, the country seemed to belong to whoever cared to use it; and although there were only four trees, it seemed certain that some twigs or branches must have fallen to the ground so we could have a fire.

We turned the horses loose in the field, unsaddled the ones we had been riding, gathered dry leaves, sticks and a few good-sized chunks of wood, and started the blaze going. We filled the kettle from our waterskin and put it to boil for maté; then we sat down, rolled our cigarettes, and lighted them in the young flames of our fire. We had built it near a big log that had been cut there and forgotten, so we had a good place to sit and to reflect that, all told, a herder's life is no worse than any other. My godfather's love of solitude may have won me; for as I looked back on my wandering life these deep communions with the silent pampa seemed the best of it all. Just the same, my thoughts hurt and were soaked in gloom, the way a saddle blanket gets soaked in blood from a wound.

The silent land gave us something of its greatness and its unconcern. We roasted our meat and ate without talking. We again placed the kettle on the embers and brewed bitter matés. Don Segundo spoke, slow, almost absent-minded:

"I'm going to tell you a story, so you can tell it to some friend that's having a run of bad luck."

More slowly I sipped my maté.

"This happened in the days of Our Lord Jesus Christ and his Apostles."

There was a pause. Don Segundo let you gradually fall like that into the realm of fiction. Soon we'd be hanging on to the thread of the story, drawn along by it—whither?

Our Lord, they say, was the sower of kindness; and He'd ride from town to town, from ranch to ranch, teaching the gospels through the Holy Land, and healing with His word. He'd take St. Peter along with Him on these rides as His helper, for He was fond of him, as he was mighty faithful and obliging.

On one of these rides, they say (and they were as hard as a herder's), just as they were cantering into a town the mule of Our Lord lost a shoe and began to limp. "Watch out for a smith," Our Lord told St. Peter, "we're getting into town." St. Peter kept his eyes open, and pretty soon he saw an old shack with tumbled-down walls, and over the door was a sign that said: "BLAKSMITH." He hurried to tell the Master, and they stopped at the corral.

"Ave María!" they called. A little cur came barking out and then an old man, all rags, and asked them in. "Good afternoon," said Our Lord, "how about shoeing my mule for me, that's lost a shoe?" "Get off and come in," said the old one, "and I'll see about it."

They went in and sat down on the chairs with shaky twisted legs. "What's your name?" asked Jesus. "My name is Misery," the old one answered, and he went out to get what he needed. The poor servant of the Lord rummaged all over the place, in boxes, in bags, in corners, but he could not find what he needed to make a shoe. He was coming back to excuse himself to the waiting ones when, poking around with his foot in a lot of rubbish, he saw a ring of silver—a big one!

"Now what are you doing there?" says he, picking it up; and he fired his forge, melted the ring, hammered it into a shoe and nailed it on the mule of Our Lord. Smart old fox he was!

"How much do we owe you, my good man?" asked Our Lord.

Misery looks Him over from head to foot. "Looks to me," he says, "like you two fellows are about as poor as I am. What the devil should I charge you? Go in peace. Maybe some day God will remember."

"So be it," said Our Lord, and they got on their mules and jogged along. After a stretch this chap St. Peter, who wasn't any too bright, says: "Look here, Jesus, we're ungrateful. This here old fellow has put a silver shoe on your mule and not charged us a cent, and he's poorer than poor, and we've gone off without leaving him a thing to remember us by."

"It's the truth," said Our Lord. "Let's go back and give him three wishes, whatever he likes." Misery, seeing them return, thought the mule must have cast the shoe, and asked them in again. Our Lord explained why they had come, and the old boy looked at Him out of the tail of his eye, not knowing whether to get mad or to laugh. "Now think," says Our Lord, "before you make your wish." St. Peter, who was sitting by him, whispers in his ear: "Ask for Paradise." "Shut up, you!" says Misery under his breath, and then he says to Our Lord:

"I wish that whoever sits down in my chair shan't be able to get up unless I say so." "Granted," says Our Lord. "Now the next wish. Be careful." "Ask for Paradise," St. Peter whispers again. "Mind your own business!" the old one snaps and then turns to Our Lord. "I wish that anyone who climbs into my walnut tree outside shan't be able to get down unless I say so." "Granted," says Our Lord. "And now the third and last wish. Don't be in a hurry."

"You stubborn mule, ask for Paradise," whispers St. Peter again. "You old idiot, shut up!" says Misery, getting mad, and then to Our Lord: "I wish that whoever gets into my tobacco pouch here shan't be able to get out unless I say so." "Granted," says Our Lord, and they take their leave and go.

Well, no sooner was Misery alone than he begins to think things over; before long he's as mad as a broncho that he did not make better use of his three wishes. "I'm a fool," he cries, and throws his hat on the floor. "If the Devil came here right now, I'd sell him my soul for twenty years more to live and all the cash I wanted!" Straight off, a gentleman knocks at the door of the shack and says: "Misery, I can give you a contract for what you ask." And he pulls a roll of paper from his pocket, all covered with letters and figures, legal-like. They read it over together, and agree about the terms, and each of them signs fair and square over a seal at the bottom of the roll.

"Now the steer's roped," I said.

"Don't you be getting ahead of the story."

We looked around us at the night, so as not to lose all touch with this world; and my godfather went on:

Well, no sooner was the Devil gone and Misery alone again, than he stumbles on the bag of gold that Mandinga has left him. He looks at himself in the duck pond and finds that he's a youth! So off he goes to town, buys himself a new suit, hires a room in the hotel like a gentleman, and that night he sleeps happy.

Boy, you should have seen how his life changed! He chummed with princes and governors and mayors. He bet more than anyone else on all the races. He traveled around the world and had a good time with the daughters of kings and dukes. . . . But years run fast in that sort of game, and now the twentieth year was up. So one day when Misery happened to drop in at his old hovel to have a good laugh at it, the Devil turns up, calling himself Señor Lili, pulls out his contract, and asks for payment.

Misery was a man of his word, and although he felt a little blue, he invited Lili to have a chair while he washes and changes his suit, for he wanted to go to hell looking decent. And as he rubs himself down he thinks that there is no lasso that doesn't break in the end and all his good times are over. When he comes back, there was Lili sitting in the chair, patiently waiting. "All right," says he, "shall we get going?" "How the devil can we go," says Lili, "when I'm stuck in this chair like I was bewitched?" Then Misery remembers the three wishes of the man with the mule, and he nearly falls over laughing. "Get up, rascal," he taunts him. "You're the Devil, ain't you?" And Lili rocks back and forth staring at Misery, but he could not budge an inch and he was sweating like a butcher.

"All right, now," says the old boy that used to be a blacksmith,

"I'll tell you what. We'll just sign for another twenty years and all the cash I want." The Devil had to do as Misery commanded, and then he got leave to go. Once more the old boy was young and rolling in money, and he began the rounds of the gay world. He hobnobbed with princes and magnates, spilled money like no one else, and played with the daughters of kings and great merchants. But the years fly when they are happy, and now the twentieth year was over, and Misery set out for his old smithy to keep his word.

Meantime Lili, who was a gossip as well as a pimp, had told them all in hell about the bewitched chair. "You got to keep your eyes skinned," said Lucifer; "that old boy's a fox, and he's got a pull somewhere. This time two of you had better go to make him keep the contract." So Misery finds two devils waiting for him at his ranch, one of them Lili.

"Come in," says he, "and have a seat while I get washed and fixed up to go to hell in proper fashion."

"I'm not sitting," says Señor Lili.

"Just as you say. Go out and wait in the yard, then, and help yourselves to some of my walnuts; they're the best you've ever ate in your devil's lifetime."

Lili was a bit leery, but his friend said he'd take a turn in the yard and taste the nuts if any were lying on the ground. Pretty soon he comes back and says he has found a handful and nobody could deny that they were the best-tasting walnuts in the world. So the two go out and start hunting; but devil a nut more do they find! At last Lili's friend, whose mouth was watering, says he is going up the tree to get more. Lili warned him to watch out, but the greedygut paid no attention, and up he goes into the tree and begins stuffing and saying once in a while: "Golly, they're good. Golly, they're good!" "Throw me a few," shouts Lili from below. "There goes one." "Throw me some more!" begs Lili. "I'm too busy," says the greedygut. "If you want any, climb the tree and get 'em." Lili hesitates a second, and then up he goes.

Pretty soon Misery walks out, and when he sees the two devils in the walnut tree, he lets out a laugh. "At your orders," he shouts. "I'm ready when you are." "But we can't get down," say the two devils, who were like stuck to the branches. "That's fine," says Misery. "All we got to do now is sign another contract for twenty years and all the money I want." And the devils do what he asks, and then he lets them go.

All over again comes the running round the world and the hobnobbing with swell folk and the making love to the grand ladies. But the years rolled just as fast as before, and when the twentieth was up,

Misery went back to the smithy where once he had worked in the sweat of his brow to pay his debt.

Meantime, the devils had told Lucifer the whole story, and Lucifer was angry. "Hell!" he said, "didn't I warn you chaps to watch your step because the man was a fox? This time we'll all go with you."

So when Misery got to his shack, there were more folks there than at a roundup. But they were all drawn up like an army, and at the orders of a leader who wore a crown. Hell's camping at my house, he thought, and he looked at the devils' gang like a dog at a whip. If I come through this time, he thought, I'm saved for good. But he wasn't as cool as he made out to be when he walks up to them and asks: "Are you looking for me?"

"We are!" shouts the guy with the crown.

"I never signed any contract with you, that you should come burning candles at my funeral."

"You're coming with me, for I'm the king of the devils!"

"How do I know?" says Misery. "If you're really who you say, why don't you prove it? Get all the devils inside yourself, for instance, and turn yourself into an ant."

Anyone else would have been suspicious, I reckon. But bad ones, they say, lose their head easy with pride and anger. Lucifer was fighting mad and gave a yell; and before you knew it, he was an ant and all the other devils were inside him.

Quick as a wink Misery grabbed the little beast that was crawling over the bricks of the floor and stuck it into his tobacco pouch. He laid the pouch on the anvil in his smithy, picked up a hammer, and began pounding away with all his might till his shirt ran sweat.

Then he washed up, changed his clothes, and went for a walk around the town. And every day the sly old fox slapped that pouch on the anvil and gave it such a drubbing that he had to change his shirt again and take another walk around town to cool off.

This went on for years.

And the result was that in his town there were no fights, no lawsuits, no slander. Husbands did not beat their women, nor mothers their children. Uncles, cousins, stepchildren, got along as God bids; spooks and pigs stayed in their sties; nobody saw a ghost; the sick got well; the old folks did not die, and even the dogs were chaste. Neighbors never argued, horses kicked their heels only in happiness, and everything ran like a rich man's watch. They didn't even have to clean the wells, for all water was good.

"Hurrah!" I cried.

"Hold your horses!" advised my godfather.

There's no road without a turn, no destiny without tears; and so it came that the lawyers, the district attorneys, the justices of the peace, the quacks and medicos—all the important ones, in fact, who live off the troubles and vices of the people—began to get so hungry you could count their ribs, and to die off. One day such as were left of this vermin were so scared that they marched up to the Governor to ask for help. The Governor, who was of the same breed, said there was nothing he could do, gave them some of the people's money, and warned them not to come for more, because it was not the state's business to feed them. Months went by, and by now the lawyers and judges and suchlike brutes were getting real scarce, for most of them had shuffled off, I hope to a better life. At last, one of them, the biggest scamp of the lot, got wind of the truth and invited the others to the Governor's again, promising them that this time they would win.

When they were all in His Excellency's presence, the lawyer told them how this calamity had befallen them: it was because the black-smith Misery had all the devils of hell shut tight in his pouch.

You can bet the Governor lost no time having Misery brought in, and in front of them all he let loose: "Oh ho! So it's you!" says he. "A nice mess you are making of the world with your conjures, you old scamp. You put things back the way they were and quit trying to right wrongs and chastise devils. Don't you see the world, being what it is, can't get along—not for a minute—without evil and laws and sickness? And that those who live by them, and there's aplenty, need to have the devils trotting round? You get back to your ranch this minute as fast as you can and let hell out of your tobacco pouch!"

Misery sees that the Governor is right; he confesses to the truth and hurries home to obey. He was bored anyway with the world and too old to care if he did leave it. But before he let the devils out he slapped the old pouch on the anvil and gave it a last good drubbing till his shirt ran sweat.

"If I let you loose," says he to the *mandingas*, "are you going to hang around here any more?"

"No!" they all shouted like one. "Let us out and you'll never see us again." So Misery opened the pouch and told them to come. Out hopped the little ant and swelled till he was the Bad One, and then from Lucifer's body burst all the little devils, and the herd of them stampeded down that street of God's world, rolling up clouds of dust like a windstorm.

Well, we're getting to the end. . . .

The day came when Misery was at the last gasp of his kettle, for every Christian soon or late must hand in his bones, and this one certainly had made use of his! Thinking that the best way, Misery lay down on his heap of rags to wait for death. He was too weary and bored, there in his old shack, even to take the trouble to get up for food and drink. He just lay and gradually shriveled up till his body was as hard and stiff as a mummy.

And so, having left his body behind for the worms, Misery thought, what next? And, being no fool, he made straight for heaven. He got there after a long ride and knocked at the gate. As soon as St. Peter opened, they recognized each other, but the old rascal figured it might be just as well not to remember, so he acted blithe and begged to come in.

"Hm," says St. Peter, "when I last saw you in your smithy with Our Lord and told you to ask for Paradise, you said: 'Shut up, old fool!' It's not that I hold it against you; but it's against the rules to give a man heaven when he's turned it down three times."

Without a word more the keeper of the blessed gates slammed them shut, and Misery, thinking that of two evils one should choose the lesser, went down to purgatory. But, brother, when he got there, they told him they could admit only souls as were ticketed for heaven; and as this glory was not to be his who had three times refused it, they were sorry but they could not invite him in. It looked like eternal torment in hell. So Misery squared his shoulders and went to hell, pounding on the door the way he used to pound his pouch on the anvil to make the devils holler. The door opened at last, and Misery got mad when he found himself face to face with Lili.

"Damn my luck," he shouted: "wherever I go, I've got acquaintances!" But Lili thought of the poundings on the anvil and lit out with his tail behind him like a flag and never stopped till he got to the feet of Lucifer. He told him who was knocking to get in.

The whole damned devils' herd was scared; the Prince of Darkness himself remembered the blows of that hammer and began to squawk like a broody hen and ordered all the doors shut against the nuisance.

There was Misery with no place to go, for they had turned him down in heaven, in purgatory, and in hell. And that's why from that day to this Misery and Poverty remain on earth, and they'll never leave for no one will take them in.

The tale had lasted an hour, and all our water was gone. We rose silently to get ready for the night.

"Poverty," I said, and threw down my saddle pad to lie on.

"Misery," I said, and made a pillow of my blanket.

I lay down upon this world, but without sorrow, and in a little while I was sleeping like a log.

JORGE LUIS BORGES

(1899–   )

LIKE GÜIRALDES, Borges is an Argentine of cosmopolitan, European formation whose work contains the essence of the poetic reality of his native land, and particularly of the city of Buenos Aires. It is not the new modern city he is concerned with, but the memories that haunt its forgotten, by-passed corners. His poetry, whose themes he has dredged up from the past, his own and that of his country, has a boldness and a freshness of imagery, an unerring sense of language, and a quality of ironic tenderness that assure Borges an outstanding place among the great modern poets in the Spanish language.

At the age of eighteen Borges went to Spain where he remained for three years, collaborating in the literary movement that developed there after World War I. When he returned to Buenos Aires in 1921 he became one of the initiators of the new movement there. Borges is a man of unusual literary background. He is completely familiar with the literature of his own language, as well as with German, French, English, and the classics. The richness of his formation is apparent in the brilliance, assurance, and penetration of his work. He is not only a poet, but probably the greatest critic of his generation.

General Quiroga Goes to Death in a Coach is one of his best-known poems. In it he has managed to convey the drama of the life and death of that famous *caudillo* who was the hero, or villain, or both, of Sarmiento's masterpiece, and who had taken such a hold on the popular imagination that it had made a legend of him even before Rosas the dictator, the Juan Manuel of the poem, found him a stumbling block in his path and had him "rubbed out."

General Quiroga Goes to Death in a Coach *

[JORGE LUIS BORGES]

The river-bed bare stones now, without a thirst of water,
And the moon bumming around in the chill of the dawn,
And the country dead of hunger, poorer than a spider.

---

* Translated with the author's permission from *Poemas* by Jorge Luis Borges.

The coach rocked back and forth, grumbling up the hill,
A huge emphatic vehicle, lumbering, like a hearse,
Four blacks with the look of death in the darkness,
Six fears in harness, and a single courage alert.

Alongside the postillions there trotted a Negro,
Traveling to death by coach, now what could finer be!
General Quiroga was headed for Hell's black hole,
With a bodyguard of six or seven to keep him company.

All that hullabaloo they cooked up in Cordoba,
Meditated Quiroga, is but child's play to me.
Here I am firm fixed and grappled fast to life,
Deep-driven in the pampa, like a Pampa Indian's spear.

I who have outlived thousands, thousands of sunsets,
And at whose name a shudder runs through the lances,
I am not unhanding life among these rocky wastelands,
Does the west wind ever die? What is a sword's life span?

But as they reached the place known as Barranca Yaco,
Sabers, point and blade, on him like a cloudburst fell.
Death, an evil death, mustered out the Riojano,
And stab upon stab repeated: "Juan Manuel."

Later, refreshed and hearty, he strode like a chieftain,
Into the black Hell God had staked out for him,
And at his orders followed, ragged, wan, and bleeding,
The torment-branded souls of horses and of Christians.

GERMÁN ARCINIEGAS

(1900–   )

GERMÁN ARCINIEGAS has packed into his forty-seven years as many and such varied activities as most men rarely encompass in a life-time. He would seem to have made his Goethe's precept: "*Wie das Leben, ohne*

Hast, aber ohne Rast." Teacher, diplomat, journalist, public servant, writer, he has served his native Colombia in all these capacities, and in all he has distinguished himself. He has spent considerable time in the United States as visiting professor at different universities, and his books have been widely read in English translation.

It is as a historian that Arciniegas displays his greatest originality. He has reinterpreted certain fundamental chapters in the history of Latin American from a wholly new point of view. He has by-passed the trappings and fanfare of the conquest and the colonization, the captains and the crown functionaries, and has brought into the light the true heroes, the anonymous soldiers who sweat and suffered and died in the jungles and the icy mountains to win the land, and the common folk who settled and worked it. Without detracting one whit from the achievements of the leading players who alone had been re-membered, Cortés, Pizarro, De Soto, Jiménez de Quesada, he proves conclusively that they could have done nothing without the help of the men they led and that they had been selected for leadership by these same men, who recognized their ability. The conquest was essentially a democratic achievement, as Bernal Díaz del Castillo had recognized four hundred years earlier in his *History of the Conquest of Mexico*. The same thing was true of the independence. It began as a series of sporadic movements—the uprisings of the peasants of Colombia in protest against oppressive taxes, the revolt of the *comuneros* in Paraguay, the rebellion of the Indians of Peru under Tupac-Amaru. These were all put down, but the movement had been initiated that after many disasters finally ended in the triumphs of Junín and Ayacucho and the liberation of America.

In the culture of Latin America it is the popular elements that in-terest Arciniegas most, the Hispanic folk heritage and the native Indian and African contributions that make up the bases of its civilization and on which the superstructure of its future rests. As a consequence of his revised evaluation of the past, many phenomena that seemed con-tradictory or inexplicable fall smoothly into place. He has studied the history of the conquest and colonization of Colombia in *The Knight of El Dorado* and *The Germans in the Conquest of America*, the beginnings of the independence in *Los comuneros*. In *Caribbean, Sea of the New World* he has written with wit, brilliance, and penetration the history of the Caribbean—sea of America—from its discovery to the opening of the twentieth century. The importance of this region in the American and the international scene had never been properly assessed before. Arciniegas's love for his own country has never interfered with his vision of America as a whole. His is a continental viewpoint.

In the following selection from *America, Tierra firme*, he describes with great delicacy and understanding one of the few manifestations of their native, pre-Colombian culture the Indians of Colombia have preserved.

The Little Horses of Ráquira *
[GERMÁN ARCINIEGAS]

Hostile kingdoms may destroy one another; cities may be leveled, and castles, towers, and fortresses fall and be razed to the ground, but against that which God builds in the humble heart, which, free of self-confidence, puts its trust only in God, nothing shall prevail; for the eyes of Him whose seat is in Heaven, and who dwells in His temple, those eyes watch over the poor man who is defenseless and has no riches of his own.

MOTHER MARÍA JOSEFA DE LA CONCEPCIÓN DE CASTILLO

IF you ever go to Chiquinquirá please inquire about the little horses of Ráquira. There are many things to see in that city of miracles. There is the faded painting worshipped by the pilgrims in its famous frame of hammered silver; and the crown of the Virgin set with diamonds as fine of water as those which gleam in the diadem of the Queen of England. You can gaze at yourself in the mirror of a well, underground now because above it stands the high altar, but to which you may have access if you ask the sexton to let you see it, saying to him: Take us to the spot where the painting made its miraculous appearance. You should also see the Dominican friars, most of them Indians, whose ignorance, shrewdness, and irony show themselves simultaneously, as at a window, in their dark, rudely cropped heads, their broad faces, and their quick eyes. You will enjoy hearing the miraculous tradition of the shrine from the lips of these guardians of the cult, and as they talk, take a look at their billowing habit, not as clean as it might be, over which descends a cataract of rattling rosaries. But none of these things will please you as much as the little horses of Ráquira. For this reason, I beg of you, before you do anything else, go to the toy shops and ask for the little horses of Ráquira. They are Chiquinquirá's greatest attraction.

On the most fantastic, on a fairyland Christmas tree, there never hung so many toys as in the ring of shops that line the square of Chiquinquirá.

When an Indian goes to fulfill a vow, for the first time in his life the hard-fisted economy of his poverty is transformed into munificence.

* Translated with the author's permission from *América, tierra firme*, by Germán Arciniegas.

For years the housemaid hoards in her little bank the pennies she filches from her mistress in marketing, and the Indian lays away the profits of a good year or augments his working day by cutting down the hours of stupefying pleasure in the tavern, or contracts a debt that amounts to selling himself into slavery for the rest of his life, but somehow, somewhere they get hold of the money for their vow. And it is then that their rags are traded for new garments, that their cartwheel hats are adorned with silken bows, that their verses and *bambucos* fill the air with music, that the forty knots of the handkerchief are untied to hand over with trembling hands the money for salves and Masses, and it is then that the children receive—for the first and the last time in their lives—toys: toys of wood, of vegetable ivory, of leather, of clay—the little horses of Ráquira.

There are linked to this custom of making pilgrimages tales and traditions that antedate by centuries the day that the horses of Lazaro Fonte, Suárez Rendón, and the licentiate from Córdoba first set foot on this land. Just as now it is Boyacá that is the land of shrines, where a hermitage crowns the brow of every hill, in other days the pilgrims went from stone to stone leaving the priests offerings of gold to win their favor. An easy labor or a good harvest, health or wealth, all were sought by an appeal to the supernatural, the miraculous, which is the way of the lowly. There were villages that became famous for their ability to model the most curious little toys of gold, and others that put all the resources of their ingenuity into shaping in clay images of toads, lizards, or warriors, in order to present to the priest gifts in keeping with his mysterious powers. For such occasions emeralds were bought in Somondoco in exchange for the cotton blankets in whose manufacture they occupied their spare moments; and the clay flutes and horns echoed the sighs of the race, and liquor of corn and cakes of corn were prepared for the occasion with special care.

The newly arrived Spaniards graciously permitted the Indians to continue their offerings at the new shrines, to preserve the custom of the pilgrimages, to travel the same roads to implore the same consolation. And to rivet the tradition more firmly, the sacred images emerged from the lakes in the same fashion as Bachúe the goddess of the Indians. Thus the Christ of Sopó and of Pueblo Viejo, to enhance their veneration among the people. But none surpasses in symbolic value the Virgin of Chiquinquirá, because, like Bachúe, she represents the mother of all mankind. And just as the Indians worshipped the child that Bachúe brought out of the waters and carried in her virgin arms, foretasting the joys of motherhood, and bestowed upon the goddess gifts of such value, according to the chroniclers, as a representation of the child in solid gold, so our Virgin has received the greatest tributes, particularly the Madonna of Chiquinquirá, who was found in a pool of water.

It would be remarkable, indeed, if from the most remote epochs the images of the gods had not been linked to the water in these plains where the entire economy, where the harvests, which were the basis of all wealth, depended upon the timely rain, or were at the mercy of the rivers, which, overflowing their banks, transformed the fields into a mirror of blasted hopes. For this reason the first animals the Indians chose to carry their pleas to the goddess of the waters were the amphibians, the toad, the snake, or the lizard, which form the basic decorative motif in the Chibcha ceramics. This was only natural. Who has not heard the friendly, familiar voice of the toads as they transmit to the water the messages and advice of the earth? Little by little these myths became transformed until they took shape in the great symbolic figures of which Bachúe is the final flowering. And later, when the new gods arrived, the natural preference of the Indians led them to select as their favorites those saints connected with water, such as the gigantic St. Christopher, whose image bears a striking resemblance to Chibchacum, the god who bore the world on his shoulders.

In one way or another Chiquinquirá is an Indian shrine. The windowless rooms of its inns overflow with the waves of humanity washed up from all the valleys, plains and hills, mountains and savannas of the eastern range. The monastery skims off the cream of the pilgrims' pockets. And the shops are piled high with the most beautiful toys ever beheld by the wondering eyes of little Indians. Little clay horses of Ráquira, some covered with bright enamel, others white and porous, just as they come from the kiln. Whip tops, peg tops of vegetable ivory. Bilboquets, which we call *Cocas*, of orangewood. Little boxes covered with rabbit skin. Crude tambourines and gourd dishes, painted and shiny like no others. Little guitars, on which the youngsters strum their first *bambucos*. Shoulder bags, half a handspan wide, but complete with decorations and sections like an accordion and diminutive pockets, which make a child's cup of happiness run over. Sets of dishes of vegetable ivory, in which each piece is less than half an inch high, and chess sets, still smaller, which are a miracle of the miniaturist's art. Plates and bowls of wood, painted red and black, for doll houses that recall Russian toys. Little glass boxes in which the image of the Virgin is all but hidden behind foliage of tin of every color, like modest reproductions of the icons that sustained the faith of the muzhiks. Tiny ivory angels with eyes popping out like wee telescopes. Rosaries of Job's-tears. Little crosses that, when held close to the eye, reveal through an opening the image of the Virgin. Clusters of scapularies. But, best of all, the little horses in which the ingenuousness of the Indian has stamped on clay a message of sincerity.

Ráquira or the Indian and the Clay
[GERMÁN ARCINIEGAS]

NOWHERE else have I seen man so close to the earth as in Ráquira. To be sure, in all America and since time immemorial vessels and pots of clay have been fashioned, but what happens in Ráquira is that the clay seems to seek the hand of man with a voice of greater intimacy. The earth takes pleasure in serving him. For this reason all the way from Ráquira to Leiva you will not see, in the space a horse takes three hours to travel, a single straw-thatched hut. The villages of this region, each with its clay-tiled roof, are almost unique in Colombia. Even in the country, against the ocher plains, whose sole adornment is the cactus, furrowed with gullies and washes left by the rains, the houses of the peasants form such an integral part of the landscape that they can hardly be distinguished from the hillside. There are many that are nothing but a hole opened on the edge of a ravine. Others that rise above the ground have for roof a layer of clay and pebbles that is no different from the surface of this wasteland. In Leiva everything is clay and adobe, and just as this old and vast city has shrunk, so the winds and the rain have washed away its houses, its old colonial homes, restoring them to the earth so skillfully that no one can say whether that gully was once a city, or that rise in the ground was the façade of a great house. In Leiva you will observe that the counters in the stores are of adobe, that the benches that line the entrance halls of the houses are of adobe, and, as a rule, the beds are of this same material. The floors of houses having more than one story are made of clay, which is spread out while still damp over a foundation of bamboo; and the clay is so grateful that with time it takes on a luster equal to that of the parquetry of our pretentious modern dwellings. A Vidal de la Blanche would make this the basis of a lesson in human geography and explain why every region selects certain materials for building or for ornamentation; why, once you have passed a certain point beyond Ráquira, the straw-thatched huts reappear and the beds of boards. The Indian is satisfied to look upon the landscape and re-create himself in his own image out of the clay from which he emerged, with his earthy face and the mud still dripping from his legs.

Cast a random glance over the distribution of the ceramic art in the American landscape, and you will find that there was not a spot where this industry and art did not flourish, producing its workmen and its artists. In graves that have been dug up in the region occupied by the Quimbayas and the Guaqueros, there have been found, along with utensils of local pottery, vessels painted black proceeding from the land of the Incas. In La Guajira, on the site occupied by the Tayronas, of whom nothing is known, there are jars like funeral urns containing the ashes of their chieftains. Referring to the remote Amazon basin inhabited by the Omaguas, Father Gaspar de Carvajal, chaplain to Gonzalo Pizarro in the sixteenth century, says that they found in one village "a house of pleasure in which there was much pottery of different shapes, such as large jars and jugs, some holding up to twenty-five arrobas and more, and other small pieces, like plates and bowls and candlesticks, of the finest pottery ever seen, for that of Malaga cannot be compared to it. It is glazed and enameled in different colors so bright that they dazzle the eye."

Yes, there were potters throughout America, but in few places was the life of man so intimately linked to the clay as in Ráquira. In other regions blessed with greater wealth the potter was just one of the multitude of workers who formed part of the complex army of artisans and artists under the dominion of the different chieftains engaged in weaving blankets, smelting gold, making feather tapestries, or carving the images of their gods in stone. In Ráquira there was nothing but man and clay. If today you travel the roads that link the town to the market places of the vicinity, you will see the procession of Indians, each with a pile of pots upon his back, on their way to sell them in the villages of Boyacá and Cundinamarca. And lining the road you will see bare little huts, each with its adobe kiln beside it, in which the potter's wares are being fired.

These villages are as poor now as they were before the conquest, and the people have not become much more unhappy, withdrawn, and silent under the domination of the masters who brought them servitude, tithes, *corvée*, taxes—in a word, civilization. The potter does not take the time now to decorate his pottery as he did in the days of his native overlords. He just smoothes the sides and bottom of his pots, firms the handles in place, so he can provide a cheap utensil that satisfies the rudimentary needs of his fellow men. But, in spite of everything, the potter loves his clay, his earth, and when he comes upon a vein of white clay he puts it aside to model in it the reflection of his hours of idleness. The women, the children, even the old people, slip their toys into the oven to be fired. Whereas in other regions the worker, when his day's toil is over, stretches himself out on the ground letting time while itself away amidst clouds of tobacco smoke, in Ráquira he spends his leisure hours shaping knickknacks out of the damp clay. Potters have always done this.

> For I remember stopping by the way
> To watch a Potter thumping his wet Clay;
>   And with its all-obliterated Tongue
> It murmur'd—"Gently, Brother, gently, pray!"

says the author of *The Rubáiyát*.

And this is all that has remained to the Indians of their primitive handicrafts. Of that early art that was beginning to create a world in America the conquerors left nothing. From the dark hands of goldsmiths and silversmiths greedy white ones snatched their rich metal. Cloth was imported from Castile that the merchants might profit. The stonemasons were forbidden to hew the images of their gods. All that was left the Indian was his clay—clay that is the index of his poverty and of his withdrawal to the secret places of his heart which the potter's spirit never quite reveals.

ALCIDES ARGUEDAS

(1879–1941)

ALCIDES ARGUEDAS was a great writer, a great scholar, and a great gentleman. No other Bolivian of our day has achieved his eminence, and he is rightfully considered one of the most distinguished historians and novelists Latin America has produced in the last fifty years. He received a part of his education in France, where he studied at the École Livre des Études Sociales, and he represented his country in Paris, London, and various South American capitals. But his heart lay always in Bolivia, and his foreign associations and experiences only sharpened his awareness of his country's problems. His *Historia general de Bolivia* is a penetrating analysis of that unhappy country's tragic century of independence, torn by anarchy and civil and foreign wars since its foundation. Its lack of many natural resources, its isolation through absence of means of communication, the concentration of its wealth in a few hands, its tremendous social problems, have all conspired to make any working solution of its ills impossible, at least until now.

Arguedas's novel *Raza de bronce*, published in 1924, was one of the earliest and best of the many fictional works that have since appeared in different parts of Latin America dealing with the oppression, exploitation, and degradation of the Indian. Arguedas was a forerunner in his realization of the problems that must be solved in those countries where the Indian is the forgotten man, the hewer of wood and the drawer of water, the creator of wealth in which he has no share, if they are to achieve stability and prosper. Arguedas is not the exponent of any ideology. He writes in a terse, limpid, almost aloof style; but underneath one feels a plea, not so much for an impersonal social justice, as for a Christian justice, a sense of the brotherhood of all men. What makes the problem of the Bolivian Indian particularly poignant is that his oppressor is less often the white man—only ten per cent of the population of Bolivia is white—than his own kind or the half-breeds.

This selection from *Raza de bronce* is a description of betrothal customs that undoubtedly date back to the Indians' remote, autochthonous past, when they were the masters of their own land, not serfs.

Race of Bronze

[ALCIDES ARGUEDAS]

AGIALI looked about him, took deep breaths of the thin, cold air, and walked along the mesa until he came to where Wata-Wara was pasturing her sheep.

The shepherdess was sitting on the ground, in the lee of a pile of rocks, mending a fishing net. She had fastened one end of it to her big toe, and her fingers darted back and forth weaving the white-threaded needles through the mesh.

"Good day, Wata-Wara," Agiali greeted her, smiling.

Without answering his greeting directly or raising her eyes from her tedious task, she asked in a calm voice, as though they had separated only the evening before:

"Did you bring back seed?"

"Yes."

"And fruit?"

"That, too."

"Some for me?" she asked, still with her head bent over her work.

He unwrapped the apples and handed them to her.

"Aren't they beautiful! How good they smell!" said Wata-Wara, taking the gift and sniffing the aroma of the fruit with delight.

Then she lined them up in her lap, on the net, and began an imaginary distribution, beginning with the biggest:

"This one is for my mother, this one for Choquehuanka; this one for my little brother, and this one for me."

And picking up the one supposed to be for her mother, she buried her teeth in it, breaking the bright, terse peel.

Agiali watched her covetously, and her voracity seemed to please him. How he would have enjoyed devouring that lovely, round little face with the caresses of desire and love!

"Is it true that Manuno died?" she asked, her mouth full and her lips wet with juice.

As the memory of the misfortune came back the lover's face clouded over. And he began to describe what had happened in detail.

"Poor soul!" said the girl indifferently, and then was silent.

"And what about you? What did you do? My mother told me you had gone to work at the ranch house."

The shepherdess paused in her work, and for the first time looked steadily at her sweetheart.

"Yes. The overseer sent for me the day after you left, and I had to go."

"Were you there many days?"

"The whole week."

"Did he treat you bad?"

The girl made a vague gesture without answering. Then she put her hand in her bosom under the tight-fitting bodice, and pulling out a little woven purse, new and of many colors, held it out to her lover, trembling with anxiety:

"He gave me this."

Agiali took it. It was warm to the touch. Through the soft mesh the circular contours of the coins showed.

Anguish like a knife thrust struck at the lad's heart at the sight of the gift. Trouche was never generous with anyone, and this must be payment for value received—

"Then," he said, and his voice was harsh, "you slept at the ranch house?"

"Yes," answered the girl in a low, guilty tone.

"Every night?"

"Every night—but—"

Agiali gave her no chance to make excuses. With one bound he covered the distance between them, grabbed her by the hair, and began to rain blows on the girl's head. Wata-Wara dropped the net and the apples and covered her face humbly with her two hands, without whimpering and with a docility like that of her dog, which was yelping timidly, circling around the couple in surprise.

"No more, Agiali, that's enough," she pleaded in a supplicating voice when it seemed to her that her fault had been sufficiently punished.

When he heard her moan he looked fixedly at her for a moment and without answering a word moved away a few steps and sat down on an outcropping of rock, his head resting in the palms of his hands, motionless, silent, looking into the distance. He was choking with rage. Not because of the act itself, but because she had disobeyed him in going to sleep at the big house.

Wata-Wara did not move from her place. She sat crying with her head bent over her lap, gently, uncomplaining; she was crying for happiness, because her lover when he learned of her fault had not asked for his ring, nor had he scorned her as though she were a beast of the field, and his blows, which had been few and almost light, revealed his love for her and his natural kindness.

After a time, seeing him sitting without making a movement, she ventured to say:

"It wasn't my fault, Agiali; he made me—"

Without raising his head, he answered in a low, dull voice:

"You're lying."

"I'm not lying, Agiali. Do believe me. As God is my witness."

The youth got to his feet and came over to her.

"You're bad; you hurt me," she said, her eyes swimming in tears as she rubbed the bruises on her face.

Agiali sat down beside her and opened the purse. It contained eight ten-cent pieces.

"Now you can buy four hens or a lamb when we get married," he said calmly.

"No, I'm saving up to buy myself a shawl, but I'm not going to marry you. You've hurt me," she replied coyly, smiling through her tears.

"If you had done as I told you, you wouldn't have stayed at the big house and we wouldn't have quarreled," the youth argued evasively.

"Do you think I did it because I wanted to?" the girl interrupted, pleased at the sight of her sweetheart's distress. "He made me do it, and if I hadn't, he would have driven us off the place, as he has done others, without letting us gather the harvest, or he would have sent my brother to the valley to wear out his oxen or to die, like Manuno. They say the reason he sent him was because his wife wouldn't give in to him."

Her allegation was reasonable, and Agiali knew it. He answered gently and humbly:

"You're right, but I'm not bad. I lost my head—"

"You won't ever whip me again because of *that?*"

Agiali frowned for a moment, and then his face turned serene.

"Never. It wasn't your fault; but him—if I could, I would eat his heart."

"So would I. We hate him, don't we?"

Agiali did not answer. He sat stroking the girl's head, his brows knitted and his jaw clenched, while his mind seemed to be far away.

In a little while he got up to go home. He told his mother the whole story.

Choquela flew into a rage. "Why should you still want to marry her?" she stormed. "You'll be fathering someone else's brat, and children cost money."

"But they're a help, too."

"No, no, they just cost money. How well I know it! Didn't I have you and the others that died?"

"If she wants to, she can do like the others: throw it into the lake or the river."

"Well, that would be a different story. But she's still such a fool. She tells everything. Why did she tell you all this, when she could just as well have kept it to herself?"

"The poor thing was probably suffering. And as she can't tell that brother of hers anything—"

"She deserves to be killed," answered Choquela, with that vindictiveness of the poor mother living at the expense of an unmarried son.

"Not her, him," the boy answered sullenly.

Days later he said to his mother:

"Forget all about what has happened, as I have done, and go pay a visit to the Coyllors. They have not come to ask for Wata-Wara's ring back, and they must be expecting you."

"Have it your own way, but you're going to father someone else's brat," she answered spitefully.

"I tell you I won't. She'll throw it to the pigs. They raise lots of them at her house, and they won't leave even the bones," the youth cut her short.

Choquela shrugged her shoulders with a contemptuous air, and went into the room where she kept her clothes and other prized possessions, and came out in a little while wearing her feast dress and carrying in her hands the gourd ornamented with multicolored fringes.

The youth looked her over and said:

"Why don't you wear your earrings and your silver pins? They'll think you have sold them and that we have nothing."

Choquela had to do as he wished. The lad's tone admitted of no argument, and besides his demand was reasonable. The poor are always looked down on, and it was her duty not to put her son at a disadvantage.

She was welcomed with much greater attentions than she had expected, and this soothed her resentment against her prospective daughter-in-law. Wata-Wara's mother came out to meet her, her arms extended toward the gourd, which Choquela offered to her at the threshold. She took a few leaves of coca from it, and put them in her mouth:

"May they be happy and never lack for food or clothing," she said, raising her eyes to heaven.

The children imitated their mother, chewing some of the leaves in sign of acceptance of the new kinship.

"Go find your sister and tell her her betrothed is here," said the mother to one of the little ones.

He went out, and the two women set to work organizing the young couple's future. They must ask for a piece of land of their own, assume the status of "people," not mere members of a family. Wata-Wara was very hard-working, saving, and knew how to run a house. From the time she was a little girl she had taken the fancy of old Choquehuanka, and had learned at his feet object lessons of order and good sense. There was not another girl who could weave such shawls and blankets or manage things so well as she. Beyond question she would make Agiali happy. For the moment she did not need a thing; she had an abundance of fine clothes, and her flocks had multiplied greatly in the last years. Like everyone else, she had little money. The bad years had swallowed up their savings, and they had to struggle without a letup to recuperate what had been lost.

Choquela did not fall short in her praises of the merits of her son. There was no better or steadier worker. Who could plow a field like him, or make use of every idle moment to catch a mess of fish in the lake? His activity, his dependability, his thrifty ways, were the envy of all. And if for the moment he was not exactly rich, he knew how to manage things so as to keep the wolf from his door.

They spent almost half a day at this game of mutual deceit.

At sunset Coyllor-Zuma and his sons came to Agiali's house. They were all dressed in their best clothes and bore the *chimo*, that is to say, another gourd full of coca. Behind them followed Wata-Wara, attired in her best finery. Over her head she wore a little square shawl covered with tassels, and she walked shyly, her head low, her cheeks red with blushes.

Agiali came to the threshold of the house to receive them. Coyllor-Zuma opened the gourd and handed it to the young man, who took a few leaves, made the sign of the cross over his mouth, and began to chew them. Choquela imitated her son.

The patio of the house was swept clear of all trash and rubbish. In the middle stood a little table, on which there was a bottle of liquor and three glasses. New blankets had been spread upon the stone seats, and their gay colors gave the gray house a cheerful air.

They began to drink.

As the sun sank from sight Agiali gave the brother of his betrothed a drum and stuck a white flag in the ground beside the table. The boy went over beside the sheepfold, and the gentle calm of the twilight was shattered as he began to beat the instrument in a special fashion, first with long, spaced blows, and then faster and louder. Tun . . . tun . . . tun . . . Tu,tun,tun,tun . . . Tu, tun, tun, tun, tun. . . .

In the neighboring houses there was a stir of activity. The peons to whom the drum had brought the news appeared behind the fence walls or at the doors of their houses. Some of them, the more curious, climbed up on the walls to see where the drumbeating was coming from. In a little while another drum answered from the house nearest that of Agiali, then another from the farthest one on the opposite bank of the river, and in a few minutes a reverberation was coming from every house, until the plain was throbbing with the deafening tumult of celebration of the joyful event. Then, plaintively, came the lament of a flute, answered first by one and then another. All echoed the same air, and the new ones that joined in augmented the sound.

Then began the procession of the peons. They came in groups of two or more. Each group was beating a drum and playing a flute. They were followed by the women, wearing their newest or least worn finery, and on the faces of all there was an expression of rejoicing and sly mischief. When they reached the patio, the women greeted Wata-Wara and the parents of the bride and groom and sat down on the stone benches, before which the gourds of coca lay. The men took off their hats, and with both hands raised in the air, hat in one, and in the other, drum, drumstick, or flute, they advanced halfway across the patio as far as the table, made a stiff bow, and then joined the group of relatives gathered by the barnyard fence.

The house was filling up. The late arrivals had to wait around the outer fringe until the first glass of liquor, served by Agiali himself and passed from hand to hand, reached them to drink a toast to the couple. Flutes and drums went on playing, and the dance began.

As the patio was too small to hold so many people, the dancers overflowed onto the plain through which the river ran. Men and women formed a circle, holding hands. Agiali began the dance, leading the chain with his sweetheart, tracing circles, obtuse angles, as the fancy moved him, sometimes alongside the river, sometimes within the shadow of the house, and from a distance the chain looked like a huge red snake dragging itself over the gray, barren plain.

Night closed in. In the high-vaulted sky the stars winked on, and the snake moved along in the darkness, tireless, and all that could be heard was the beating of the drums, the plaintive, wailing lament of the flutes, and the triumphant shout of the girls: *"Huiphala! Huipalita!"*

Suddenly as with one voice a gleeful roar echoed above the quiet plain: "Thief! Thief!"

Drums and flutes ceased to sound; the rattle of pebbles followed, and the sparks struck from the broken stones flashed in the dark.

Agiali, carrying out the age-old rite, with a swift movement had pulled his sweetheart loose from the chain, and was dragging her behind him, she feigning reluctance, while the others pretended to attack him to free the captive.

The shouts gradually died down, and silence fell, deep, deathlike, over the plain. Only in the distance rang the lover's chant of triumph:

> I bear away, away
> A little white dove I bear away. . . .

The couple reached the house, now empty and silent. They were covered with bruises from the stones that had found their mark. Agiali's head was cut, and the girl complained that her back hurt, but the breasts of both throbbed with happiness.

The youth pushed Wata-Wara into the bedroom, and locked the door behind them. . . .

Venus glowed with all her splendor in the sky.

ENRIQUE LÓPEZ ALBÚJAR

(1875–   )

FROM THE DESCRIPTIONS that have come down to us in the writings of
the Inca Garcilaso de la Vega and other early historians of Peru, it is
apparent that the laws of the benevolent despotism by which the Incas
ruled their subjects were wise, just, and inexorable. Any infraction of
the law carried severe penalties. The more exemplary the punishment,
the less frequently would it have to be employed. The smallest unit in
the vast structure of government was the *ayllu* or village, which was
ruled over by its elders in accord with laws that had been formulated
for all by a supreme council, and which were observed to the letter.
The following dramatic account of the execution of a sentence pronounced against an unrepentant criminal, literally a "fourth offender,"
by the council of elders of his village in our own times is proof of how
little the white man's civilization has impinged on the Indian's traditional way of life in the remote mountain regions of Peru. Except for
the presence of the church in the village square, and the dogs, cows,
and shotgun, all of which the Spaniards contributed, the scene might
well have taken place in pre-conquest days.

Few writers have had the opportunity and the natural gifts to observe
the Indians of the coastal plains and highlands of Peru as has Enrique
López Albújar. His duties as circuit judge made it necessary for him
to visit many remote parts of the country, and his talents as narrator
and observer have enabled him to describe the people and their customs
with unusual accuracy and dramatic vividness. He is the author of a
novel and several volumes of short stories. *Ushanan Jampi*, which is
Quechua for "the last resort," is one of his most famous.

Ushanan Jampi *

[ENRIQUE LÓPEZ ALBÚJAR]

THE square of Chupán was swarming with people. The whole village,
agog with curiosity, had assembled there from the early hours of the
morning in expectation of the solemn act of justice to which it had
been summoned the night before.

* Translated with the author's permission from *Cuentos Andinos*, by Enrique
López Albújar.

All private work and all public services had been suspended. Gathered there were the laborer, his poncho over his shoulder, smiling a foolish grin at the comments of the different groups; the tousle-haired shepherd, with his bronzed, muscular calves, serpentined with veins like lianas girding a tree trunk; the silent, crafty gaffer, chewing endlessly at his coca; the shy, neat young girl, in her billowing, black skirt, her feet clean and rubbed like bright, polished metal, her nails broken and worn down, twirling her spindle back and forth in the air as she murmured a litany of spells to ward off evil; and the young boy, in his characteristic hat with drooping brim and conical crown—a clown's hat—who shivered under the fictitious warmth of a poncho that barely reached the bend in his elbows.

And, intermingled with the crowd, dogs the color of dirty amber, sullen, consumptive, with long, angular heads, like violin cases, ribs that could be counted, shaggy hair, eyes of wolf and tail of fox, and long, jointed sinewy, legs—like those of some arachnid. Back and forth they moved, sniffing insolently at the people, questioning them with glances of restrained ferocity, letting out impatient yelps, demanding food.

The purpose of the assembly was to see justice done a member of the community from whom another, Cunce Maille, an incorrigible thief, had stolen a cow a few days before. It was a crime that had shocked everyone, not so much because of the theft in itself, as because it was the third offense. This was something unheard of in the community. It amounted to a challenge, a flouting of the stern, inflexible justice of the *yayas*, the village elders, and demanded swift, condign punishment.

Seated in front of the community house about a rustic table that had the solidity of the Incan furniture, the plenary council of the *yayas*, acting as a court of justice, sat solemn, impassive, showing no other signs of life than the steady, rhythmic movement of their mouths, which seemed to champ some invisible bit.

Suddenly the *yayas* stopped chewing, spat out the greenish wads of coca, wiped the foam from their lips with the back of their hands, and old Marcos Huancachino, who presided over the council, spoke:

"We have chewed enough. The coca will guide us when it comes time to do justice. Now let us drink, to be sure we shall do right."

And one after another they took long swallows from an enormous jug of *chacta*, served by a decurion.

"Have them bring in Cunce Maille," ordered Huancachino, when all had finished drinking.

With hands tied behind his back and led in by four stout youths, there suddenly appeared before the tribunal an Indian of indeterminate age, tall, muscular, haughty, who seemed indifferent to the insults and threats of the crowd. In this attitude, with his clothes bloodstained and torn by the rough handling of his pursuers and the teeth of the sheep dogs, the Indian looked rather the symbol of rebellion than of defeat. His pure Indian features were so well cut, his body so lithe, his glance so uncringing, his bearing so proud, that, in spite of his blood-shot eyes, he radiated attraction, the attraction aroused by those men who possess beauty and strength.

"Untie him," ordered the same voice that had ordered him brought in.

Once he was free, Maille crossed his arms, lifted his bare, disheveled head, cast a subtly contemptuous glance about the court, and waited.

"José Ponciano accuses you of having stolen his spotted cow last Wednesday and selling it in Obas. What have you got to say?"

"It's true, but last year Ponciano stole a bull from me. Now we're square."

"Why didn't you make a complaint then?"

"Because I don't need anybody to do justice for me. I can take care of it myself."

"We the *yayas* allow nobody to take justice into his own hands. Anyone who does that forfeits his rights."

Ponciano spoke up at this point:

"Maille is lying, *taita*. That bull he says I stole from him I bought from Natividad Huailas. He is here; let him speak."

"That is true, *taita*," answered an Indian, stepping forward to the table.

"You dog!" shouted Maille, turning fiercely toward Huailas. "You're as big a thief as Ponciano. Everything you sell is stolen. Here everybody steals."

At this insult the *yayas*, who had seemed to be dozing, came to with a jerk, while many of the villagers raised their cudgels in protest and brandished them, muttering fiercely. But the head of the council, more imperturbable than ever, after imposing silence with a commanding gesture, spoke:

"Cunce Maille, you have committed an outrage that is an offense to all. We could punish you by handing you over to the justice of the people, but that would be taking unfair advantage of our authority."

And turning to the plaintiff José Ponciano, who from the end of the table where he stood was looking menacingly at Maille, he said:

"How much do you calculate your cow was worth, Ponciano?"

"Thirty soles, *taita*. She was ready to calve."

In view of the answer the presiding *yaya* turned to the assembly:

"Who knows Ponciano's cow? How much would Ponciano's cow be worth?"

Many spoke up at the same time to say that they knew the animal and that it was really worth the thirty soles at which its owner had valued it.

"Did you hear, Maille?" asked the president of the defendant.

"I heard, but I have no money to pay him."

"You have cattle, you have land, you have a house. We shall impound one of your herd, and as you cannot stay here, for this is the third time you have been brought before us charged with stealing, you will leave Chupán at once and forever. The first time we advised you what you should do to mend your ways and become an honest man again; you did not do this. You scoffed at the advice. The second time we tried to settle things between you and Felipe Tacuche, from whom you stole ten sheep. Again you paid no heed to the advice, for you have not made up with the man you offended, and you threaten him constantly. Today, it was Ponciano's turn to lose, and tomorrow it will be someone else. You are a danger to all. The moment has come to drive you out and apply the *jitarishum*, the expulsion, to you. You will go and never return. If you come back you know what awaits you; we will take you, and you will suffer *ushanan-jampi*. Have you listened carefully, Cunce Maille?"

Maille shrugged his shoulders, looked disdainfully at the council, put his hand into his coca pouch, which by some miracle he had managed to keep when he was captured, and, taking out a pinch of coca, began to chew it slowly.

The president of the *yayas*, not in the least daunted by this tacit defiance of the accused, turning to his colleagues, spoke once more:

"Fellow members, this man standing before us is Cunce Maille, who has been accused of stealing in our community for the third time. The crime is evident; he has not denied it; he has not proved his innocence. What shall we do with him?"

"Drive him away from here; apply the expulsion to him," answered the *yayas* with one voice, then turning silent and impassive once more.

"Have you heard, Maille? We have tried to make an honest man of you, but you have not wished it so. You are now banned from the community forever."

Then, rising to his feet and addressing the villagers, he added in a solemn tone, louder than he had used heretofore:

"This man you see here is Cunce Maille, whom we are expelling from the community as a thief. If he should ever attempt to return to our lands anyone of you may kill him. Do not forget it. Decurions, take that man and follow us."

And the *yayas*, followed by the accused and the multitude, left the square, crossed the village, and began to descend a steep path in the midst of an awesome silence broken only by the slapping of sandals. Everyone was dumb, bemused, awed. Even the dogs, restless and noisy before, trotted along silently, ears and tail hanging, as though aware of the solemnity of what was taking place.

After a quarter of an hour's march down a steep path rough with stones and hedged by thorned, tentacled cactus like menacing octopuses, the president of the *yayas* raised his mayor's wand, adorned with multicolored ribbons and tin-foil flowers, and the strange procession stopped at the edge of the brook that separates the lands of Chupán from those of Obas.

"Let go of that man," said the *yaya* carrying the wand.

And turning to the criminal:

"Cunce Maille, from this moment you are not to set foot on our lands again, because our protecting spirits would be angered and as a result of their anger our crops would fail and the streams dry up and the plague come. Cross the brook and depart from here forever."

Maille turned to the crowd, which with an expression of horror and indignation more feigned that real had followed the solemn words of the *yaya*. After spitting contemptuously on the ground with that contempt that only the face of an Indian can express, he snarled at them:

"Shit faces."

And with four bounds he crossed the waters of the Chillán and disappeared from sight behind the bushes on the opposite bank, while the dogs, startled at the sight of a man running, broke their long silence, barking furiously, but without venturing to enter the clear, swift-moving waters of the brook.

If to any man expulsion is an affront, to an Indian, and an Indian like Cunce Maille, expulsion from the community is all possible affronts, the sum of all suffering and the loss of everything worth while: cabin, land, cattle, gods and family. Above all, the cabin.

Jitarishum is the civil death of the culprit, a death from which there is no return, which condemns the Indian to perpetual ostracism and marks him with a brand that closes the doors of the community to him forever. All that is left to him is his life, to wander about ravines, highlands, hills, and woods, or to go down to the cities, to live under the yoke of the white man, which for an Indian used to the free, untrammeled life of the highlands is a torment and a disgrace.

And Cunce Maille, with his rebellious, fractious nature, would never be able to resign himself to the expulsion he had just suffered. There were two things that drew him irresistibly to the land he had been driven from: his mother and his cabin. What was going to become of his mother without him? This thought nagged at him and led him to conceive the most reckless plans. Roweled by his memories, his homesick heart charged with hate, like a cloud with electricity, quickly wearied of the aimless, marauding life that had been forced upon him, late one night he returned across the same brook he had passed a month before, in broad daylight, under the silence of the hostile villagers, and the yapping of the pack of starved curs.

In spite of his bravery, which had stood the test a hundred times, as Maille set foot on the forbidden land he felt as though a cold hand had clutched his heart, and a shiver of fear ran through him. Fear? Of what? Of death? But what did death matter to him who was accustomed to risk his life at the drop of a hat? Besides, didn't he have his rifle and his hundred bullets? Enough to fight the whole village and make his escape whenever he wanted to.

And the Indian, gun cocked, ear alert, eying every bush warily, crept along the *via crucis* of the hillside path down which the natives of Chupán descended but never returned, as it was reserved for the solemn occasions of their stern justice. It was the Tarpeian Rock of the village.

Maille overcame all the difficulties of the ascent, and once in the village he stopped before a cabin and uttered a short, guttural cry. The door opened, and two arms twined themselves about the exile's neck as a voice murmured:

"Come in, my son, come in. For many nights your mother has not slept waiting for you. Do you think anyone saw you?"

Maille's answer was a shrug of his shoulders as he crossed the doorstep.

But the council of the *yayas*, knowing from experience how dear an Indian's home is to him, the sorrow that comes over him when he has to leave it, and the desperation with which he clings to everything that is his, to the point of dying of grief if impotent to recover it, reasoned: "Maille will be coming back one of these nights; Maille is bold, he has no fear of us, he holds us in contempt, and when the desire comes upon him to chew coca under his own roof at the side of old Nastasia, nothing in the world will stop him."

And the *yayas* reasoned correctly. The cabin would be the trap into which the criminal would fall one day. And they arranged to watch it day and night, with truly Indian cunning and tenacity.

For this reason that night Cunce Maille had hardly crossed his threshold when a spy raced with the news to the president of the *yayas*.

"Cunce Maille has just gone into his house, *taita*. Nastasia opened the door to him," he gasped, out of breath, trembling, still gripped by fear, like a dog suddenly come face to face with a lion.

"Are you sure, Santos?"

"Oh, yes, *taita*. Nastasia threw her arms around him. Who else would old Nastasia be putting her arms around, *taita?* It's Cunce—"

"Is he armed?"

"He's carrying his rifle, *taita.* If we're going to get him we must all go armed. Cunce is bad, and he's a good shot."

The news spread through the village with the speed of electricity. "Cunce Maille has come back. Cunce Maille has come back." The phrase ran from lip to lip. Groups were immediately formed. The men got out their big clubs—the clubs for such moments of tragedy; the women squatted in circles at the door of their houses; and the dogs, nervous, instinctively aware that something was happening, began to call and dialogue among themselves.

"Listen, Cunce," whispered old Nastasia, who with her ear to the crack of the door was alert for every sound, while he sat on a bench, impassively chewing coca, as though he had forgotten everything else in the world. "I hear steps, and the dogs are asking each other who has come to the village. Don't you hear? They must have seen you. Why did you come, oh, my son!"

Cunce gave a disdainful shrug and said only:

"Well, I've seen you, old lady, and I've had me a good chew in my own house. I'm going now; I'll be back another day."

The Indian got to his feet, avoiding his mother's embrace with feigned brusqueness, and, opening the door, bent to the ground and peered out. Nothing—neither noise nor suspicious shadows; a faint, rose-colored light was beginning to tinge the crest of the mountains.

But Maille, Indian that he was, was too astute and suspicious to trust this silence. He ordered his mother to go into the other room and lie on the floor face down; then he took a step back to gain momentum, and with a great sideways leap was out of the door and running like a deer. A volley rang out, and a hail of lead perforated the door of the cabin, as innumerable groups of Indians, carrying arms of different sorts, appeared on all sides shouting: "Death to Cunce Maille! *Ushanan Jampi! Ushanan Jampi!*"

Maille barely managed to run some hundred paces when another volley of fire made him turn back, and in four feline bounds he climbed the bell tower of the church, from which point of vantage, determined and fierce, he began to fire with unerring aim at the vanguard of his pursuers.

A scene began to unfold the like of which had never been seen, even among those men accustomed to every kind of horror and cruelty, something which beginning as an act of defiance, bade fair to become a monstrous heroism worthy of an epic.

To every ten shots of the besiegers, harmless shots from antiquated rifles, ailing shotguns made for unsteady hands, the exile answered with one that invariably found its mark, giving rise to one groan and a hundred screams. At the end of two hours he had put out of the fight a dozen of his attackers, among them one of the *yayas*, which further infuriated the whole village.

"Take that, dogs!" shouted Maille each time he dropped an Indian. "Before you take me I'll kill fifty of you. Cunce Maille is worth fifty of you dogs of Chupán. Where is Marco Huacachino? Would he like to put a little lime in his mouth with this *shipina?*"

And the *shipina* was the barrel of the gun, which moved, menacing and deadly, from side to side.

Confronted with this situation, whose horror seemed as though it would never end, the *yayas* after long deliberation decided to parley with the rebel. The spokesman was to offer him everything, even his life, and once he was down among them, they would see how to get out of keeping their promise. The man needed for the job was someone as stouthearted and sly as Maille himself and able to win over the most suspicious with his guile.

Somebody suggested José Facundo. "That's the man," exclaimed the rest, "Facundo can fool a fox and talk a bird off a bush."

Facundo, after calmly accepting the honorable commission, leaned his gun against the wall behind which he had been parapeted, sat down, took a handful of coca out of his pouch, and chewed it religiously for some ten long minutes. Satisfied with the taste, which augured well for his undertaking, he jumped over the wall and rushed toward the church tower, leaping, zigzagging, shouting as he ran:

"Friend Cunce! Friend Cunce! Facundo wants to talk to you."

Cunce Maille let him come on, and when he saw him sit down on the first step of the stairs, he asked him:

"What do you want, Facundo?"

"I am here to ask you to come down and go away."

"Who sent you?"

"The *yayas*."

"The *yayas* are sons of the devil who when they sniff blood want to drink it. Maybe they want to drink mine?"

"No; the *yayas* have told me to tell you that if you wish, they will embrace you and take a drink of *chacta* from the same jar with you, and will let you go if you promise never to come back."

"They wanted to kill me."

"Not they; *ushanan jampi*, our law *ushanan jampi*, the same for all. But this time they will waive it for you. They are astonished at your bravery. They have consulted our great *jirca-yayac*, and he has said they are not to touch you. The coca has told them the same thing. They are sorry."

Cunce Maille hesitated, but realizing that he could not continue indefinitely as he was, that a moment would come when his ammunition would get low and they could starve him out, he finally said as he came down the steps:

"I don't want any embraces or *chacta*. Let all the *yayas* come here unarmed and from a distance of twenty paces swear by our gods that they will let me go without bothering me."

What Maille was asking was something unheard of, something that Facundo could not promise, not only because he had not been authorized to do so, but because the power of *ushanan jampi* was such as to make an oath worthless.

Facundo hesitated, but only for a second. Then laughing, with a gesture like that of a dog whose tail has just been stepped on, he answered:

"I am here to offer you anything you ask. You are like a brother to me, and I offer my brother whatever he wants."

Then holding out his arms, he added:

"Cunce, haven't you an embrace for your brother Facundo? I am not a *yaya;* tomorrow I want to be able to tell all Chupán that I have embraced a man as brave as you."

The frown disappeared from Maille's brow, he smiled at the flattering words, and, setting down his rifle, flung himself into Facundo's arms. Instead of the brief, warm embrace he expected, what Maille felt were two sinewy arms fastening about his neck, almost strangling him. Maille instantly realized the trap that had been set for him and, as swift as a tiger, he clasped his adversary still more tightly, lifted him off his feet, and attempted to climb back up the stairs with him. But as he set his foot on the first step, Facundo, who had kept his wits about him, gave a sharp jerk of his hips, making Maille lose his footing, and they both fell to the ground, vomiting insults and threats. After a violent struggle Maille managed to get on top of his opponent.

"Dog! Bigger dog than the *yayas!*" screamed Maille, quivering with rage. "I am going to cut you into meat for the dogs up there, but first I'm going to eat your tongue."

Facundo closed his eyes and did nothing but scream at the top of his lungs:

"Here he is! Here he is! Here he is! *Ushanan Jampi!*"

"Shut up, traitor!" roared Maille, driving his fist into his mouth, and, grabbing him by the throat, he squeezed it so hard that Facundo's tongue burst out, a huge, slavering tongue that threshed about like the tail of a hooked fish, while at the same time his eyes rolled up in his head and a long shudder ran through his body.

Maille smiled diabolically; he pulled out his knife, severed his victim's tongue with one slash, and got to his feet to return to the bell tower. But the besiegers had taken advantage of the fight and had closed in upon him. A blow over the head from a club dazed him; a knife thrust in the back made him reel; a stone hit him in the breast, and he dropped his knife and put his hand to his wound. Yet he had strength enough to clear a path for himself through the crowd with his fists and his feet and, fighting a rearguard action, he managed to reach his house. But the villagers who were on his heels swarmed in after him just as he fell into his mother's arms. Ten knives buried themselves in his body.

"Don't do that to him, *taitas*, it makes my heart hurt," pleaded old Nastasia as she fell backwards, her face splashed with blood, under the weight of the inert body of her son and the fierce attack.

A horrible scene, a cannibal-like orgy, followed. When the knives were weary of stabbing they began to slice, cut, dismember. As one hand tore out the heart, another gouged out the eyes, another slashed out the tongue, another ripped out the bowels. And all this accompanied by shouts, peals of laughter, insults, maledictions, and the fierce barking of the dogs, which, through the legs of the assassins, snatched mouthfuls of flesh from the corpse and buried their sharp muzzles in the pool of blood.

"Let's drag him," a voice called out.

"Drag him," echoed a hundred more.

"To the ravine."

A rope was quickly tied about his neck, and the dragging began. First around the village, by order of the *yayas*, so that all might see how the law *ushanan jampi* had been carried out, then down the cactus path.

When they reached the bottom of the ravine, through which the Chillán runs, all that was left of Cunce Maille was the head and part of the spine. The rest had been left on the cactus, on the rocks, and between the insatiable jaws of the dogs.

Six months later under the lintel of the door of the deserted, ill-omened house of the Mailles there could still be seen a kind of festoon of dry, twisted, greasy, yellowish tatters: the intestines of Cunce Maille, which had been ordered hung there by the implacable justice of the *yayas*.

VENTURA GARCÍA CALDERÓN

(1885–   )

THE PRECEDING selection, *Ushanan Jampi*, affords us an example of the survival of a pre-conquest concept of justice among the descendants of the Incas. In *The Pin*, Ventura García Calderón, another Peruvian, gives us an equally dramatic instance of the survival of the medieval code of honor among the descendants of the conquistadors.

The colonial epoch was the Middle Ages of Latin America. The conquistadors lived like medieval barons on their vast estates, which they had received from the crown in return for their services. A special code of laws had been drawn up by the Spanish monarchs for the protection of the Indians, but these were more honored in the breach than in the observance, and the powerful landowner on his remote holdings was more often than not lord of life and death, not only over his servants, but over his whole family. As for a man's wiping out with blood an offense to his honor, this was not only accepted, but almost demanded. Until recently the conditions of life outside the cities had changed very little in the last three hundred years. It is not surprising that the mental outlook of the people should resemble that of their forefathers.

Ventura García Calderón is one of the group of Latin American writers who won their early prestige in Europe shortly after the turn of the century. He lived for years in Paris, where he was one of the founders of the *Revue de l'Amérique latine*. He is a poet, critic, journalist, novelist, and short-story writer. His work is characterized by that refinement, mordant wit, and grace which, if not the prerogative of the sons of Lima, is certainly typical of them. He has represented his country in a number of foreign capitals, and is at present Minister of Peru in Geneva.

In *The Pin*, from his volume of short stories *La venganza del condor*, he has skillfully depicted the adaptation of the stern Calderonian code of honor of Spain to the Peruvian background.

The Pin *

[VENTURA GARCÍA CALDERÓN]

THE horse collapsed, dying, soaked with sweat and blood, as the rider leaped to the ground at the foot of the massive stairway of the Ticabamba ranch. Above the heavy cedar balcony appeared the stern head of the owner Don Timoteo Mondaraz. In a bantering bass voice the imposing old man called out to the visitor, who was trembling:

"What ails you, Borradito? Why, your knees are knocking together. Speak up, man, we don't eat people alive here—"

Borradito, so nicknamed through the valley because of his pockmarked face, clutched his straw hat desperately in his hands and tried to explain so many things at the same time—the sudden tragedy, his gallop of twenty leagues that night, with orders to get to his destination as quickly as he could, even if it killed the horse—that for a moment he could not get a word out. Suddenly, without breathing, he poured forth in a jumble:

"Master, I am here to tell you that Mr. Conrado told me to tell you that just last night Miss Grimanesa took sick and died."

It must have been by a special dispensation of Providence that Don Timoteo did not whip out his revolver, as he always did when excited, but he clutched the servant's arm as though to tear further details out by the roots.

"Last night—dead—Grimanesa?"

He must have sensed something in Borradito's vague explanation, for without saying any more, leaving orders that his daughter Ana María was not to be awakened, he went himself to saddle his best riding horse. In a few moments he was on his way to the ranch of his son-in-law Conrado Basadre, who the year before had married Grimanesa, that lovely, pale Amazon, the best catch in the whole valley. The wedding was like a festival, with fireworks, Indian women dancing in their purple dresses, Indians still lamenting the death of the Incas, which took place centuries before, but which still lives on in the dirges of the downtrodden race, like the lamentations for Zion in the sublime stubbornness of the Bible. Then along the best paths through the planted fields there had come the procession carrying ancient images of saints. And the happy marriage of his lovely girl to handsome, dashing Conrado Basadre had ended like this—

Burying his buck spurs in the horse's flanks, Don Timoteo recalled that festival with horror. He was trying to make it to Sincavilca, the estate of the Basadres, in four hours.

* Translated with the author's permission from *La venganza del condor* by Ventura García Calderón.

Late that afternoon there came the sound of another swift gallop clattering over the stones of the mountain road. To be on the safe side the old man fired a shot into the air, calling out:

"Who goes?"

The rider coming toward him reined in his horse, and in a voice that could not conceal his emotion, called out in turn:

"Don't you know me, sir? The overseer of Sincavilca. I'm going for the priest."

The rancher was so upset that he did not ask why he was hurrying so fast to get a priest when Grimanesa was dead, or why the chaplain was not at the ranch. He waved good-bye with his hand, and urged on his mount, which set off at a gallop, its flanks running blood.

Over the huge gate that closed the courtyard of the ranch the silence hung like a pall. Even the dogs were silent in the presence of death. The great doors, with their silver nailheads of colonial days, were draped with black crepe in the form of a cross. Don Timoteo crossed the vast, deserted rooms without removing his spurs till he reached the bedroom of the dead woman, where Conrado Basadre sat sobbing. In a voice choked with tears the old man asked him to leave him there for a moment alone. And after closing the door with his own hands he gave himself over to his grief for hours, insulting the saints, calling Grimanesa by her name, kissing her limp hand, which fell back upon the sheet, covered with Cape jessamine and wallflowers. Grave and solemn for the first time in her life, Grimanesa lay like a saint, her hair hidden under the coif of the Carmelite nuns, and her lovely body imprisoned in the habit, as was the religious custom of the valley. On her breast they had laid a tremendous silver crucifix that one of her grandfathers had used to brain Indians in an uprising long ago.

As Don Timoteo bent over to kiss the sacred emblem the corpse's habit parted, and he observed something that horrified him, for he drew back from the body with a strange revulsion. Looking quickly about him, he hid something under his poncho, and without taking leave of anybody, mounted and returned to Ticabamba that same night.

For six months there was no communication from one ranch to the other, nor was there any explanation of this silence. They had not even gone to the funeral. Don Timoteo spent his time shut up in his room redolent of storax, deaf to the pleas of Ana María, as beautiful as her sister Grimanesa, who lived in adoration and fear of her strong-willed father. She was never able to find out the reason for the change that had come over him, or why Conrado Basadre never visited them.

But one bright Sunday in June, Don Timoteo arose in a good humor and suggested to Ana María that they go over to Sincavilca after Mass. The decision was so surprising that the girl wandered about the house all morning in amazement, trying on in front of the mirror her long riding habit and her Panama hat, which she had fastened to her glossy hair with a long gold hatpin. When her father saw her he said sharply, looking at the pin:

"Take that ugly thing off this minute."

With a sigh Ana María obeyed, resigned, as always, to her father's unpredictable moods.

When they reached Sincavilca, Conrado was breaking a colt, his head bare to the sun, as handsome and dashing as ever in his black saddle with its silver nailheads and trimmings. He leaped clear of the horse with one bound, and at the sight of Ana María, so like her sister in beguiling charm, he stood gazing at her for a long time, forgetful of everything else.

Nobody spoke of their bereavement or mentioned Grimanesa's name, but Conrado filled Ana María's arms with his beautiful, flesh-petaled Cape jessamine. They did not even visit the dead woman's grave, and there was a painful silence when the old nurse came in sobbing to embrace "*la niña*":

"Jesus, Mary, and Joseph, as beautiful as my mistress! Like a cherry!"

From then on, the visit to Sincavilca was repeated every Sunday. Conrado and Ana María spent the day feasting their eyes on one another and holding hands when the old man turned his head to look at a new field of ripe cane. And one glorious Monday, after the bright Sunday of their first kiss, Conrado appeared at Ticabamba, attired in all the splendor of a feast day, his violet poncho thrown across the sheepskin saddle pad, and his horse, curried and combed until it shone, prancing elegantly and with neck arched until its muzzle touched its breast, like the palfreys of the liberators.

With the solemnity befitting a great moment he inquired for the rancher, and when he spoke to him he did not use the usual respectful "Don Timoteo," but murmured, as in the days when he was courting Grimanesa:

"I should like to speak to you, Father."

They went into the old-fashioned drawing-room, where the portrait of the dead daughter still hung. The old man sat in silence while Conrado with great embarrassment explained in a hesitant, abashed voice that he would like to marry Ana María. A long pause followed. Don Timoteo sat with his eyes closed, as though he had fallen asleep. Then swiftly, lithely, as though the years had passed over his robust rancher's body without leaving an impress, he got up and opened an iron box, whose old and complicated lock had to be gently coaxed open. Still silent, he took out of it a gold pin. It was one of those stick-pins the Indian women use to hold their shawls together, the head shaped like a coca leaf, but longer, sharper, and stained dark with blood.

When Conrado saw it he fell to his knees, whimpering like a convicted criminal.

"Grimanesa, my poor Grimanesa!"

But with a brusque gesture the old man indicated that it was not the moment for tears. Making a superhuman effort to control his growing distress, he muttered in a voice so blurred that his words could hardly be made out:

"Yes, I took it from her breast as she lay dead— You had driven this pin into her heart— Isn't that true?— Had she been unfaithful?"

"Yes, Father."

"Did she repent as she died?"

"Yes, Father."

"Does anybody know it?"

"No, Father."

"Was it with the overseer?"

"Yes, Father."

"Why didn't you kill him too?"

"He ran away like a coward."

"Do you swear to kill him if he comes back?"

"Yes, Father."

The old man cleared his throat solemnly, clasped Conrado by the hand, and said in a voice almost too low to hear:

"If this one deceives you, do the same with her. Here!"

And he solemnly handed over to him the gold pin, as in olden times a sword was handed to a newly made knight. Then pushing him roughly away, and putting his hand over his aching heart, he made a sign to his son-in-law to leave the room, for it was not good for anyone to see stern, implacable Don Timoteo Mondaraz weeping.

CIRO ALEGRÍA

(1909–   )

Ciro Alegría is generally recognized as the outstanding novelist of his generation in Latin America. His first novel, *La serpiente de oro*, in 1935 won first prize in a contest sponsored by the publishing house of Nascimento in Santiago de Chile; his second, *Los perros hambrientos*, obtained a similar award from Zig-Zag in that same city in 1938; and in 1941 he was awarded first prize in the Latin American novel contest sponsored by Farrar & Rinehart of New York for his novel *El mundo es ancho y ajeno*, which is known in its English version as *Broad and Alien Is the World*. All these novels have been translated into a number of different languages.

Perhaps the fact that he was born and raised in one of the outlying provinces of Peru, and that he spent seven years in exile in Chile because of his activities against the governments of Sánchez Cerro and Benavides, has given Alegría perspective and that broad, all-encompassing vision of his country which is one of the unique features of his work. *La serpiente de oro* deals with the life of the inhabitants of the banks of the Marañón River; *Los perros hambrientos*, with the life of a group of outlaws in the mountain highlands. In *El mundo es ancho y ajeno* these and the other distinct and separate worlds that make up Peru come into being, and there is an interplay between them that gives the work a symphonic quality.

Like many others of his contemporaries, Alegría is pleading for justice for the Indian, and for his incorporation into the fabric of Peruvian society. But his art surpasses his thesis. He has that greatest of gifts a novelist can possess, the ability to create characters who really live. No one who has read *Broad and Alien Is the World* can ever forget the wise, prudent old Indian mayor who is blood kin of Pedro Crespo, the Mayor of Zalamea in Calderón's great drama of the same name, or the bandit Fiero Vázquez, Natasha, the old wise woman, and so many others. Moreover, Alegría's artistic intuition transcends the limits of the local problem of the Indians of Peru, and their tragedy acquires universal proportions. It becomes the tragedy of the poor and helpless everywhere who by the tricks of a law at the service of the powerful are despoiled of their little possessions, their dignity, and their hopes.

Alegría has the eye of a painter for the various aspects of his land: the lush, tropical lowlands, the cool uplands with their austere beauty of light and coloring, the overpowering jungle, the bleak, frozen mountains. His style is peculiarly his own: a blend of the language that has been preserved in the more remote regions of Peru, rich, sober, with a somewhat archaic flavor, the crisp, direct manner that has probably come from his work as a journalist, and with a lyrical tone that reveals the poet who walks hand in hand with the novelist.

The folklore elements are unusually abundant in Alegría's work. In it are to be found the age-old rites and traditions of the Indians, the superstitions and beliefs brought in by the Spaniards; in many cases the two have become fused and indistinguishable. The following selection from *Broad and Alien Is the World* is a typically Indian legend.

Ayaymama *

[CIRO ALEGRÍA]

IN the quiet of the forest Augusto saw many birds. He was surprised by the strangeness of the *huancavi*, a brave hunter of poisonous snakes, and by the kingfisher, which feeds on fish. Sitting on a branch that overhangs the water, it lets its droppings, which contain seeds, fall in as bait, and then plunges in and brings out the fish in its beak the minute it comes near. He used to watch the toucan shake the chalice-shaped leaves to get the water out of them into its thick, coarse beak, or, when it rains, stand with its bill open, because it cannot drink any other way; and the *mariquinas*, with their sweet, merry song, that fly in flocks along the riverbank. These were the most visible. The others lived in the high, sunlit foliage of the jungles and, once in a while, flitted before the rubber gatherers like a wisp of fire or gold or emerald or snow. But their gay chirping told of their presence.

And one night when an *ayaymama* was singing near Canuco a rubber gatherer told one of the many legends about it. Because in the depths of the tropical forest, while the moon silvers the tops of the immense trees and the waters of the vast rivers, the *ayaymama* sings long and mournfully. It seems to say, "Ay, ay, mama." It is a bird nobody has ever seen and is known only by its song. All this comes from an evil spell cast by Chullachaqui. This is how it happened.

* Reprinted from *Broad and Alien Is the World* by Ciro Alegría, translated by Harriet de Onís, by permission of Rinehart & Co., Inc. Copyright 1941 by Rinehart & Co., Inc.

Long ago, a very long time ago on the banks of a river that flowed into the Napo—which is a river that winds through the jungle and empties into the Amazon—the Secoya Indians lived whose chief was Coranke. Like all the natives he had a cabin of palm-tree trunks, thatched over with leaves from the same plant. There he stayed with his wife, who was called Nara, and their little daughter. Yet to say he stayed there is just a manner of speaking, for Coranke was almost never at home. He was a strong, brave man who was always in the heart of the jungle engaged in fighting or hunting. Wherever he turned his eye there his arrow flew, and he wielded his wooden club with a strength nobody could equal. Wild turkeys, tapirs, and deer fell, pierced through, and more than one jaguar, trying to spring on him by surprise, dropped to the ground, its skull crushed with a blow from his club. His enemies fled from him.

Nara was as beautiful and industrious as Coranke was strong and brave. Her eyes were deep like the river, her lips were red like ripe fruits, her hair was black as a raven's wing, and her skin was as smooth as cedar wood. She could weave cotton into tunics and blankets, and plait hammocks from the fiber of the *shambira* palm, which is very supple, and mold pots and water jugs from clay, and cultivate the garden that lay beside the cabin where corn, yuccas, and bananas flourished.

Their little daughter, who was still very small, had Coranke's strength and Nara's beauty, and was like a beautiful jungle flower.

But at this point Chullachaqui had to begin his meddling. He is the evil spirit of the forest, who looks like a man except for the fact that one of his feet is the hoof of a goat or a deer. There is no more perverse creature living. He is the scourge of the natives as well as of the white men who go into the jungle to cut mahogany or cedar, or to hunt lizards and anacondas for their skin, or to gather rubber. Chullachaqui drowns them in swamps or rivers, makes them lose their way in the maze of the forest, or attacks them in the shape of a wild animal. It is bad to cross his path, but it is worse if he crosses yours.

One day Chullachaqui happened to be passing in the neighborhood of the chief's cabin and saw Nara. To see her and fall in love with her was all one. And as he can take the form of any animal that he wants to, sometimes he changed himself into a bird, and at others, into an insect, so as to be near her and to be able to look at her as much as he wanted to without frightening her.

But soon he tired of this and wanted to take Nara away with him. So he went into the forest, changed himself back to his own shape, and so as not to appear before her naked, he lay in wait for a poor Indian who was hunting there, killed him, and stole his tunic which was long and covered up his goat foot. Disguised this way he went to the river and took a canoe which a boy, who had been sent by his parents to gather some healing herbs, had left on the bank. He is so wicked that he did not mind killing the Indian in the forest nor leaving the boy there in the jungle with no way to get home. He rowed along till he came to the chief's house which was on one of the riverbanks.

"Nara, beautiful Nara, wife of Chief Coranke," he said as he drew in, "I am a hungry traveler. Give me food—"

Beautiful Nara filled half a gourd shell with yuccas and sweet corn and bananas. Sitting at the door of the cabin Chullachaqui ate slowly, looking at Nara, and then said:

"Beautiful Nara, I am not a hungry traveler, as you think, and I am here only because of you. I adore your beauty and I cannot live without it. Come with me!"

Nara answered:

"I cannot leave Chief Coranke."

Then Chullachaqui began to plead and weep and weep and plead with Nara to go away with him.

"I will not leave Chief Coranke," said Nara.

Chullachaqui went sadly toward the canoe, very sadly got into it, and rowed down the river, disappearing in the distance.

Nara noticed the footprints the visitor had left in the sand on the riverbank, and when she saw that one print was that of a foot and the other of a hoof, she exclaimed:

"That was Chullachaqui."

But she did not say anything to Chief Coranke when he came back from his travels, so as not to expose him to the wrath of the evil one.

Six months went by and, late in the afternoon of the last day of the six months, a mighty chief stopped his great canoe in front of the cabin. He wore a rich tunic and his head was adorned with beautiful plumes, and his neck with heavy necklaces.

"Nara, beautiful Nara," he said, coming ashore and showing her a thousand gifts. "You can see that I am powerful. The jungle is my domain. Come with me and it will be yours."

He had brought the most beautiful flowers of the forest, and all the sweetest fruits, and all the most beautiful things—blankets, dishes, hammocks, tunics, necklaces of teeth and of seeds—that the different tribes of the jungle make. On one of Chullachaqui's hands sat a white parrot and on the other a wild turkey as black as night.

"I see and know that you are powerful," answered Nara, glancing at his footprints which confirmed her suspicions. "But for nothing in the world will I leave Chief Coranke."

Then Chullachaqui called out and the anaconda came out of the river, and he gave another cry and the jaguar came out of the forest. And on his one hand the anaconda rolled up its huge flexible body, and the jaguar arched its back on the other.

"You see, now," said Chullachaqui, "I am the master of the jungle and of the animals in the jungle. I will kill you if you do not come with me."

"I don't care," answered Nara.

"I will kill Chief Coranke," replied Chullachaqui.

"He would prefer to die," answered Nara.

Then the evil one pondered a moment and said:

"I could take you by force, but I don't want you to be sad with me for that would be unpleasant. I will return, as I have today, in six months, and if you refuse to come with me I will give you a terrible punishment."

The anaconda returned to the river and the jaguar to the jungle, and Chullachaqui went back to the canoe carrying away his gifts, sad, very sad, and got into it and disappeared once more down the river.

When Coranke returned from his hunting Nara told him everything, for she had to, and the chief decided he would stay home at the time Chullachaqui had promised to return, to protect Nara and their daughter.

And so he did. He put a new cord on his bow, sharpened his arrows, and stayed around the cabin. Then one day, when Nara was out in the cornfield, Chullachaqui suddenly appeared before her.

"Come with me," he said. "It is the last time I'm going to ask you. If you don't come I will turn your daughter into a bird who will mourn forever in the forest and will be so shy that nobody can ever see her; for the day she is seen the spell will be broken, and she will resume her human shape. Come, come with me, I am asking you for the last time. If not—"

But Nara, mastering the fright the threat had caused her, began to cry out:

"Coranke! Coranke!"

The chief came quickly with drawn bow and swift arrow, ready to pierce Chullachaqui's heart, but he had already fled into the jungle.

The parents ran to the spot where their little daughter lay sleeping, but the hammock was empty. And out of the rustling depths of the jungle they heard for the first time that mournful cry, "Ay, ay, mama," which gives its name to the enchanted bird.

Nara and Coranke grew old quickly and died from the sorrow of hearing the sad voice of their little daughter who had been changed to a bird so shy it could not even be seen.

The *ayaymama* still sings, especially on moonlit nights, and the men of the jungle always peer into the thick foliage in the hope of liberating this unfortunate human being. It is very sad that nobody has yet been able to see it.

MARIANO LATORRE

(1886–   )

WHETHER OR NOT Mariano Latorre is the founder of the school of Creole literature in Chile, as certain critics assert, might be open to discussion, but there can be no doubt that he is its most gifted cultivator. All of Chile—mountain, valley, and sea—is to be found in his novels and short stories. In part his work is that of a landscapist; he has painted the different physical aspects of his country with the brilliance and sweep of a mural decorator, and at the same time with the delicacy and eye for detail of a miniaturist. With equal skill he has depicted the inhabitants of these different regions. "Depicted" is an inadequate term for Latorre's accomplishment. He has really created them by the keenness of his observation and the depth of his understanding. In his early work his characters form a part of the landscape and are in a sense an outgrowth of it. But in his later work, as his art matures, they emerge from it, formed and conditioned by it, to be sure, but with a vigorous, pulsating life of their own.

Although he has devoted his life to his writing and teaching, Mariano Latorre has not inhabited an ivory tower. He knows every inch of his native land and has spent his leisure hours in close contact with its people. Fortune has not pampered the Chileans. They have had to struggle hard to wrest a living from their meager little patches of land in the narrow valleys or hire themselves out to work the mines or the ranches of the wealthy landowners. Many of the men have left their homes to earn a living from the sea, and the women have had to remain behind, taking over the men's duties. In spite of the contact with the outside world which their seafaring life has given them, and in spite of a large foreign immigration, the Chileans have preserved to a remarkable degree the traditional, folkloric elements of their Spanish and Indian heritage. In the following short story, which is one of Latorre's favorites among his work, from the volume *Hombres y zorros*, he gives a remarkable account of the customs and ceremonies attendant upon the funeral services for a woman who had sinned greatly and whose soul seems the certain prize of the Devil.

The Old Woman of Peralillo *

[MARIANO LATORRE]

STRETCHED out on the hard floor of the rustic room, she lay dying, as I stepped over the thick plank that served as the threshold of the low door. It was as though I had entered a cave shrouded in cobwebs. A flickering candle on the window sill cast moving outlines of objects and people against the murky background.

This was how my real acquaintance with Doña Bonifacia Retamales de Aravena of Peralillo began. Doña Moñi, as she was familiarly called in the hills.

I had never heard her voice before. The death rattle, the same in all the dying, was an inadequate basis for reconstructing the deep tone of her masculine voice, which was one of Doña Moñi's peculiarities, according to those who knew her. I had never even seen her on the mountain roads going to the port or to Chillehue, riding a little dun mare, La Pulga, as well known a figure in the hills as its mistress herself. It was a miracle that the frail back of that little animal, which resembled a toy horse, could bear the weight of the majestic corpulence of the owner of Peralillo; but miracles of this sort are not uncommon in the hills. Vitality and resistance are never in keeping with the vessel of clay that holds them. Thus the moving little clod of earth that is a lark in the spring pours itself out in a flood of unsuspected melody.

I had never crossed the little brook purling over its clear bed which divides the yellow humps of the hills where Doña Moñi lived; but I was not ignorant of the fact (the mountaineers have no secrets, especially over a glass of wine) that Doña Moñi, twice widowed, had for half a century ruled her two husbands—farmers of the locality— with a rod of iron, making them work like hired hands in the vineyards and fields. She was as strong and hard-working as any of the men. But she kept all the money in her own hands. It must have been buried somewhere, because there was no sign of it. I had heard more than once of her Herculean strength—how she could lift up her horse, saddle and all, or a wagonload of wheat—and when it came to drinking, she

---

* Translated with the author's permission from *Hombres y zorros* by Mariano Latorre.

could hold her own with Pedro Mono, Taquilla, and other famous drinkers of the hills.

Women of this type are not unusual in the mountains along the coast. I have seen many of them in the country and villages. Life is hard, the men emigrate to the central valley, crossing the whole mountain range, or follow the banks of the Maule River to the coast in search of work that will pay them better. In their absence the women look after the vineyards and plant the small wheatfields. They end by becoming men themselves. Such physical strength is matched by corresponding sexual appetites. A few glasses of wine or brandy unleashes their passions, and they stop at nothing. In the case of Doña Moñi, it was said that she offered herself to any boy who took her fancy at the threshing or grape harvest; or, without making any bones about it, put it on a money basis, whichever suited her best. It was a common thing for the *huasos* to assemble at her house and drink with Doña Moñi and some nieces of hers who came across the hills in their shawls and wooden shoes as soon as they heard the strumming of the harp and the songs of the singers or the shouts of the drunken *huasos*.

I had learned that afternoon from a little grandson of the old woman's, who came to the ranch store to buy some candles, that Doña Moñi was dying, and I invited my brother, the owner and manager of this property of our father's, to go to the wake.

We arrived just as her soul was taking off from its native hills for eternity, or to hide near by, according to a *huaso* whose acquaintance I made that night, for her soul was condemned to eternal torment. On the earth floor, which her wooden shoes had trod so many times, her vigorous, firm-jawed head lay bowed. Her tawny red hair, in which hardly a gray hair showed, was spread out as though to make a pillow for her rest. The yellowish light, dimmed by the heavy air of the room, which was crowded with people, threw into relief her strong-willed, leonine face. Her yellowish teeth, sound in spite of her seventy years, were clenched as though biting on something, because her firm jaw had dropped.

Everyone had gathered around the old woman. Someone had picked up the candle from the window, and the flickering of the flame brought out vividly those hard faces that bent over expressionless to observe every detail of the death agony. The death rattle died away. This was followed by such a dead, intense silence that the very light of the candle seemed to quiver with the gentle flutter of a butterfly's wings. Suddenly the room came to life with shrill cries, inarticulate lamentations, hysterical sobs. There was something at once mechanical and grotesque about it. It was the custom. The sounds stopped as suddenly as they had begun. I heard murmurs: a woman's firm voice was giving orders. Men and women moved away. The dead woman was carried from the hard cold floor of the little whitewashed room to the monumental bed, an old four-poster with gilded columns. It was at this point I asked myself a question that had been troubling me for some time: Why had the old woman died on the ground and not in her bed? Was it perhaps an old funeral ceremony handed down from the Spanish settlers or their Indian serfs of the Maule region?

This was not the only thing that perplexed me from the beginning of the wake for Doña Moñi Retamales de Aravena to her burial in the cemetery of Chillehue.

A feverish activity began, especially on the part of the women. There were whispers, hurried orders, the moving about of boxes and furniture. A little window that looked out over the fields was opened. The night came into the room with its ever pristine coolness, and the flame of the candle, ridged with coagula of wax, like a watering eye, flared up. The men began to file out of the room. I stood quietly in a corner. Doña Moñi was washed and fixed up as she had never been in life. I saw her naked for a moment: her back was strong and well shaped, and her ankles and legs slender and graceful in contrast to her feet, misshapen by hard work. A violent argument broke out among the women as to what she should wear. But the voice and authoritative air of a big, dark, hook-nosed woman prevailed, who as she talked had pushed the dead woman's jaw into place and fastened it with a handkerchief tied at the back of her neck. I saw the oldest son come in, a dark-bearded man with an inoffensive air. It was his duty to close the eyes of the dead. He performed the task with unctuous slowness. The four candles were burning in candlesticks and bottles. The trembling little reddish flames rose and fell. Fragments of shadow fluttered over the corpse. The women had knelt to pray. The first rites had begun. The hum of the Rosary came monotonously and sadly from beside the bed. Hugging the wall, I slipped outside.

Night had draped the blunt, sleeping hills in mourning. The icy breath of August chilled the thick, pervading darkness. It had rained the week before, and the swollen waters of the brook roared in the distance. The winking of the far-off stars seemed the silvery echo of the streams unending rumble. To one side of the house a group of the mountaineers had built a fire. The first flames snapped timidly at the heavy shadows to lunge at them later with their red paws. Dark torsos bent over the fire, ponchos hanging at angles. I did not go into the kitchen where my brother probably was. Leaning against one of the posts of the porch, I listened to the muffled mutter of the prayers and the clear sound of the water in the night. I liked being there in the darkness. My poncho enveloped me in a warm, protecting embrace.

With every passing moment each noise, each word wafted me by the wind took on a more pronounced individuality. My ears had become as keen as those of a fox. This silent process came to give me a kind of morbid pleasure. When I heard the screech of an owl, I could see it, wrapped in a scrap of the darkness, fall upon a sleeping bird. If a cricket chirped near me, I sensed the saws of its hind legs, rubbing against each other as if they were cold. It would have surprised me to discover that this world of noises that was coming to life within me differed from the way I had imagined it.

Thus it was that I became aware of the presence of a countryman I had not noticed, so motionless was he leaning against the stone corner of the porch. He had seen me; of that I was sure. As I lighted up a cigarette he asked me for a light, the classic formula for beginning a conversation. The unknown was not an introvert. After a few words I had learned that his name was Chano González and he was from Nirivilo. To be sure, sharing a cigarette in the country is almost the equivalent of an introduction. The momentary gleam of the match showed me the face of a typical old man of the mountains, with a thick white beard and strongly marked features but devoid of animation. All expression was concentrated in the bluish sparks of the eyes, hidden amidst bristly hairs. He was a distant relative of the old woman's. He felt that something was due him, if nothing more than a share of the funeral baked meats. Doña Moñi was rich, as the term is understood in the hills. She had a little vineyard on the slope where the house stood, a field below for corn and beans; a young planting of vines and also a hillside where grew a few sacks of wheat dotted with red poppies. Besides, there was that money accumulated by the old woman, coin by coin, whose hiding place had not yet been discovered and would never be.

"On" Chano regarded himself as a connection; possibly his relations with Doña Moñi had not been too cordial. Later on I was to learn that my suspicions were not ungrounded. He lived several miles from Peralillo and seemed to be familiar with all the ins and outs of Doña Moñi's life. His voice had a kind of singing quality, like that of a bird, and his words had that typical shrewd cunning that gave them the tart-sweet flavor of wild berries. He puffed contentedly at his cigarette, and his words, wrapped in smoke, dripped slowly into my ears. They were accounts of country squabbles, village gossip, references to lost sheep and to oxen that had got loose in the crops. Now and again the conversation came back to the dead woman. Suddenly a phrase caught my attention.

"They'll have to sit up with her for two days like the mistress of the house she is and to keep off the Evil One, who has been lurking around here this many a long year."

"You say the Evil One is around here, On Chano?"

"Twice the owl has hooted behind the barn. Didn't you hear it? That's a sign that he is going to do everything he can to keep her from being buried in consecrated ground."

There flashed into my mind the memory of the old woman stretched out on the hard floor of the room, and it occurred to me that this old mountaineer could tell me the reason for this strange custom; but he did not give me time. He sententiously brought his remarks to an end with this pronouncement on the fate of the old woman:

"This is what comes of the loose life she lived."

My curiosity was aroused. I asked him:

"Wasn't Doña Moñi a decent woman, On Chano?"

"A slut, that's what she was—ever since she was a little bit of a thing, asking your pardon. May I go to hell if I am not telling the truth. The mourners lifted her out of the bed where she had sinned, so she could die on the good earth and God might forgive her. With her feet to the east and her head to the west."

He became silent. He had thrown away his cigarette, and it seemed to me that he crossed himself devoutly.

"But you musn't talk ill of the dead, for they say they will haunt you. Aren't you coming down to the canyon?"

"Not yet, On Chano. I'm going to wait here for my brother."

The fire was calling him, and the hubbub that could already be noticed in the hollow of the canyon. His hour had come. The stew was bubbling in the pots by now, and the wine was circulating from hand to hand and gurgling in the glasses. For a moment his figure came to life, a light poncho illuminated by the glow of the flames; then it melted into the mass of shadows that surrounded the fire.

I turned back to the little room where Doña Moñi had lived and sinned. I felt a sympathy for her after what I had heard from Don Chano, her poor relative. She was already in the coffin, which must have been hidden out of sight under her bed, for I had not seen it anywhere before. It had been covered with black cotton cloth, and the corners were bound with white insets. Her pale face, tanned by the sun of many summers, was quietly serene. Hers was a strong head with a rounded forehead framed by reddish hair just touched with gray. There was nothing Indian in its contours. A mole in which stiff hairs bristled showed at the left corner of her mouth. The interminable recital of the rosary continued beside the coffin. The breath of night, which made its way through the window, was unable to dissipate the thickness of the gray atmosphere, and when fatigue occasionally interrupted the monotonous passing of the beads, the sputtering of the charred wicks could be heard as they curled back on themselves.

I went back to the porch. There I was surrounded by solitude. In the distance the crowd was milling about the comforting fire. The appetizing smell of roast meat reached my nostrils. The meal had begun. A great deal of drinking must have been going on, for the shadows shifted about and the mountaineers were gesticulating in endless arguments. Scraps of words came fluttering through the black air and melted into the darkness like drops of shadow falling into the immense shadow. I went to look for my brother, who was probably with Doña Moñi's son near the fire. Don Desiderio Aravena got to his feet as he saw me coming and solicitously offered me a piece of the roast meat. I ate it hungrily, and this astonished me. And now I must have a glass of liquor. He was mumbling incoherent words. He was drunk, like all the others, who were sitting with their arms about each other and crying, while the flames played upon their coppery, inexpressive faces. I understood that he was greatly flattered by our presence at his mother's wake. He offered us meat and wine all over again when we told him that we were going to accompany Doña Moñi's remains to the cemetery of Chillehue.

At last we were on our way through the hills. The night seemed to roll down over us, spatter us with the silvery dew of its stars. The horses guided us through the labyrinth of trails and roads. Every now and then an unexpected madroño branch grasped at us, and at times a breeze so pure that it seemed to have come down from the sky made us shiver.

I kept thinking of Doña Moñi and of the unforeseen way she had entered my life. The day before I would not have moved from the ranch to cross the hills and go to Peralillo. Now, as though she were an old friend, I was prepared to accompany her to the cemetery of the distant village. I was consumed by a desire to know more about her.

I abruptly asked my brother, who was smoking in silence:

"Did you know that the reason Doña Moñi died on the ground was because she had sinned so many times in bed?"

"Of course. They did the same thing years ago with an old miser who lived in Rinconada. And in Doña Moñi's case there was more reason for it. An old fellow from Nirivilo, who was a tenant of mine, told me a lot about her. They were distantly related and had quarreled over a field the old woman said belonged to her and had fenced in. When she was a young girl she used to go off to the hills with anyone who took her fancy, with nothing but a blanket and a little food. In a few days she'd be back at work again, and always alone. Every one of the fellows she had her fling with was her enemy afterwards, and they didn't leave her a leg to stand on. Once a baby was born. Old Fidela who lived with her helped her to do away with the child, and they buried it under some stones, but the dogs dug up the body, and that's how the thing came out."

"Did she go to jail for it?"

"No, that's not the custom around here. The less they have to do with the law and the courts the better they like it. They settle their own affairs. Everybody knows all that has happened, and when they get into a fight at threshing time, they blurt it out. In the case of Doña Moñi, they were afraid of old Fidela, who is a witch, so they just said that she was a lost soul and nothing could save her from the devil."

"That's what I heard from an old-timer from Nirivilo, On Chano González, who was on the porch when you went down with the old woman's son."

"He's the one I was talking about, who was a tenant of mine and a relative of Doña Moñi's. Being on bad terms doesn't keep anyone from going to a wake. Death puts everything right, anyway as long as the liquor and the food last. That old fellow is the one who has slandered her most. In spite of his saintly looks he's a mean, sly old codger. He's the one who gave her house the nickname of the Church. He'd always say with a very solemn air when he saw anyone going that road: "Are you going to the Church?" "No, On Chano, can't you see I'm on my way to Peralillo?" "Then you're going to church."

People finally caught on to what he meant, and the name stuck. It was that anybody could go there the same as to church. The old woman sold liquor, and they could carry on all they liked, provided they paid for their liquor. It finally got to Doña Moñi's ears, and she took her revenge by presenting the priest of Chillehue with a keg of wine, so he would upbraid the country people when they went to Mass for the sacrilege of calling a house of ill repute a church.

II

The sun was unable to break through the mist—hoarfrost turned to vapor—that blotted out the outlines of the hills and hemmed in the little valley between two walls of dense whiteness. The old oak trees of the coast, the grandfathers of those that had gone down to the sea or had been used in the shipyards, twisted and gnarled, stood out through the chill pressure of the fog. On the hillside the knotty vine-stalks were almost one with the dark earth. Hardly rising above the ground, the birds passed, songless.

About noon the figure of a horseman emerged against the milky background. The diminutive silhouette of a pony of the hills, a brownish poncho.

My brother recognized it at once.

"There comes On Chano. They've sent him after wine."

I stood beside the counter to get a good look at him. His white whiskers, which the wind was blowing to one side, were like the moss hanging from the old oak trees.

He greeted us politely.

"How did the gentlemen rest? You were greatly missed at Peralillo."

The faded blue dots of his eyes were brimming with quiet complacence. He tried to dismount, and as he did so, rider and saddle slipped to one side. He straightened himself out with a comical lurch to the other side. He was probably still half drunk. To cover up he put the blame on the horse. And nothing could have been a greater injustice than to hold the gentle animal responsible.

"The rascal is full of tricks."

With elaborate precautions he dismounted again. On foot he had a grotesque look, frail and rickety. Only his head, with the straight nose and large mouth, was strong and well shaped. Like Doña Moñi, he did not seem to have any Indian blood. His head might have been that of a Castilian or an Andalusian.

My brother knew perfectly well what he had come for, but he asked him:

"And what brings you this way so early, Don Chano?"

"Your Worship hasn't seen what I've got in my hand?"

And with this he brought out from under his poncho a limp goatskin, all wrinkled and twisted.

"I hadn't noticed, Don Chano. Excuse me."

"Well, now that you have, let's fatten it up with wine, if you don't mind, because it's not good for it to be empty like this; it dries up. Besides we still have to sit up with Doña Moñi to keep away the Evil One, who has been hanging around since last night. The hills have been full of howls and hoofbeats."

"How's that, Don Chano?"

"Look, Your Worship, even the priest of Chillehue, who never misses a wake, wasn't able to come to administer the last rites, because he's sick, they say. Imagine On Luterio getting sick, when he's like an ox! It's the Evil One's doings. We're going to have trouble burying her in consecrated ground. That's what I told Desiderio and Fidela. You just wait and see."

My brother, a jovial soul, never took the superstitions of the hill folk seriously, but he was interested, or pretended to be interested, in their everyday life. He solemnly glossed the old man's words:

"It is strange, Don Chano, that the priest didn't come to the Church, for that's where the priests like to go."

On Chano caught the joke at once, and a look of alarm came into his light eyes:

"It's not a good thing to make jokes about the dead, *patrón*."

We went down to the cellar. The wine gurgled through the funnel in purple bubbles. The skin took on new life as it filled up with liquid. Its dark wrinkled surface grew smooth and lighter. On Chano tied the leg that served as a mouthpiece into a tight knot and thrust it under his arm. With the elasticity of a reptile the skin adjusted itself to the old man's body, swelling out into two great dark balloons.

On the porch just as he was about to mount, On Chano asked for candles.

"The others are just about used up," he explained.

My brother invited him to have a drink while he went into the ranch store to get the candles. The old man downed two glasses, one after the other. I offered him a cigarette. Sitting on the edge of the porch, he puffed away voluptuously.

"Tell me something, On Chano," I asked him, "how is it that Doña Moñi left so many children if she got rid of the babies?"

His little eyes showed his surprise that I should be aware of this. He hesitated but decided to answer.

"As soon as she began to show that she was carrying, if Your Worship will excuse me, her husband didn't let her out of his sight and watched every move she made. If he hadn't, who knows what she would have done?"

And then, repentant of having talked this way about the dead, he rose to her defense with the sly shrewdness of the mountaineer. The taste of the funeral feast was still on his lips, and there was more to come.

"But all this happened years ago, while my poor father was still living. Years ago. Moñi was young then and a very pretty woman. And vain! She used to clean her teeth with herbs, and she would laugh at anything just so folks would see them. The men that swarmed around her, Your Worship! Even the Governor of Maule stopped there once when he was campaigning. But she never neglected her work for anything. There was no one like her in the fields or the vineyard. The two husbands she had were old and not much good, and if it hadn't been for her, there wouldn't be one vine left by now. She used to take a stick to her second husband to make him cultivate the vines, and then they'd wind up in a fist fight. She'd tear off all her clothes and foam at the mouth like a crazy person. Moñi was like a lion."

As soon as my brother came back the old man got up. He put the wineskin over the saddlebow, and the packages of candles in the saddlebag. He took his leave with many thanks. And he insisted that we ought to go to the cemetery the next morning. We'd have a good time.

"There'll be plenty to eat, for Desiderio has killed four sheep. We're taking along two sacks of meat and another skin of wine the mourners told me to buy for them to wash it down. We're starting at dawn, because there's going to be a funeral Mass said in the church of Chillehue."

"All that won't stop the Devil, Don Chano," observed my brother.

"It's hard to say, Your Worship. He's so mean that he'll make trouble when you least expect it. He's determined to have her if he can. The owl goes on hooting in broad daylight—"

With comic haste he crossed himself several times after making these remarks. He climbed on to the horse with elaborate precautions. It was as though he were afraid the fragile framework of his *Chincol* might collapse, but he finally got himself settled. A slap of the reins set the horse in motion.

Blanket, beard, and tail followed the course of the wind, which was beginning to roll the mist up the slope of the hills.

For a moment they stood out against the clearing air, then disappeared amidst shreds of clouds, as though engulfed in the white tide.

III

The high ridge of the sierra lashed by the north wind. Sharp gusts, more icy and cutting every minute.

The red machete of the road divided the young oak grove into two great groups of skeletons. The land lay a gray dirty blotch under the high overcast sky. Over the pebbles of a gully a brook carded the snowy fleece of its current.

My brother and I had been waiting half an hour for Doña Moñi and her cortege. The only sound to be heard was the brook and the whistling of the wind. Not a bird showed itself among those crags, lords of the wind.

"Let's stand over here," said my brother. "The wind is coming from this direction, and you can't hear a thing. They won't be long now."

As though called up by a magic spell, hoarse voices began to make themselves heard in front of us. Then the slither of hoofs on the rocky path. A cliff hid the procession from our sight. First there appeared an enormous cross, newly planed. A stout countryman, walking with long strides, was carrying it on his shoulder. Behind came the swaying black blotch of the coffin on a bier whose shafts rested on the shoulders of four men. They were breathing heavily. Four streams of vapor, four puffing, gray cones, came out of their mouths. Against the corners of the coffin their faces showed red from their exertions, but their step was firm and steady.

On their shaggy ponies some twenty *huasos*, wrapped in their ponchos, followed the coffin.

The black coffin, with its grotesque white trimming, looked like a huge bird gliding down the hillside about to settle. And it came to rest on the dun earth in front of us. Doña Moñi's son came over to greet us. His words became entangled in his thick black beard, the wind carried them off, and we were unable to understand anything he said. It didn't matter. We nodded agreement. A sudden silence fell over the procession as it waited there. This was something unexpected and had impressed the party favorably.

Once more the coffin was back on the shoulders of its bearers. Black and grim, blind and hurried, it moved over the rises and falls of the rough road with its funereal load.

I fell behind. My brother was with Desiderio Aravena at the head of the party. I looked the *huasos* over. I knew many of them. They were regular customers of the ranch store or the wine cellar. I greeted them as I recognized them. It is amazing how much they resemble each other. All cast in the same mold out of the same dark material. The bronzed shade of their skin identical, but not the shape of their heads. Some have long faces and dark eyes; others, full cheeks and light pupils. The features are regular, with strong jaws. I have rarely seen a face of Indian type in the hills. The Indian had disappeared in remote colonial times, when the hills, now bare, were covered with the green of sycamore and oak; yet his spirit lived on in the customs, in the soul of the hills, to form a strange compound of heathen superstitions and Christian practices. There was a morbid fear of the hereafter, especially of the devil, the ruling spirit of the mountains. Satan had flourished at God's expense. It was a Satan who had much of the *huaso* about him, who wore poncho and a spur on his left ankle, and who knew the ins and outs of all the gossip and intrigues of the neighborhood, like any native. Their lives flowed, with the changeless uniformity of running water, between christenings and burials, harvests and vintages. The only difference was in the number of lambs slaughtered or the skins of wine consumed, depending on each one's means.

"Your Worship is going to be left behind," spoke up a voice I recognized as soon as I heard it.

Don Chano, riding his old nag, came to arouse me from my contemplation.

"You know how tricky these mountain roads are. You might take the wrong one and ride into the river."

He had taken charge of the horses of the *huasos* who were carrying the coffin on the first lap of its journey. I noticed that he was also the custodian of the skins of wine and the sacks of meat. This filled him with a comical vanity. He was half drunk, and every minute he would let out a shout at the horses, which with stirrups and reins tied to the saddlebow, lingered by the roadside to nibble at the dry grass.

"Come on, you devil! You half-broken son-of-a-bitch—"

When he calmed down a little I offered him a cigarette.

"How about us having a smoke, Don Chano?"

"A cigarette is always a good thing, Your Worship."

"When will we get to Chillehue? Have we still got a long way to go?"

"We've barely started, Your Worship. We've not even reached the top of Peñalquin. When we get there, then we have to come down the other side."

"If we get there."

His light eyes clouded over. He looked down, really disturbed. Without his saying a word, I understood all the frightening premonitions that were going through his mind. I dropped the matter. To change the subject I asked him:

"Did you tell me what Doña Moñi died of, Don Chano?"

"How could I tell you when you never asked me."

"Well, I'm asking you now."

We rode along in silence for a few moments.

"Of old age, I suppose. Oña Fidela says she had just finished eating a piece of corn cake when she rolled over to one side and her tongue went all thick. Doña Cata came to see her and said it was a seizure. They put hot cloths on her, but it was no use; she couldn't move her body. They say twice she raised her arm to her mouth, pointing to her gold tooth. They say you must pull it out or the person will go to Hell. But her son wouldn't have it, and there she goes with her gold tooth and a pair of silver earrings her second husband gave her. Doña Fidela did cut the heels off her shoes, and you can't tell about the teeth, because the old woman is a sly one."

"Why the heels, Don Chano?"

His quizzical glance rested on me for an instant. He was at a loss to understand my ignorance of such vitally important matters. Finally he must have remembered that I was an outsider, and he explained with a certain air of condescension:

"You take off the heels, sir, so the dead person won't come back to haunt the house."

We had lost sight of the procession.

Don Chano urged on the horses, and we quickened our pace. We came to the crest of the ridge. The wind lashed at the bare rocks in furious gusts, like the crack of an icy whip. We hurried down the slope. A great gulch opened out, filled with thick, sodden mist. I had the impression that all the clouds of the mountains had gathered there, wearied with their wanderings. Corpse and mourners had disappeared in that thick, nebulous mass. Voices could be heard close beside us. They had halted. The horses drowsed, tied by their bridles. The men were sitting on the ground or on stones or tree trunks along the road. There was the coffin, black and sinister. This was the first stop, according to my informant Don Chano. Breakfast. Here they would eat and drink, two paces from the corpse. It was the custom, a custom of over a century.

When we came up, the oldest son, Desiderio Aravena, held in his hand a little cross tied with a withe. I saw him go over to a weather-beaten oak tree that stood by the right of the road. At the foot of the old tree, with its gnarled trunk covered with knotty excrescences, the little cross was set up. With amazing rapidity Don Chano wove a wreath of withes and hung it on the arms of the cross. A pile of dark stones, like a boundary marker, rose against the tree's rough trunk. There were fallen crosses among the stones, gouts of candle wax, and the black lickings of flames. I saw the whole cortege bend down when this was done, gather up stones, and throw them upon the heap. It was a time-honored resting place, the first lap of the journey, after crossing the crest of the ridge. There they restored themselves and at the same time left a pious tribute to the spot where the dead had rested. The dead person shared their rest. He was a comrade of misfortune. Perhaps happier than the living, because he would go to Heaven as all the poor do. Death had set a halo of sanctity upon his head. They perpetuated his memory so that he might intercede with God for the friends left behind, those who went on struggling with the sorry vines and the grudging wheat patches of the hills.

The wind stirred the old sanctified oak. The network of dark twigs along its boughs moved with the hollow rattle of a skeleton's fingers. The gray beards of hanging moss slapped back and forth with each gust of wind.

Don Chano began to pass out the food. A hunk of dull, porous meat, a piece of hardtack. Appetizing, both meat and cracker. And better still with a swallow of cold wine and a cigarette. The conversation came to life. The members of the party exchanged rough jokes.

"Give us another swallow, On Chano, to keep up our strength."

The old man hurried over, and the wineskin poured out a steady gurgling stream.

"The old lady weighs more than a two-hundred-pound sack of wheat," added another.

Don Chano, unflagging, kept squeezing the belly of the skin into the horn that was used as a cup, and to a wisecrack of one of the *huasos*, he replied in a mocking tone:

"Don't show off, Don Parrot Shanks, you know people don't have money on work days."

His interlocutor, a skinny, bowlegged, little *huaso*, snapped back:

"Parrot Shanks, yourself, you with the glass eyes!"

And he advanced toward Don Chano with a threatening gesture of defiance. The latter's little blue eyes twinkled, and his rough, gnarled hand held the horn steady. The chief mourner stepped between them.

"No need to take offense and to show disrespect for the dead."

And he added, philosophically:

"We're all going to rest in the same earth."

The cavalcade mounted once more. On other rested shoulders Doña Moñi continued her trip through the denuded hills that ridged the coast. The procession was silent. Only the men carrying the coffin kept up a steady conversation, as though to lighten their tiresome task. Once more the recollection of the old woman I was so piously accompanying to her last resting place took hold of my mind. It did not seem to me that she was dead, there between the rough boards of her homemade coffin, or that I was going to a burial. It was a neighborhood threshing under the hot summer sun or a grape harvest, golden in the autumn light. Doña Moñi was wearing her best country finery: a freshly laundered blouse, skirt stiff with starch, and her Sunday shoes. Down her strong back hung two braids like red snakes. Like a queen she walked among the sheaves or the baskets piled high with fragrant grapes. The wind of the hills billowed out the cool thinness of the percale skirt. Her firm breasts showed under the folds of the blouse.

Then in a quick change I could see her, half drunk, hoarse with singing, lying in the shelter of a straw stack or under the green complicity of the sweet-smelling vines. Shameless and bold, without modesty or remorse. A symbol of the woman of the country, passive and as untroubled by scruples as the earth itself. And like the earth, fruitful and eternal.

We were descending rapidly. The valley was growing ever wider; the hills towered majestically, rearing high their flat peaks, shrouded in mist. Every minute another farmhouse of adobes appeared, square, unadorned, like an excrescence of the barren earth. Not a soul was to be seen in the deserted yards, not a sound came from the windows, with their board shutters. Only the chickens, huddled together against the cold, on the poles leaning against the walls.

Like the hem of a long skirt, winding by the foot of the gray hills, gleamed the unrolling ribbon of a river. The projection of hills and the skeletons of second-growth oaks were reflected in its steely surface. Also the pallid face of the August sky. The entire procession was gathered at the river's edge beside the ford. Men and horses formed a single mass. The wind tugged at the men's ponchos and stood on end the horses' winter coats, as soft as a fledgling's down. From a distance that silvery mirror had seemed lifeless, but when we reached the bank I realized how deep it was and how treacherous its current, which swirled in swift, silent eddies. The *huasos* were taking counsel before they crossed. Finally the coffin on its bier of poles and branches started across. The men had rolled up their pants and were moving steadily. Further on, the current grew stronger. It closed furiously around the bronzed calves of their legs. They were now walking cautiously, their backs bent under the weight of the coffin. Their strong breasts were panting. From the bank Desiderio Aravena was directing the operation.

"More to the north, On Chuma, there's a deep hole to the south."

Don Chano, sitting on a stone was smoking and dozing. As though unintentionally, I joined him.

"The river looks deep, Don Chano," I remarked, to open the conversation.

"It's swollen with these rains we've had, but the worst of it is the mud, sir. Just so no one misses his footing— Otherwise Doña Moñi will be in the water."

He spoke in that slightly ironical and at the same time solemn tone so typical of the mountaineers. But I did not have time to question him further. A hoarse cry that ended in an oath rang out. We turned our heads quickly. One of the bearers had slipped in a whirlpool of dark water, and the coffin, like a porpoise submerging, had sunk into the silent waters. There was a swift splash; then the rear end rose only to sink again, like the tail of a fish. The other men had fallen into the water too. The thick bubbles went gurgling over them. They got to their feet dripping. Heavily they made their way toward the bank, leaving behind coffin and bier, which floated down stream as though in search of its burden. Several of the *huasos* mounted. Others forded the stream, and groups on both sides of the river rushed after Doña Moñi's coffin, carried further and further away by the swirling waters, shouting orders and waving their arms as though trying to catch a runaway animal. It was a comic and macabre sight; but funniest of all was the expression of terror stamped on Don Chano's face. His predictions, which may have started as idle gossip, were coming true.

"If only the box doesn't come open," he muttered.

Only later did I find out what those words of his meant.

"It's going to stop in that shallow, On Ñica," shouted one of the riders to another, who had managed to outdistance the coffin and was swinging his lasso in ever swifter circles, ready to throw it over the head of the coffin.

The coffin had suddenly picked up speed as it entered the main stream of the current, which was swinging toward the left bank in a wide curve.

"It'll stop there because there are a lot of roots there," observed one.

"Watch it, On Ñica," called out another.

The lasso whistled over the water. It hit the surface with a sharp crack and managed to catch the foot of the coffin, which came to a quick halt crosswise of the stream.

The *huasos* applauded the feat. They had completely lost sight of the fact that they were on their way to a funeral. There were excited comments, loud peals of laughter. Suddenly someone warned:

"Your lasso is slipping, On Ñica. Don't let it get loose again."

The man gave the lasso a slight tug at the same time spurred his horse in the opposite direction. The noose now gripped the coffin tightly. On Ñica gave it a gentle pull. Slowly it rose out of the oozy mud of the bank, moving heavily like an alligator. Part of the dark covering had been torn away and showed the naked wood, dripping water. But the nails had held. As it had no handles they lifted it bodily on to solid ground. There they cleaned off the mud, rubbing it with leaves, and someone tried to fasten the wet lining back in place. Others went off for the bier, which was caught in the roots of an old willow tree that had been carried down by the swollen stream.

When the crossing of the river had been effected, I found myself once more with my brother and Don Chano beside Doña Moñi's coffin. Everyone was still talking about the feat of On Ñica, the best roper in the hills.

"It must have been a charmed lasso, because it got the better of Old Nick," said my brother jokingly. "What do you think, Don Chano?"

Everybody looked at the old man. His pale eyes blinked. It was a moment of responsibility for him, and his answer was grave when it came. He knew how his neighbors felt about such matters.

"One should not joke about such things, Don Jorge. The Evil One is hanging around here. Did you see the way the box floated?"

Everyone looked solemnly at the coffin, as though trying to guess what lay under the poor, rough-hewn boards.

"The poor soul might have been lost. The Evil One, as the master of the waters, could have dragged her down into the earth under the river. Let's hope the same thing didn't happen as with Peiro Chávez, when the box was empty when they took out the pillow."

Desiderio Aravena interrupted him angrily:

"You're like the hoot owls, you old mischief-maker."

Not a word did he answer. His protest was smothered in a deep puff at his cigarette.

The bier had been put together once more, and this time it was Don Chano's turn as bearer. Desiderio Aravena's decision was motivated by a certain malicious rancor. Now the old man would see whether Doña Moñi was still inside the four planks of the coffin or in the hands of the Evil One in some cave of the highest hills, Peñalquin, Mingre, or Name.

On the shoulders of the bearers the coffin moved swiftly over a kind of arid mesa. The heavy cloud masses above the hills began to shift, as though they had suddenly lost the balance that supported them in space. The wind bent the bare branches of the oaks and shook the heavy foliage of the *boldos* and *litres*.

Dirty and squalid, the village of Chillehue emerged from the very rocks. Stones and houses were the same color. The rude church tower reared itself aloft over the uneven roofs. At the sight of it the coffin moved more rapidly. It seemed to me that Desiderio Aravena's face lighted with satisfaction as he looked at Don Chano's sagging shoulder under the right forward end of the bier. He may have been thinking that there in the old, brick-floored church, to the tolling of the bells, the decisive battle between the Evil One and Doña Moñi would be fought out. God would weigh in the balance the good actions and the bad of the old woman of Peralillo. Her kin had done all they could to save her from Satan's snares. Purified by the Mass, her orgies and crimes would be forgotten. The Evil One, lurking in some corner of the church, his head turned to avoid the sight of the Blessed Cross, would flee through some broken window pane with his tail between his legs to his lair in the steepest peak of the costal range.

IV

The village bell tolled for the soul of Doña Bonifacia Retamales de Aravena. Like shivering doves the tones came forth, and the wind carried them over the roofs into the open above the lowering ridge of the hills.

The priest, an old man, his hair gray and his face weathered, clad in his vestments, received Doña Moñi at the door of the church. This was a good sign, for the priest had sent word that he was sick. The whole village had assembled in the barren lot that was the square. The *huasos* had removed their old, battered hats, and their thick hair rose up in release. The coffin was set on a kind of dais. Upon the cotton-covered box, gray with mud, fell the drops of holy water and the priest's harsh Latin, half mumbled through his thick lips. The *huasos* were kneeling on the brick floor. Through the church, as square as a cellar and acrid with the smell of barn-owl droppings, the guttural voice of the priest and the coughing of the country folk echoed strangely.

Again the priest accompanied the coffin to the door. Once more the procession set out under the gray sky, facing the wind this time, which whipped the folds of the ponchos and the men's beards about, down the village's only street. The women peered out from the doors, behind the sagging porches, the paneless windows. Some of the villagers mounted and joined the cortege. The drinking was not yet over.

The cemetery lay on the slope of a hill, a few blocks from the settlement. The road, gashed along the side by deep gullies of red clay, went almost straight up the hillside. Four irregular walls of gray adobes formed the cemetery. In front of the wide, worn oak gate, the bier came to a halt. The *huasos* dismounted. The weary horses huddled beside the entrance. The village cemetery had a desolate air. Rough, tile-roofed shacks, similar to the houses of the living, with narrow slits of windows, were the vaults of the well-to-do villagers. The dull, barren earth bristled with rude crosses, on which hung the skeletons of funeral wreaths. There Doña Moñi's grave was being dug. Near by, the coffin rested. The *huasos* had sat down to wait. They were smoking and talking. The blows of the pick on the hard earth made a dull, heavy sound.

The cold was growing more intense. The white immobility of the fog had become a ghostly procession of black clouds. The countrymen eyed the sky from time to time and made comments on the weather.

"Wind's coming north by northwest," said one.

"It would be a good thing if it rained and broke up the cold spell," added another.

"This freeze isn't doing the wheat any good," a third rounded out the conversation.

The grave was ready. The diggers had thrown their spades on the ground and were waiting. The *huasos* got to their feet; but the strange ceremonies of the mountaineers were not yet over. I went from one surprise to another. In spite of my recollections (I had spent many of my vacations as a child on my father's ranch) the whole thing had a strange, primitive quality for me. It was as though I were in another epoch, in distant colonial times. The superstitions inherited from Spanish forebears, and disfigured by the Indians as they became civilized, persisted almost unchanged. They all had the same object: to get into God's good graces on departing this life. Only at this moment were these people generous. Generous, materially and spiritually. The roast lamb and the liquor that flowed without measure went hand in hand with the strange ceremony of expiring on the bare earth, and with the one I was about to witness: removing the pillow from beneath the corpse's head.

Desiderio Aravena had pried open the lid of the coffin with the edge of a spade. The corpse lay uncovered. Everyone crowded eagerly about to look. Nobody seemed to notice the sharp smell that emanated from the body. On the contrary, it seemed to me that a satisfied expression came over the impassive faces. Here was proof that the body was still in the coffin and that the offerings and prayers to God had taken effect. Now nobody doubted Doña Moñi's salvation. Even I, without being conscious of it, gave a sigh of relief. I looked for Don Chano. His eyes were obstinately fixed on the corpse, but they revealed nothing. Perhaps he was ashamed of his doubts and was performing an inward act of contrition. I seemed to hear him say what he had repeated so many times:

"You mustn't joke about the dead, sir."

Desiderio Aravena had gently raised (probably for the first time in his life) the old woman's head, and another *huaso* pulled out the little pillow. The head sank back in the coffin. The lid was nailed in place once more. Then Desiderio picked up the pillow and with a solemn gesture threw it to one end of the cemetery, beside the wall.

The coffin was lowered into the hole. The stony earth of the hills dropped noisily upon it. Each of the *huasos* gathered up a handful of dirt and threw it into the grave. It gave me a curious feeling to see their clumsy hands emerge from under their ponchos and bury themselves in the dirt. Like the earth, the rough hands were brown. How similar that living earth was to the dead earth!

Then the mountaineers began to file out of the cemetery. They mounted and set out toward the village. They were talking loud now, laughing, riding their horses against each other in rough fun. In the confusion I had lost sight of Desiderio and Don Chano. My brother finally joined me. We dropped slowly behind to take another path and withdraw from the cortege. It was an idea of my brother's, who knew the hills well, but we did not have time to put it into practice. The whole party had gathered before the hitching rail of an old house on the outskirts of the town. They called out as they tied their horses. The door opened, and a tall woman with red hair and gray eyes appeared in it. A cry almost escaped me, because it was as though Doña Moñi had come to life again. She had a stout door bar in her hand, and her attitude was one of defiance. The *huasos* paid no attention to this, because they were gaily dismounting and tying their horses. They greeted the dour-visaged woman jokingly, and she answered them in the same tone:

"How's everything going, Oña Rosa?"

"We dropped by to see you so you wouldn't be alone."

"Has the wine from Maule come?"

"We saw a load come by the other afternoon, past Peralillo."

"Let us in; it's starting to drizzle, Oña Rosa."

The woman had an answer ready for every one of these remarks, as gruff and crude as those of the mountaineers, but she did not put down the thick bar. This is what Doña Moñi must have been like, I thought to myself, when a crowd of *huasos* came to her house for wine and tied their horses at the hitching rail. I looked at her with interest. Here was a new element that brought back to life for me the late Doña Moñi, whom this countrywoman of Chillehue must resemble. Theirs had probably been a similar fate. This one seemed poorer, for the bare room we entered when she finally put down the bar was her only possession. There was not a fruit tree or plant in the barren ground that surrounded the house. A grape vine had wrapped its tendrils around some rotting boards. A neglected hawthorn managed to keep alive beside the wall. She reminded me so much of the dead woman—her whole air, the coppery flame of her hair, the hard, gray eyes—that I looked in vain for the little mole with the red bristles I had noticed at the lower left corner of Doña Moñi's mouth two days before by candlelight at Peralillo. I learned afterwards that their name was the same, Retamales, which was as common through the hills as the oaks and foxes. A racial product that had its male counterpart in the highwayman.

The *huasos* had begun to drink. They were talking excitedly while the red-haired woman filled their glasses, which the wine of the hills tinted purple. I noticed that she wore no stockings and her shapeless feet were thrust into wooden shoes that clattered with every step she took. At this point we took our leave. The drizzle had become a steady rain. We had no more than turned the corner when Desiderio Aravena caught up with us. I felt a surge of anger. Was this *huaso* going to make us go back to that room where they were drinking the sour wine of the hills?

My brother laughed knowingly.

"Wait a minute," he said.

And, sure enough, the *huaso's* words were an enigma to me.

"Are you gentlemen going back to Peñalquin or are you staying here?"

What difference did it make to him if we were staying in the village or going back to the ranch? But my brother calmly replied:

"We're going back right now, neighbor, before the rain gets heavier. Don't be afraid."

The wide, bovine face lighted up with satisfaction. Renewed thanks. Excuses for having troubled the gentlemen. We must not forget that his house in Peralillo was ours. He reined his horse about and disappeared in the rain.

"And what's the reason for all that?" I asked my brother.

"That's another custom of the hills. They say that if the chief mourner gets home before the others, he will die within the year. He's still got a lot to do. He's got to round up all the *huasos*, get them on their horses, and start them home. We'll meet him on the edge of the town. Wait and see."

We did not meet anybody as we forded the river. The whole horizon was in motion. A ridge of dark clouds was moving southward in a swift gallop. The wind was howling through the twisted branches of the oaks. The mountain range lay stretched northward like the wet back of some gigantic monster.

In the shelter of a rock a rider was trying to protect himself from the wind and the rain. His water-soaked poncho flapped heavily.

"What did I tell you?" said my brother. "There he is waiting for the rest of the mourners."

He came toward us as soon as he saw us. I could see his thick lips, pale with cold, moving, but I could not make out a word he was saying. Probably the usual ones: thanks, good wishes, expressions of friendship. The wind snatched the sounds away as fast as they came from his mouth. My brother answered him at the top of his lungs. It was nothing, the least one neighbor could do for another. Then he invited him to ride along with us to Peñalquin.

The expression on his face changed swiftly from humility to anger, and a flash of hatred gleamed in his black eyes.

"How can I move from here, Don Jorge? Nobody can find that good-for-nothing old On Chano. All the others went by on their way to Peralillo a while back."

His teeth were chattering and his words melted into the wind.

"But he'll pay me for this, that slandering old devil!"

For hours we rode with the wet wind buffeting our faces. And for hours I seemed to hear his high-pitched, mournful, tragic complaint.

RÓMULO GALLEGOS

(1884–   )

VENEZUELANS MAY DIFFER on the subject of Rómulo Gallegos's political views—he has held a number of cabinet posts and is now president—but they all agree that he is their country's greatest novelist. Critics generally regard him as one of the finest in all Latin America.

Venezuela is made up of a number of regions, each with its own personality and characteristics: the coast, hot and tropical with a large Negro population; Caracas, the capital, the center of the country's intellectual life and politics; the vast rolling savannas, where the cattle range; the remote, aloof Andes region; the jungle.

In his different novels Gallegos has given us a vast kaleidoscopic picture of these various regions of his land. And the principal character in all his works is Nature, so powerful, so exuberant, so indifferent, that man is dwarfed and helpless beside it. In *Doña Barbara*, his masterpiece, the heroine herself is more a symbol of the irresistible power of natural forces than a real person, vividly as she is drawn.

Few writers of his epoch have been more aware of and more attracted by the folkloric elements in the tradition of his native land than Gallegos. His works are pervaded with the folk songs, the customs, and the superstitions in which his country is so rich. In the following selection from *Pobre negro* he gives us a dramatic description, full of lyrical beauty, of the feast of St. John—Midsummer Night—which is the religious festival the Negroes have made peculiarly their own. They have combined in it the pagan and Christian elements of its European origins along with half-forgotten vestiges of their own African tradition.

[RÓMULO GALLEGOS]

Poor Nigger *

MIDSUMMER EVE. In the cacao groves of La Fundación the slaves were working with might and main.

* Reprinted from *The Green Continent* by Germán Arciniegas, translated by Harriet de Onís and others, by permission of Alfred A. Knopf, Inc. Copyright 1944 by Alfred A. Knopf, Inc.

"This is the job for today," the overseer Mindonga had told them, pointing to a wide space overgrown with brush. "By evening you're to have this as clean as a dance floor, like this was the place where you're going to have the celebration this year. Hit those canes as though you was playing a tune on a drum."

Eager hands wield grub hoe and machete without pause; but no one works so contentedly as Bad Nigger, for while the sharp blade in his powerful hands clears the field of brush, his thoughts are busy with the malicious couplets he has thought up for the night's celebration.

So satisfied is he with the work of his mind that without slackening that of his arms he begins to laugh, showing his strong white teeth, for it is impossible for him to keep quiet long:

"Oh, brothers, what verses I have thought up for tonight! Not a nigger or a mulatto anywhere in this part of the world that won't split his sides laughing seven days and seven nights when he hears me make my vows to St. John."

But the overseer, who allows no idling at the work, and who winces every time he hears the word "mulatto," and who does not like this joking nigger anyway, calls out sharply:

"Swing that machete, flannelmouth. All your strength goes to wagging that tongue of yours."

"What did I tell you?" grumbles Bad Nigger between his teeth. "That damned mulatto is always hounding me. One of these days he's going to get me at a bad moment, my patience will give out, and I'm going to bury this blade in his neck, even if they chop me to bits for it. These mulattoes behave like they were white. What am I doing? A poor Negro can't even talk to make his work easier. Damn that Father Las Casas for bringing us here! If the story that fellow from Coro, José las Mercedes, told when he was around here trying to get the slaves to rise is true. Maybe now I would be with him, shooting up the hills, if they hadn't got him in Panaquire, may he rest in peace! What a life! To have to plant and gather cacao for the white man, with your back bent at the orders of that mulatto!"

An upstanding, robust fellow, tireless at his work, always ready for a joke or a trick—it was from this and not because of a bad disposition that he had got his nickname—well built, proportioned like a statue, and with extremely fine features for his race, this Negro was very popular with all the slaves, and the master thought a great deal of him.

When this was mentioned the slave would say ironically:

"He is grateful to all the animals who do good work. Just day before yesterday the black mule said to me as I was filling up its manger: 'Brother, the master sure appreciates us.' "

It was only the overseer Mindonga who could not bear him, and he was always picking on him for the least little thing, tormenting him so he would give him an excuse to use the whip on him. But the shrewd Negro saw through him, and as he knew that even though the master was always kind to him, the smooth-tongued, tricky mulatto would always be able to show him that he was in the right, he never gave him an excuse to carry out his threats and merely muttered his complaints to himself. Besides, he got over things quickly, because he did not bear a grudge.

And his irritation that morning disappeared as soon as the overseer went to inspect the work the women slaves were doing.

Besides, it would be hard for him to stay mad when that very evening the dance was to begin when the Negro forgets all his troubles. Tapipa and Roso Coromoto, the best drummers in all Barlovento, would have their drums in good shape, and if the master was generous, as he usually was, and as he well might be this year with the good harvest, the old women slaves, who were no good for field work any more, would already be in the quarters preparing the corn and molasses liquor and the good things for them to eat at the dance, which would go on all night and all the next day.

"You swing your machete and keep your trap shut, Bad Nigger," he repeated to himself. "Tonight you'll have your fun dancing with that little black Saturna, who has agreed to be your partner. And is she a fine-looking girl. You know, if I don't watch my step with that black girl, one of these days you're going to hear me saying to the master: 'Boss, sir, give me permission to marry that Saturna, for I can't keep my mind on my work any more on account of her.' Whoa there, Bad Nigger! What about maybe there's where the trouble with that yellow Mindonga comes from? Remember what they told you two days before yesterday? Suppose maybe it's true that the overseer is trying to meddle with that black girl? I'd better keep my eyes peeled. This very night I'm going to find out the truth and see if I'm going to have to sharpen up my machete for something besides chopping brush."

And now he kept quiet all the way down to the bottom of his soul, while the fumes of jealousy lent strength to his herculean arm moving the machete.

The rays of the sun were coming straight down through the motionless foliage. The slaves panted as they bent to the inhuman task. The bantering sparrows hopped about through the foliage of the tall *guames* and *bucares* that shaded the cacao grove, the agile, wary squirrels jumped from branch to branch, and the fallen leaves rustled as the snakes, driven from their nests, slipped away. One coiled and reared up before Bad Nigger, prepared to defend its nest, where it probably had its young. He cut off its head with one slash, and the anger that was boiling in his breast muttered as he looked at the color of the snake: "You would be yellow."

The sun was sinking behind the *araguato* trees, which are the color of the monkeys of this same name, who now came trooping back in noisy bands to the thick leafy trees where they spent the night. They were like a howling gust of wind sweeping through the forest, like the sound of a wailing multitude.

The long day's work was done, and the overseer smiled perfidiously as he looked upon the wide space they had cleared of brush and snake hills.

"This is what I call a good job," he said to the slaves, who were busily finishing up. "You've earned your pleasure tonight, and tomorrow is another day."

The Negroes smiled back at him, thinking Mindonga was referring to the dance of the drums, and swinging the grub hoes to their shoulders, they started off toward their quarters behind the overseer, who was on horseback. There were thirty of them, naked from the waist up, wearing nothing but pants rolled up to their thighs. But they were clothed in the human beauty of their powerful muscles, made sinewy with work, and the sweat of the day's toil adorned their black skin with bronze reflections in the sun.

They walked through the cacao plantation in Indian file down the path, which twisted, snakelike, through the staggered trees. They left the shade of the woods and came out upon the open banks of the Tuy. Down the slow-flowing muddy stream came a canoe. The boatmen, slaves of the Fundación de Arriba, shouted a greeting. They all belonged to Don Carlos Alcorta.

"Hello, friends."

"Hello, friends," came the answer. "Where do you come from?"

"From Boca de Paparo," answered those in the canoe.

"Has the schooner sailed?" asked Mindonga.

"We left her riding at anchor, with all the cacao loaded, waiting for the wind to change."

And to their fellow slaves:

"Good-bye, friends. We'll see you tonight at the dance."

"God willing," answered those walking along the bank. "Bring along good verses to match Bad Nigger's. He's made up some dandies."

And Mindonga smiled perfidiously.

Down another pathway came the women, carrying on their heads the baskets of cacao they had gathered. Saturna led the group, and she smiled under the gaze of Bad Nigger. Her powerful limbs moved in a majestic, rhythmic sway, and under her dirty blouse the virginal breasts with their erect nipples quivered. The eyes of the man who desired her fixed upon them, and she made a gesture of modesty and showed her gleaming teeth, small and even as the grains of a well-filled ear of corn, in a wide smile as she remembered the dance she had promised him.

"I'm going to dance that weed-pulling nigger down tonight."

But as he kept staring at her without saying a word, in contrast to his usual talkativeness, she became embarrassed and grumbled:

"Lord, what a man! Does he want to eat me with his eyes? *Ave María Purísima!*"

Talking and bantering back and forth, the two rows of workers reached the patio of the plantation, where the cacao that had been spread out in the sun to dry during the day was already gathered into the sheds to keep it from the night dew. As the overseer dismounted he said to the slaves:

"All right. You've worked hard today, and I know you're tired, so you don't have to say the Rosary tonight. And as soon as you've eaten, you can all go to bed."

This was the humiliating fashion in which he treated them when the master was away; when he was there, on the contrary, he pretended to be kind to them. But now, in addition, they felt that they had been cheated, and they looked at each other, asking silent questions, which only Bad Nigger ventured to put into words:

"To bed? And what about the dance we always have on this night?"

"I said this morning that the machete and grub hoe were the only musical instruments there would be this year," answered Mindonga, more insolent and domineering. "The master doesn't want any more dances around here, because he doesn't feel like it. He's the boss and he doesn't have to give any explanations, any more than he would to a horse when he gets on its back. So you've heard what I said: every Negro to his pallet, and I don't want to hear a word out of anybody. Or I'll take my whip and make someone's back into a drum tonight. I wouldn't mind playing a tune on it."

But there were protests, even though they were only muttered ones:

"This is going too far. Now they've even taken away the dance, the only fun a poor nigger had."

"But twice as much work, and hard, like today."

"That's what being a slave is, all right."

"Nobody is one because he wants to be or if he can help it; nor should those of us who are, be, for there's been laws about that since 1821. And the masters might obey them, for they're white and free, and they never did anything to get that way. And then they wonder why things happen."

"I don't believe the master had anything to do with this, myself," interrupted Bad Nigger. "This is the doings of that damned mulatto. Why, his name is almost *Mandinga*.[1] There's no wedge harder than one of the same wood. He's gone to Don Carlos with some kind of lie so he won't let us have the dance."

Tapipa, less excitable, more resigned and bitter, said:

"I wonder if it's because of the white blood in him."

"I don't know why it is, but the fact is that so far I've never seen a good mulatto. They just can't be. They're not one thing or another, and it's always the bad and not the good that comes out, because they're the Devil's work, for God doesn't do things on the sly, and when he's making something, he doesn't mix up the recipes."

Roso Coromoto broke in, to egg him on and make him talk, since there was nothing else they could do for amusement:

"Stop talking about your betters, Bad Nigger. You're not too pure-blooded yourself. Don't you say that all you'd have to do to look like a white man would be to paint yourself white, because you don't have either the nose or the lips of a Negro?"

"Why, brother, till a little while ago you saw my father and mother around all the time."

"But in the house where your grandmother worked when she was a girl there weren't any Negro men."

"Oho!" exclaimed several of the group, resigned to the fact that the only fun they were going to have would be at the expense of their companion. "So that's how things are? What have you got to say to that, Bad Nigger?"

"You let me alone, boy. Don't you come messing with me now."

Tilingo went back to the subject that had started them off.

"What I want to say is that if the master didn't want us to have the dance, all right, he's the boss and he doesn't have to ask anybody's permission; but why did Mindonga, who must have known about it, wait till the last minute to tell us, fooling us as though we were children."

"Because he likes to humiliate us," answered Bad Nigger. "Can't you see he's mean just for the fun of it? But I swear by this cross," making a cross of his thumb and forefinger, "that I am going to dance tonight, even if it is on *Mandinga's* front doorstep."

Those who heard his oath were sure afterwards that the Devil had taken Bad Nigger at his word.

Men and women had already gone to their separate sleeping quarters and were soon fast asleep, recovering the strength they had expended in the hard day's toil, when Bad Nigger, kept awake by his

[1] Devil.

anger and resentment, began to hear the sound of a distant drum through the silence of the night.

He sat up on his pallet, listened attentively, and said to himself:

"That's coming from El Sitio, and that's where I'm going, no matter what it costs me."

He pulled from under the pallet the change of clothing and the new sandals he had hidden there in readiness for his furtive escapade, and clutching them under his arm, he crawled to the door. He opened it cautiously, peered out into the empty patio, crossed it on tiptoe, climbed over the wall, and dropped into the field on the other side.

In the hot Midsummer Night the full moon shed its radiance over the hills and bathed the quiet guamo trees with its spectral glow. Everything about the quarters lay in silence, and only in the distance could be heard the throbbing of the drum.

The dried leaves in the cacao grove were crackling under his feet when he noticed that the sound of the drum was coming from a different direction. He stopped to see if he could locate it.

"It's not at El Sitio. It's at La Fundación de Arriba. Is it possible that they are letting them have a dance there and won't let us have one? It wouldn't surprise me, because Mindonga isn't in charge there. But if that's the case, I've just wasted my time getting up, for if that's where it is, the minute I show up there they'll send me back so Mindonga can do a job on me. And won't he like that! Wouldn't it be better for me to go back? Wait a minute, Bad Nigger. It's not at La Fundación de Arriba either. It's coming from the other side."

A goatsucker flew by, almost brushing his ear, and a shudder ran through him. Far away, in a tree on the other side of the Tuy, an owl hooted. Bad Nigger raised his right hand to the inseparable conjure bag he wore around his neck to ward off the spell of these unlucky birds, but the prayer he was about to say died on his lips as he noticed a strange thing that was taking place about him. With the passing of the clouds over the face of the moon, the cacao grove was alternately bathed in splendor and in a wan pale light that broadened and then narrowed the field of vision as if by magic, making the silent loneliness of the spot even more frightening.

In the soul of the Negro the abysses of millenary superstitions opened wide. Those were ghosts moving among the trees, perhaps the souls in torment of old plantation slaves, who were still working there, doing penance for the sins they had not confessed when they died, or perhaps they were the souls of the redeemed, who were blocking his path so he would not go to the drum that *Mandinga*, who had taken him at his word, was playing at the door of Hell.

He shivered and clutched tighter in his right hand the dirty conjure bag, which enclosed the protective powers of the piece of naval cord that kept him spiritually bound to his mother and protected him from harm and danger. And he murmured the prayer to ward off evil:

"Blessed Mother, you are at rest, and I with you because of this by which you nourished me when I was in your womb. Keep me and hold me fast when I am about to fall, intercede for me with God in time of peril and the hour of danger."

And with this he resumed his crossing of the growing and shrinking grove, which seemed bewitched. He could not turn back, because he realized that, despite his faith in the incantation, if he took one step back he would be seized by panic.

As for the sound of the drum, he could no longer tell from which direction it was coming. There were moments when he was not even sure there was such a noise anywhere. Yet he tried to persuade himself that he really was hearing it and that it was a normal thing:

"Now it's coming from over at El Sitio again. It must be the wind that carries the sound from one direction to another as it shifts. But there's not a breath of wind stirring, for not a leaf moves anywhere. There's a fox! Look at its eyes glowing like coals. Is it a fox? Was that someone laughing in there? I'm beginning not to like this too well."

He clutched the conjure bag tighter to insure its protection, and he tried to keep up his courage:

"Listen to that double drum! Doesn't it sound good! Hear that kettledrum! What a time they must be having! Wonder where it is? It's not at El Sitio, and it's not at La Fundación de Arriba either. But if you walk straight ahead without looking back and ask the road which way to go and listen sharply, you get to Rome, they say. That's just the opposite of Hell. There's that laugh again! Could that be Mindonga who's been sneaking along behind me through the trees? Mindonga— *Mandinga*—it sounds almost the same. Mindonga! Who ever heard of a Christian having a name like that! Though I doubt if that mulatto was ever baptized. Quit fooling, Bad Nigger, Mindonga has nothing to do with this. You swore you were going to a dance tonight, no matter where it was, and you have to keep your oath. Who said anything about being afraid? By the Holy Trinity and the Blessed Virgin of Carmen, mother of all men by the navel of Christ! Let's see if it's true the Devil took me at my word. Tonight I dance to the music of that drum. It's coming from down there now, and there's where I'm going."

He strode firmly ahead, leaving the winding trail of the bewitched cacao grove, and came out on a broad, straight, cleared path, lined with thick mahogany trees evenly planted along the sides, whose pleached tops formed an arch above his head. He had almost reached the end when he stopped, saying to himself:

"But what am I doing here? This is the road to the Big House, and I just realized it."

True enough, there was the master's house, built in a large open clearing and surrounded by gardens. On its weather-stained roof and on the pillars of the veranda the moon poured a flood of white light, and the silence of the night wrapped it around.

"There are the white folks sleeping so sweetly in their beds, with seven mattresses and their feather pillows," murmured Bad Nigger. "It won't hurt if I go on by, as long as I've come this way."

But then:

"Wait a minute. What's that moving on the porch? A white shadow that comes and goes. Suppose it's the master! Now it's stopped, and it seems to be looking this way. Can it see me from where it's standing? I wonder if these white clothes are going to give me away. Look! It's not a real person. Look how it grows! Is it coming toward me? But it doesn't seem to move. *Ave María Puríssima*. It's a ghost. Let me recite the Magnificat to it."

Suddenly he shuddered, overcome by blind terror. The shade, after stretching to a fantastic height, higher than the roof of the house, suddenly grew small and, without seeming to move, was out in the middle of the path beneath the arch of the mahogany trees, and then, as though witchcraft were at work, it was coming toward Bad Nigger.

"Oh, sister," he babbled, shaking from head to foot and clutching the conjure bag in his right hand, convinced that he was face to face with the most terrifying ghost mortal eyes had ever beheld, "in the name of God, please let me by!"

The vision gave a groan and dropped to the ground. Bad Nigger stood rooted in his tracks, not daring to breathe. Then he muttered hoarsely:

"Listen to it moan! Like a real person!"

As though drawn by a power stronger than his will, he took a few steps forward. The mysterious drum was beating in his temples.

Boom, boom, boom.

He stopped, and then said incredulously:

"Why, it's White Missy."

It was Ana Julia. She had stealthily left her bed, where she had been tossing about, unable to sleep, to see if she could find air. She was beginning to feel that choking sensation that preceded her attacks. She had walked about the veranda, like a restless spirit, in the silence of the night, until suddenly the fascination of the dark, breathless forest

that lay about the house took possession of her soul. She stood for a
moment at the top of the stairs that led to the proud mansion, and
then, in her folly, descended them, crossed the garden, and set out
upon the path bordered by the mahogany trees. There she hesitated
for a moment as she saw the white blotch of the fugitive's clothes, and
then, overcome by the vertigo of her deep-seated disorder, she fell,
her soul having fled, at the feet of the reckless slave. Her pale delicate
face in the moonglow of the witching night still wore the stamp of
gnawing pain, of deep, tormenting suffering . . .

He had gazed upon the face of magic, and when this happens, nothing is ever the same again. He was bewitched.

Dawn found him lying upon the side of a hill, face to the sky, dreaming with eyes open, spellbound, his brier-torn clothes soaked with dew.
In his soul echoed the last words his lips had murmured before the en-
chantment:

"White Missy."

It was like the muddy waters of a mountain flood that little by little
grow clear until they give back the pure tranquil reflection of the sky.
Or like the radiant dawn of an unending day that has penetrated into
a cave. What a beautiful, unforeseen happening, what a divine thing
had suddenly taken place in his life!

Where had he wandered that glorious night? What soft grass car-
peted that path he had traveled without tiring? His whole body
bloomed with memories, and yet there was no one thing his memory
could lay hold of. It was as though all that had happened to him had
taken place in another man's dream.

The moon had walked beside him to light his wandering steps, and
the clouds had parted to open a blue path dotted with tender stars.
Because in his unexpected leap across the abyss, wings had sprouted
on the man's heels, and never again would he tread the hard earth
or the thorny briers, but would fly through the gentle air. And he
seemed to melt into the glory of the dawn, all gold and glistening silk.

Below, while it was still dark, there had been the flickering of torches
and the beating of drums through the hills. But the sound was of a
general returning victorious at the head of his troops, in a uniform of
shining silk, with epaulets of gold, on a white charger shod with silver,
naked sword flashing in the air. Below, the sea gave back the glittering
reflection; through the hills came the roll of the drums. From the highest peak a king gazed smiling upon his kingdom, which was the whole
earth as far as the eye could reach. A man who was no longer black
and who had never been a slave.

But all this took place in the dream of the other man. The one lying
on the hillside only murmured over and over again:

"White Missy."

But when a man goes beyond his boundaries, there are always others who go out to hunt him back, and it was not to be wondered at that these should be the very slaves of La Fundación. Mindonga was urging them on like a pack of bloodhounds.

"This way. They've picked up the trail here."

They were already coming over the brow of the hill when the enchanted one got to his feet. At the head of the party came Tapipa and Roso Coromoto; and as he saw them so intent in their pursuit, he muttered:

"You, brothers?"

But instantly the great inward light that had come from the flight beyond the pale made him realize that what they were doing was only natural, and he stood watching them affectionately—they had not seen him yet—like friends he would never see again.

"I'm telling you good-bye, brothers," he said to himself. "For now I belong to the world of free men, free, free. The men who have taken to the hills that have been calling them this long time."

Then he slipped on hands and knees through the bushes till he came to a wooded ravine that cleft the hillside, and through this he quickly made his way toward the sharp cliffs that rose up abruptly before him, offering him refuge from his pursuers, for only a man whose life was in danger would venture among those rocky precipices.

But they picked up his trail, and all morning he could hear Mindonga's shouts urging them on:

"There he goes! There he goes!"

It was past noon when Tapipa, who was always ahead of the party—not in the hope of catching him, but, on the contrary, to take another direction if he should see him—stopped on the summit of one of those cliffs, and, waiting for the others and especially the overseer, who was frenziedly whipping on the chase, said when they had caught up with him:

"Bad Nigger is finished."

And he pointed out to the overseer a bush hanging over a cliff that dropped sheer to the bottom of the chasm:

"Look! He's lost the protection of his mother, who has saved him from harm and danger up to now. Look at his conjure bag caught on that bush. He has fallen into the bottom of that gorge."

It was not possible that anyone who had fallen down there could come out alive, and Mindonga, after peering down the chasm, beyond which it was impossible to go in any case, finally accepted Tapipa's explanation.

"Cut a pole and put a hook on the end of it, and let's see if we can bring up that mess of dung."

They did this, and late that afternoon the overseer returned to La Fundación, where Don Carlos Alcorta was impatiently waiting for him. All day he had done nothing but stride up and down the courtyard where the cacao was spread to dry.

Mindonga dismounted and walked over to the master, holding out the conjure bag of the runaway. Don Carlos thought he meant that he had killed its owner, and said to him:

"I wanted him alive."

Mindonga explained what had happened. There was a brief silence, which Don Carlos ended with:

"Throw that thing away."

But Tapipa, eager that the relic should not be profaned, broke in: "Please, master, let me take it and bury it, for it's a sacred thing."

"Give it to him," said Don Carlos, who was in no mood to combat superstitions. And turning his back, he entered the Big House.

Tapipa did not bury the amulet, although he pretended he had. But' he contributed to the growth of the legend that sprang up—according to which Bad Nigger had been carried off by the Devil because of his rash vow—by pointing out to his companions in superstition what was irrefutable proof:

"When I got to the top of that cliff you could still smell the sulphur *Mandinga* leaves behind him."

And all the others agreed that they, too, had smelled it.

ARTURO USLAR-PIETRI

(1906–   )

ECONOMIST, STATESMAN, novelist, short-story writer, teacher, Arturo Uslar-Pietri is one of the best of Venezuela's present-day writers, and a figure that is admired and respected throughout Latin America. He belongs to a family that has played an important role in Venezuela's history—one of his ancestors was a member of the British Legion that fought with Bolívar to win Spanish America's independence, another was Bolívar's aide-de-camp—and he is deeply concerned with all problems affecting his country's welfare.

His first volume of short stories, *Barrabás y otros relatos*, published in 1928, was warmly received, and his novel of one of the many civil wars that plagued Venezuela during the nineteenth century, *Las lanzas coloradas*, has been translated into a number of different languages.

Saturated as he is in his country's history and tradition, Uslar-Pietri is a master at sketching with light, deft touch, suggesting rather than affirming, the dramatic episodes of the past. The selection that follows, from his volume of short stories, *Red*, is the account of the end of that strange, sinister figure of the conquest, Lope de Aguirre the Tyrant. This madman or monster led his band of terrified soldiers—and it took a great deal to terrify the soldiers of the conquest—from Peru through mountains and jungle out to sea through the Orinoco, and then back to Venezuela, murdering, looting, sowing terror wherever he went. His plan was to return to Peru, seize the government, and defy the authority of Philip II, to whom he addressed various insolent, admonishing communications. But the awe in which the crown was held was too great, and his men deserted his bloody standard until finally he was left alone, to be shot by the king's men like a mad dog. But his memory still persists as a legend among the countryfolk of Venezuela, who believe the will-o'-the-wisp is the Tyrant's lost, tormented soul.

Ignis Fatuus *

[ARTURO USLAR-PIETRI]

ALIVE with crickets, the night was throwing the countryside into a frenzy. There was the throb of water. Two or three stars flickered in the sky. Howls fled from the dogs. The path, like a vein, came serpentining past the house to unwind itself in the night. Out of the door smoke and light from the kitchen came forming phantoms.

Said the older woman, stirring the pot:

"Mustached, long-haired, whiskered, eyes like a mad fox!"

"What did he wear?" asked the not so old one, crouched over the hearth.

"An iron sword, as broad as a tile, rowel spurs and a great red cape that covered his horse's croup, like a cardinal bird."

"And a dagger?"

"Yes, a dagger like the Devil's horn."

"And a musket?"

* Translated with the author's permission from *Red* by Arturo Uslar-Pietri.

"Yes, a musket that bellowed thunder, big and wide-mouthed like a Negro when he laughs."

"*Ave María*, save us from the Tyrant Aguirre."

"*Ave María*, save us from the Tyrant Aguirre."

When the noise of the foray began to die down, the Governor's lady, from the darkened room, showed her head at the postern door that opened on the courtyard, and called to her man with voice and eyes:

"Sir husband! Sir husband! What is the meaning of this silence? Are the attackers dead?"

The voice of the Governor made no reply, but a thousand rivulets of blood creeping over the flagstones came to tell her of her misfortune. By following the blood she reached the body. It lay with paunch distended, head black with powder burns, legs spraddled wide, and hands like the feet of a frog about to jump.

Traveling further, her glance met a pair of heavy, dusty boots, a long, slender sword whose hilt was hidden in the folds of a cape, and reached an uncovered, fleshless head in which the eyes, the teeth, and the ends of the mustache smiled.

"If your husband is not here, I am at your service, Don Lope de Aguirre, the son of my own prowess."

Without heeding him the woman began to scream:

"They have killed my husband. Help! The raiders have killed him. Help! Help!"

Don Lope came closer to the door.

"I am the raiders."

"My husband. Help! Help!"

"Where is your husband?"

"Help! Help!"

"Who is your husband?"

The fat, quivering woman pointed to the corpse with a trembling finger.

"There he is! There he is!"

Don Lope thought aloud:

"The wife of a Spanish governor will bring forth Spanish governors, who will continue to rule the colony badly. I must write the King about the matter. But in the meantime—"

And as though he were going to unfasten her dress, he pulled out his dagger and cut her through in eight directions. Her vitals tumbled out before her body fell across the tentacles of the other blood, now cold.

The thick smoke of the witches' den kitchen throws up and casts down monstrous columns.

Says the older and more wrinkled, whose every wrinkle seems a mouth that speaks:

"Killing people, he went his way, slipping over the heads of the dead."

The not so old one, in a voice that was barely an echo:

"And he slid down the rivers, too, in a boat painted the color of blood."

"The rivers came before, and what happened on the islands, too. Now he's on the mainland."

"On the mainland who was with him?"

"He had people from everywhere who followed him out of fear, for the daggers missed his body and the bullets stopped in the air not to hit him."

"Now he's on the mainland. What happened?"

"Have you seen a funeral go by? It is he going past. Have you known when the plague came? It is he going past. Have you felt in the night the hour when death comes for those that have been marked? It is he going by."

The mountains have no end. Behind one peak another rises, and behind that, another and another and another, like waves.

In front, Don Lope alone, on horseback, then his captains, on horseback, then the soldiers on foot, swords clanking, then an old woman on all fours, and La Torralba and the daughter of Don Lope on muleback, praying.

The multitude sees him in the lead, far off, entering the chill sky on stilts of shadow. At the first hill the horse falls, but the Tyrant sinks his spurs into its flanks until the blood gushes blue, and the animal gets to its feet and climbs, dragging itself along like a worm.

Halfway up the next ascent the horse collapses between the Tyrant's legs, and he is left standing above the hide, stretched out like a carpet.

Don Lope turns to the man behind him:

"Give me your horse, and you take the next man's."

Like a row of cards falling, everyone changes horses till they come to the last rider, who has to follow on foot.

Leading the row of men, joined and filled with shadow, he is now the head of an immense serpent broken into segments. Halfway up the next slope Don Lope's horse collapses again. Once more he changes. Halfway up the next slope another fall and another change.

On the ninth peak the Tyrant is mounted on the back of his first captain. A terrifying shadow silhouetted against the light, multiple-armed, panting through two mouths.

"Am I very heavy, son?"

"As light as a feather, Don Lope."

The first captain falls, and the second takes over the burden.

After a time he asks again:

"Am I very heavy?"

The answer is the thud of the captain's body falling to the ground.

The steep peaks succeed each other, and the rear troop is shrinking away.

They had crossed fourteen villages without meeting a soul. The road became a street that passed between the empty houses, past a silent church, and became road once more in the open fields. The inhabitants had deserted them in mass.

At the beginning, when they reached a village, Don Lope ordered the drums beat, in the hope that the inhabitants would return. The sharp beats pulsed against the tense hide with the rhythm of an artery, but nobody came. Meanwhile the troops were dwindling; the men dropped to the ground with hunger, deloused each other, and cursed.

"I am being deserted."

In the folds of the mountains, groups hid and melted away among the trees. Don Lope turned his head and looked at the thin line of men.

"I am being deserted."

He sent ahead spies to cut off the flight from the settlements. They turned up as beggars in the midst of the multitude on the march. In the way they walked, in the movement of their arms, in their glance, people knew them.

"One of the Tyrant's men."

The man denied it, the fugitives threatened him, and he finally admitted who he was, and urged them on in their flight.

When Don Lope arrived he found only emptiness. The spy had fled with the others.

"Beat the drum, loud!"

The monotonous rhythm throbbed in the air.

"I am being deserted."

It was a dance tempo to attract the legions of fear.

The girl crossed herself, and La Torralba spat.

The drumhead echoed like the taut paunch of a dead man.

"I am being deserted."

"And traveling from village to village, where did he come to?"

The older woman, flushed from the fire, paused before she answered:

"Traveling from village to village, he came to the one that had been marked for his last hour."

"Did he know it?"

"No, but the others felt it. They felt it in his eyes, where it shone like a prophetic light."

"A prophetic light like a star?"

"No, a light like a will-o'-the-wisp in a graveyard."

All around, behind all the hills, the lances gleamed.

The news reached the hut of the Tyrant.

A man came in.

"Is your road still open, Don Heretic?"

"It has been taken, and we can't get out by it."

The pikemen could be seen approaching in close, resolute squads. The ring was drawing tighter, and the report of muskets excited the horses.

Like a circle of fire around a scorpion, all the routes of escape had been cut off by the Spanish troops.

The last captain approached, sweating and pale.

"The last road has been taken. We cannot get away now."

He trembled as he spoke, and in the silence the vibration made his spurs jangle.

"We are not leaving, Sir Chicken."

The five captains stood around him, silent. Don Lope loaded his two pistols to the muzzle with powder as thick and dark as coffee. He went to the door and looked out upon the tightening circle of pikes and the hurly-burly of the Spanish soldiers.

He turned around and saw his daughter, who was crying on the indifferent shoulder of La Torralba.

"Why am I crying, Father?"

The Tyrant turned toward the man nearest him.

"Get out your dagger, Sir Chicken, you who know only how to tremble. And you, Don Yataghan, and you, Don Perico, and you, Don Heretic, and you."

The five blades were mottled with gleams in the shadows of the closed room.

"Because we are murderers, we must die, and no one must be left on whom the others can avenge themselves. Because we are traitors, we shall not pay for our treason."

From the throat of his daughter, tearless now, blood bubbled out of the open wound. The five captains shuddered. The silence left by the sound of the weeping that had stopped filled the room.

There was a roar from the harquebuses as they splintered the door.

The Tyrant, his eyes transparent with a glittering light, shouted:

"Kill your daughter, Don Perico!"

"I have none, Don Lope."

"Kill your daughter, Sir Cripple!"

"I have none, Don Lope."

The balls were tearing great holes in the roof.

"Then kill them in yourselves!"

Like a ring of dolls, the captains dropped to the ground, the daggers snuffed out in their sweating flesh.

The sky appeared through the holes in the roof.

"Kill them in ourselves."

One hand of the Tyrant dropped to the floor like a glove; with the echo of another shot, an ear was clipped off like a cock's comb. And another burst poisoned his blood with powder. The Tyrant spun around. He was still squealing like a pig. He was still writhing like a snake. He was still quivering like the flesh of a steer that has just been butchered.

The voice of the older woman lost reality and became of the substance of the night. The smoke dimmed the lights and wiped out the walls. Everything rested on the flickering of the flames.

The other, peering through the smoke, spoke:

"I can't hear. Did all this happen? Is he dead?"

The hearth raised up threads of crackling flame.

"I can't hear."

Out of the fire, like a lamp, like a light floating on oil, sprang a flame that sped through the night.

"Ah, he went by the road of the fire."

"He is a fire that travels through the darkness, blocking the roads."

The glow returned, rising, falling, stripping the leaves from the trees.

Only the two voices lived on in the darkness.

"*Ave María*, protect us from the soul of the Tyrant Aguirre, who passes at night in the flame."

MARIANO PICÓN-SALAS

(1901–   )

MARIANO PICÓN-SALAS is one of the leaders of Latin American thought. His *De la conquista a la independencia*, a history of the ideas and philosophical currents that shaped Latin America's formation, is one of the most stimulating and thoughtful books that has been written in this field. His recently published biography of Miranda, the father of Spanish American independence, is outstanding among the many studies that have been made of that brilliant, baffling personage. He has taught at the University of Chile, where he studied, having left his native Venezuela during the dictatorship of Gómez, in the United States, Puerto Rico, Mexico, was Dean of the Faculty of Letters of the Universidad Central of Caracas, and is now his country's ambassador in Colombia.

In *Viaje al amanecer*, from which the selection included here is taken, he evokes with charm, delicacy, and irony the memories of his childhood. In Mérida, the city in the Andean region where he was born, time has buried that once prosperous center under successive layers of forgetfulness, which Picón Salas gently moves to reveal the faded souvenirs of the past—his own and Venezuela's—that lie underneath. The scenes he calls up have the faint fragrance and smile-provoking ingenuousness of a forgotten flower pressed between the pages of a book.

The Back Yard and the Geography of the Air *

[MARIANO PICÓN-SALAS]

ON the days when "Sancocho" was not digging for buried treasure behind the house, it was my delight to take possession of the back yard. A need comes over one all of a sudden to flee the company of grownups, and nowhere else did solitude and the blue sky hold such sway as here, and the privacy necessary for one's own pursuits. The quadrangle of adobe formed by the garden wall Sancocho had built, whose top the little gray sparrows known in Mérida as *chupitas* had constituted

* Translated with the author's permission from *Viaj. al amanecer* by Mariano Picón-Salas.

their permanent aerodrome, framed the sky, and the placid horizon was limited by the snow-crested ridges of the Sierra. From other roof-tops glimpsed in the distance came the sound of bird festivals. The crowing of roosters and the cackling of hens rang out cheerfully in the sweet morning air. In the near-by stable the horses answered with spirited neighs. Bordered by wild spurge, and dragging along its flotsam of fallen lemons, fruit rinds, leaves, and flowers, ran the irrigation ditch. I would squash the ripe guavas to find in their rosy pulp the moving threads of worms. I observed the ants, the dragonflies, the lizards and the beetles. Free of the exactions and verbosity of humans, I discovered Nature, so rich in geometry and color. In contrast to people, who resemble one another so much, here there were families, species. In the metropolis of the back yard all lived their little lives. There was the bumblebee and the black ant, the red ant, the caterpillar. Even before I received as a reward for my first year at school a thick volume illustrated in color, *The Wonders of the Animal World*, a living zoology had become mine by the direct method in those hours of immersion in the back yard. Some days the companion of my hours of idleness was "Mocho" [1] Rafael, when he came in from the ranch with his loads of corn fodder, smuggling along some delicious mangoes that could be eaten only in the back yard, burying mouth and nose in their dripping, juicy, golden flesh. Rafael and I avoided our betters to transmit to one another our magic discoveries.

Rafael was my teacher of aerial geography. Looking up at those skies of my infancy—skies continually alert with flocks of birds—I came to discover that there existed a geography of the air full of signs and portents that people for the most part ignore. To foretell changes in the weather and what is about to happen there is nothing more helpful than this science of the augurs. Mocho Rafael, who was raised in the country, whose only mirror was the sky, who could imitate the calls of the birds and the noise of a hawk about to swoop down upon a chicken, handed on to me his extraordinary knowledge.

"There are things," said Mocho Rafael, "that you learn when you're by yourself in the country, chopping wood and waiting for them to bring you your gourd of food." He alone could tell me where that flock of scattered buzzards overhead was making for.

He would pause to correlate the signs of his secret wisdom; take a deep breath as though receiving direct communication from the air, and then state sententiously:

"This is April. Those buzzards are going to the uplands of Niquitao to molt, over by Trujillo. They must get there on Good Friday at three

[1] Stump-fingered.

in the afternoon, the very hour Our Redeemer died. They join the other buzzards that have come from the plains or the coast, elect their king, and then separate until next Good Friday."

Toward the end of April on a certain afternoon the first wild ducks appear, migrating from the plains and the seasonal shrinking of the streams.

"The rainy season is coming," said Mocho Rafael. "It's probably raining in Piñango and Pedraza. In two days at the outside we'll have the first heavy rains in Mérida."

And the turtle doves informed him in August that the corn of the mountain fields was completely ripe; and with the clouds of October there appeared against the sky of the back yard the timid blackbirds.

"Those are the souls of folks who did not have time to repent. They come back to earth as All Saint's Day approaches, in the hope that a prayer or a sprinkle of holy water may help them out."

"But I don't like to talk about such things," Mocho Rafael would add abruptly.

"Then tell me how you lost your finger," I begged him, although I had already heard this fabulous tale many times.

And with this he sailed off, high, higher than the buzzards, on the untrammeled wings of his lusty imagination. About that missing piece of index finger, which he probably lost cutting hay on the ranch, he had forged the most extraordinary tale. A tale that he always began with great circumlocutions, as though asking forgiveness for having been the hero of such a spectacular event.

"Those of us who live in the country, far from all help," Rafael began, "have to learn certain things that people in the city don't know. When I was a little boy they taught me the 'Black Magnificat,' which can change a man in trouble into whatever he needs to be, and defend him against lightning, thunderbolts, or a bad end. 'Rafael,' my mother said to me, 'Don't ever use it unless you're in real trouble, because they say this prayer calls up the Devil.' I had grown up on the ranch, and looked after the calves and milked the cows, and I had never had any need to say it. I didn't even say it when that big flood of the Chama River came that broke the spillway, nor in the earthquake of '94. But one afternoon I was on the ranch all by myself, mending a saddle with a pack needle, when Aunt Porcia came up to where I was sitting on the porch:

" 'Rafaelito, have you heard that they are recruiting men for the revolution of that one they call General Castro? It's always us poor folks that get it in the neck. Because those generals mak war using us, the *niguatosos*.' [1]

---

[1] *Niguatosos:* literally, those having sand fleas. Poor folks.

"She had no more than said it when I heard the hoofbeats of riders crossing the little bridge. I even heard them say:

" 'Let's see what we can find on the ranch of these *godos*.' [2]

" 'Run away, Rafaelito, hide,' Aunt Porcia had just finished saying. 'What shall I do?' I asked myself helplessly. I don't know how I happened to think of the Black Magnificat. I noticed a big beam, one of those that hold up the porch, and I thought: 'What if I were to turn into something that was hanging from that pole?' I said the prayer to myself (for things like that must be kept secret), and suddenly my body began to shrink and shrink, and up I went to the beam, as though the hands of the Devil were hoisting me through the air. Just as I stiffened out I caught a whiff of banana."

"It seems that the 'generals' went snooping all over the place. As they found no people and no provisions, because we had just sent the harvest to Mérida, they carried off the pigs and chickens. There's nothing these generals like better than drinking and eating at somebody else's expense. As they passed the porch one of them noticed the bunch of bananas. He cut a piece of one to taste it: 'They're still green,' they say he said. 'They'll give me a bellyache.' How could he expect them to be ripe, when I was nothing but a lad then, not even twenty years old! If it hadn't been for that, something worse would have happened to me."

"I can't tell you how long I was turned into a bunch of bananas. Along about morning, when it starts to get real chilly, I began to stretch out, and all my bones seemed like they were creaking. 'Black Magnificat,' I said to myself, 'if the danger is over let me become a human being again.' And I said the prayer once more. I grew, I grew, I dropped off the beam, and there I stood on the porch again. This same Rafael Francisco González, your humble servant, with my clothes all wrinkled and the end of my finger gone: the one that bandit cut off and ate, thinking it was a banana and complaining about it being green. Just like all those generals that start rebellions. But I said to myself: 'Never mind, Rafael, you got out of that pretty good, even if now you'll be nicknamed Mocho. It would have been worse if they had rounded you up with the rest of the *niguatosos*—I am not cut out for an officer—and you fell somewhere in a heap of stinking dead.' "

"And why don't you teach me the Black Magnificat?" I asked Rafael, when he had finished his story.

"Because you're just a little shaver and you're a city child and have folks to look after you. You're white, and the whites are never dragged off to fight. If I teach it to you, you'll just use it for mischief. That's

[2] *Godos:* Name given during the War of Independence to the supporters of the crown. Synonymous with "rich," "well born."

meant for us, the *niguatosos*. When you grow up you'll be somebody important, and important people laugh and don't need such things. Later on when you remember that I told it to you, you'll say: "That Mocho Rafael, what a liar he was! The things he could think up!"

JUAN BOSCH

(1909–   )

ONE OF THE distinguishing characteristics of the work of the younger Latin American writers is that mixture of irony and tenderness with which they regard their past and their tradition. It is a kind of senti-mentalism turned inside out, distorted, as though to hide the depths of their feeling. This is very manifest in the work of Juan Bosch, who since 1937 has lived in exile from his native Santo Domingo. He is a member of the Council of the Partido Revolucionario Dominicano, which looks to the overthrow of the dictator Trujillo.

Bosch is the author of several volumes of excellent short stories, a novel, a biography of the Puerto Rican educator Hostos, and several volumes of essays. A number of his short stories have been translated into various languages.

In the following selection he employs with wry humor and touching pathos the superstition that the souls in purgatory are in charge of bringing the rains. Fantasy and realism are beautifully blended in it.

Two Dollars Worth of Water *
[JUAN BOSCH]

OLD Remigia clung to the saddle, and raising her tiny face, said: "Here is a nickel for the souls in Purgatory, so it will rain, Felipa."

Felipa smoked on and made no answer. The lamentations she had heard about the drought. . . . She finally raised her eyes and scanned the sky. Clear, high, not a shadow on it. Its brightness was infuriating.

"There's not a sign of a cloud," she observed, and lowered her glance again. The brown fields showed gaping cracks. There at the

* Translated with the author's permission from *Dos pesos de agua* by Juan Bosch.

foot of the hill stood a hut. The people who lived in it, and in the other, and those far, far off were all thinking the same as she and old Remigia. No rain for so many months. The men had fired the pines on the hillsides; the heat of the flames seared the limp leaves of the cornstalks; sparks flew off like birds, leaving a luminous wake behind them, and flowered in great bonfires. All this so the smoke would rise heavenward—so it would rain. But nothing. Nothing.

"This is going to be the end of us, Remigia."

Commented the old woman: "For the years we have left—"

The drought had begun by killing off the first crop. After sucking the moisture out of the earth, it began on the brooks. Little by little their beds grew too wide for them, the stones lifted their heads covered with slime, and the little fish fled downstream. Spring after spring either dried up or turned into a swamp or mudhole. Thirsty and hopeless, many families left their little farms, hitching up their horses and setting out in search of some place where it was not so dry.

But old Remigia refused to leave. One day the rain would come, one afternoon the clouds would pile up against the sky, one night the song of the downpour would sound against the scorched palm thatch.

Ever since they had carried her son off on a stretcher and she had been left with her grandchild, old Remigia had become taciturn and saving. One by one she put her pennies in a gourd partly filled with ashes. She planted the patch of ground behind the house to corn and beans. The corn went to fatten the chickens and pigs; the beans were for her and her grandson. Every two or three months she picked out the plumpest chickens and took them to town to sell them. When a pig was nicely fattened she butchered it. She sold the meat herself and rendered out the lard. This and the cracklings she also took to town to sell. She would close the door of her cabin, ask a neighbor to look after things for her, set her grandson on a bay pony, following behind on foot. By night they would be back.

In this fashion she wore her life, with her grandson suspended from her heart.

"It's you I'm working for, son," she would say to him. "I don't want you to have to scuffle for a living or die before your time, like your father."

The child would look at her. Nobody ever heard him talk, and although he stood hardly three feet high, he was up before daylight with his machete under his arm, and the sun rose on his back bent over the garden patch.

Old Remigia hugged her hopes to her breast. She watched her corn grow, her beans ripen; she heard her pigs grunting in their sty; she counted her chickens when at night they flew up to roost in the trees. Between times she took down her gourd and counted the coppers. There were many of them, and finally silver coins of all sizes.

With trembling hand Remigia caressed the money and dreamed. She saw her grandson of marrying age, riding a fine horse, or perhaps behind a counter selling bottles of rum, yards of cloth, pounds of sugar. She smiled, put back the money, hung up the gourd, and leaned over the child, who was sleeping soundly.

Everything was going fine, just fine. Then without knowing how or why, the drought had come. A month went by without rain, then two, then three. The men who passed her cabin said as they greeted her: "Terrible weather, Remigia."

She silently assented. Sometimes she would add: "The thing to do is light candles to the souls in Purgatory."

But it did not rain. Many candles were burned, and yet the corn withered on the stalk. The springs dwindled away; the pig wallow grew caked and dry. At times the sky clouded over; thick gray banks formed against the horizon; a damp wind came blowing down the hillside, raising up clouds of dust.

"We're going to get rain tonight, Remigia," the men assured her as they went by.

"At last!" said a woman.

"It's almost coming down, you might say," a Negro confided.

Old Remigia went to bed and prayed. She promised more candles to the souls in Purgatory and waited. It seemed to her at times that she could hear the roar of the rain coming down from the high bluffs. She fell asleep hopefully, but in the morning the sky was as clean as fresh linen.

People began to lose heart. Everyone looked washed-out, and the ground was burning hot to the touch. All the streams in the vicinity were drying up; all the vegetation of the hillsides was burned. There was nothing to feed the pigs; the donkeys wandered off looking for locust pods; the cattle strayed to the swamps, chewing at the roots of trees; the children traveled distances of half a day for a can of water; the chickens got lost in the woods, trying to find seeds and insects.

"This is the end, Remigia. This is the end," the old women mourned.

One day in the cool of the morning Rosendo, with his wife, his two children, the cow, a dog, and a bony mule on which their household goods were loaded, passed by.

"I can't stand this any longer, Remigia. Someone has put the evil eye on this place."

Remigia went into her cabin and came out with two copper coins.

"Light this much worth of candles in my name to the souls in Purgatory," she said.

Rosendo took the coins, looked at them, raised his head, and stared long at the blue sky.

"Whenever you want to, come to Tavera. We're going to find us a little place there, and you're always welcome."

"I'm staying, Rosendo. This can't go on."

Rosendo turned away. His wife and children were disappearing in the distance. The far-off hills looked as though they were on fire from the sun.

The boy was burned as dark as a Negro. One day he came to her: "Mama, one of the pigs looks like it was dead."

Remigia hurried to the sty. Panting, their snouts shriveled and dry, as thin as wires, the pigs were grunting and squealing. They were all crowded together, and when Remigia drove them away she saw the remains of an animal. She understood: the dead had nourished the living. Thereupon she decided to go herself to bring water so her animals could hold out.

She set out at daybreak with the bay pony and returned at noon. Stubborn, silent, tireless, Remigia kept on. Not a word of complaint passed her lips. The money gourd was lighter; but she had to go on sacrificing part of her savings so the souls in Purgatory would take pity. It was a long trip to the nearest brook; she walked, not to tire the pony. Its flanks were as sharp as a knife, its neck so thin it could hardly support its head, and at times the rattling of its bones could be heard.

The exodus continued. Every day another cabin was deserted. The gray earth was crisscrossed with cracks; only the thorny *cambronales* stayed green. Every time she visited the brook the water was lower. At the end of a week there was as much mud as water; in two weeks its bed was like a stony old road, the pebbles giving back the glitter of the sun. The horse foraged desperately for something to nibble at and lashed its tail about to drive off the flies.

Remigia had not lost faith. She scanned the sky for signs of rain.

"Souls in Purgatory!" she pleaded, on her knees, "souls in Purgatory! We are going to burn up if you don't help us."

One morning a few days later the bay pony could not get to its feet; that same afternoon her grandson stretched out on his cot, burning with fever. Remigia went from cabin to cabin, even the distant ones, urging their inmates:

"Let us make a Rosary to St. Isidoro," she said.

"Let us make a Rosary to St. Isidoro," she repeated.

They set out early one Sunday morning. She was carrying her grandson in her arms. The child's head, heavy with fever, hung limply over his grandmother's shoulder. Fifteen or twenty women, men, and ragged, sun-tanned children, intoned mournful chants as they moved along the barren paths. They carried an image of the Virgin, they lighted candles, they knelt and raised their prayers to God. A gaunt, bearded old man, with steely, burning eyes and bare breast, marched at the head of the procession, beating his sternum with his bony hand, his eyes raised heavenward as he implored:

> St. Isidoro, Farmer,
> St. Isidoro, Farmer,
> Bring the water and hide the sun,
> St. Isidoro, Farmer.

They had all gone. Rosendo had passed by; Toribio, with his feeble-minded daughter; Felipe, and others and others. She gave them all money for candles. The last ones went by, people she did not know. They had a sick old man with them and were crushed by the weight of their sadness. She gave them money for candles.

There was now nothing to break the view from the door of the cabin across the calcined fields to the gaunt hills against which they ended. Even the bare beds of the streams were visible.

Nobody hoped for rain any more. Before they left, the old folks swore that God was punishing the place, and the young ones said it had the evil eye.

Remigia hoped. She collected a few drops of water. She knew she would have to start all over again, because there was hardly anything left in the gourd, and the little garden patch was as bare as the highway. Dust and sun. Sun and dust. The curse of God for man's wickedness had fallen there; but the curse of God could not prevail against Remigia's faith.

In their corner of Purgatory, the souls of the blessed, standing waist-deep in flames, were going over their accounts. They spent their time in the fire being purified, and, by a cruel irony, it was they who had the power to unleash the rain and bring water to the earth. One bearded old crone spoke up:

"*Caramba!* Old Remigia of Paso Hondo has spent two dollars on candles so it would rain!"

Her companions were shocked.

"Two dollars? Good Heavens!"

One asked:

"Why didn't she get any service? Is that the way to treat people?"
"We'll have to oblige her," roared another.

The order went around, the word was spread:

"Water for Paso Hondo. Two dollars worth of water!"

"Two dollars worth of water for Paso Hondo."

"Two dollars worth of water for Paso Hondo."

They were all very much impressed, almost overawed, because they had never had an order for that much water, not a half, not even a third. For two cents worth of candles they supplied a night's rain, and once they sent a small flood for twenty cents.

"Two dollars worth of water for Paso Hondo," they roared.

All the souls in Purgatory were shocked to think of the water that would have to be poured out for that much money while they burned in eternal flames until the moment when God in His supreme mercy should call them to His side.

In Paso Hondo the sky began to cloud up. Early one morning Remigia looked toward the east and saw a thin black cloud, as black as a mourning band, as thin as the thong of a whip. An hour later great masses of gray clouds were piling up, pushing against one another, scudding along. Two hours later it was as dark as night.

Full of fear, fear that such happiness might come to naught, Remigia said nothing, merely looked. Her grandson still lay on the bed, feverish. He was thin, like a rattle made of bones. His eyes seemed to peer out of two caves.

Overhead came a clap of thunder. Remigia ran to the door. Advancing like a runaway horse, a sheet of rain was coming toward the cabin from the hills. She smiled to herself, clasped her cheeks, and her eyes opened as wide as they could. It was raining at last!

Swift, pelting, singing loud songs, the rain reached the road, beat upon the thatched roof, leaped over the cabin, and began to fall on the fields. Feeling as though she were on fire, Remigia ran to the back door and saw the thick strands of water coming down, saw the earth sink to sleep and give off a dense vapor. She rushed outside jubilant.

"I knew it, I knew it, I knew it!" she cried at the top of her lungs.

The rain beat upon her head, ran down her temples, soaked her hair.

"It's raining, raining, raining!" she chanted, her arms raised to heaven. "I knew it!"

She rushed back into the house, picked up the child, pressed him to her breast, held him up and showed him the rain.

"Drink, child, drink, my son. Look, water; look, water!"

And she shook him, she hugged him, as though she wanted to fill him with the cool, joyous spirit of the water.

While the storm raged outside, inside Remigia was dreaming.

"Now," she said to herself, "as soon as the ground is ready to work I'll plant sweet potatoes, early rice, beans, and corn. I've still got a little money left to buy seed. The child is going to be all right. What a pity folks left! I'd like to see Toribio's face when he hears about this downpour. So many prayers, and nobody but me's going to get the benefit of them. Maybe folks'll come back now when they hear the spell is broken."

Her grandson slept quietly. At Paso Hondo, over the dry beds of the brooks and rivers, the muddy water began to run. There was not much yet, and it eddied around the rocks. Down the hillside it ran red, thick with clay; from the sky it fell heavy and swift. The palm-thatched roof was breaking up under the pounding of the rain. Remigia dozed; she saw her field full of thriving, flourishing plants swaying in the cool breeze. She saw the patches of yellow corn, of rice, of red beans, of swelling sweet potatoes. Until finally she fell into a heavy sleep.

Outside the rain roared with never a pause.

A week went by, ten days, two weeks. The rain kept up without an hour's interruption. All the rice and lard were used up, and the salt. Through the rain Remigia set out for Camino de las Cruces to buy food. She started in the morning and got back at midnight. The rivers, the brooks, even the swamps, had taken over the world, washing out the roads, slowly invading the fields.

One afternoon a man went by, riding a big mule.

"Listen, Don," Remigia called out to him.

The man rode up to the door, and the mule stuck its head in.

"Get down and warm yourself," she invited him.

The animal stayed out in the rain.

"The sky has turned to water," the man observed after a pause. "If I was you I'd leave this low place and go up in the hills."

"Me go away from here? No, Don, this weather will soon be over."

"Look," the visitor went on, "this is a flood. I've seen some terrible ones, with the water carrying off animals, houses, plants, people. All the streams I've just crossed are rising, and besides, it's raining heavy at the headwaters."

"The drought was worse, Don. Everybody ran away, and I weathered it."

"Drought doesn't kill, but water drowns, Doña. All that," and he pointed at what he had left behind him, "is flooding. I rode for three hours this morning through water up to the mule's belly."

As it was getting dark he left. Remigia begged him not to set out in that blackness.

"It's going to get worse, Doña. Those rivers will be over their banks."
Remigia went to look after her grandson who was fretting.

The man was right. God, what a night! There was a steady, menacing roar, punctuated by the crack of thunderclaps and the glare of lightning. Dirty water began to swirl through the crack at the bottom of the door and spread over the floor. The wind was howling in the distance, and now and again there was the crash of a falling tree. Remigia opened the door. A distant flash lighted up Paso Hondo. Water and more water, running down the slopes of the hills and turning the highway into a roaring river.

"Could it be a flood?" Remigia asked herself, doubting for the first time.

But she closed the door and went back in the room. She had faith, a boundless faith, greater than the drought had been, greater than the rain might be. Inside, the cabin was as wet as outside. The child was huddled in his cot, trying to escape the drip from the leaking roof.

At midnight a thud against the side of the house awakened her. As she got out of bed she felt the water almost up to her knees.

What a night, what a night! The water came in gusts; it ran everywhere, covered everything. Another flash of lightning blazed, and the thunder shook loose pieces of the black sky.

Remigia was afraid.

"Blessed Virgin!" she cried, "Blessed Virgin, help me!"

But this was not the affair of the Virgin or of God, but of the souls in Purgatory, who were shouting:

"Now, that's half a dollar's worth. Half a dollar's worth."

When she felt the water tugging at the cabin, Remigia stopped hoping and picked up her grandson. She clutched him to her breast as tightly as she could, forcing her way through the water, which hampered her as she walked. Somehow she managed to pull the door open and get outside. The water was up to her waist. She plodded, plodded ahead. She had no idea where she was going. The wind pulled her hair loose, the lightning flashed green in the distance. The water was rising, rising. She clasped her grandson still tighter. She stumbled but managed to keep her footing, pleading:

"Blessed Virgin! Blessed Virgin!"

The wind snatched her voice away and scattered it over the liquid savanna.

"Blessed Virgin! Blessed Virgin!"

Her skirt was floating. She was slipping, slipping. She felt something catch at her hair, hold her fast by the head. She thought to herself:

"As soon as this is over I'll plant sweet potatoes."

She saw the corn buried under the dirty water. She dug her nails into the breast of her grandson.

"Blessed Virgin!"

The wind howled on, and the thunder shattered the sky.

Her hair had caught on a thorny trunk. The water rolled down, down, carrying cabins and trees. The souls in Purgatory shrieked on wildly:

"Not enough yet, not enough. Two dollars worth of water, two dollars, two dollars."

CARLOS SAMAYOA CHINCHILLA

(1898–   )

MANY MODERN AUTHORS have retold the traditions and legends contained in the *Popol Vuh*, but none more deftly or tenderly than Carlos Samayoa Chinchilla of Guatemala. He is a man of broad cultural formation; at the age of sixteen he left his native land to travel extensively throughout South America, Europe, Africa, and the United States, where he lived for two years. On his return to his country he devoted himself to journalism and his writing. He was until recently his country's minister to Colombia.

It is in the field of the folklore of his country that Samayoa Chinchilla has done most of his work; he is the author of several volumes of tales dealing with the legends and traditions of Guatemala, Indian, colonial, and of the immediate past, the nineteenth century. *The Birth of Corn*, one of his best-known stories, is a version of one of the traditions of the *Popol Vuh*.

The Birth of Corn *

(Seventh Tradition of the *Popol Vuh*)

[CARLOS SAMAYOA CHINCHILLA]

To determine the epoch, even approximately, would be impossible, for the stelæ of Piedras Negras, Quiriguá, Palenque, and Tikal have

* Translated with the permission of the author, Carlos Samayoa Chinchilla.

stubbornly kept the secret of their inscriptions so far. Yet, by a flight of the imagination spanning an arc of not less than three thousand years, we can return to the early days of the infancy of America.

By order of their gods, the tribes were migrating from north to south in search of a better climate and more fertile lands. Dawn was breaking. The shuffle of the sandals of the multitudes on the march echoed like the earth's own breathing through the depths of the forest. High in the tender sky of daybreak gleamed Icokij the guiding star, and at the head of the wandering peoples went bands of parrots and leopards, setting the route.

The peoples had already safely passed the swamps of Xicalanco and the steaming jungles of lower Usumacinta, and now the new land before their eyes was growing ever sweeter and more inviting. Game and fish abounded, and the region seemed favorable for bringing their journey to an end and settling there, but the stern gods of their race when consulted always returned the same answer: that they were to continue their southward exodus toward the unknown continent.

The sun climbed higher and began to gild the landscape. Above the violet hills floated flocks of white clouds, and to the south, silhouetted against the distant horizon, stood various blue pyramids. Volcanoes. There could be no doubt. There was the land of promise their gods had so often spoken of.

All the animals, large and small, were filled with joy. Queletzú the parrot screamed with delight, and all the birds rustled their plumage. But the hearts of the men, in spite of the bright prospect, were downcast. "We have lost Tulán," they said. "We separated, and there we left our kin and friends. Where are they now? We have seen the sun arise over new lands, but where were they when it dawned?"

They had lost their language by this time and were in danger of losing their religion, for during the long exodus there had been neither time nor a suitable place to pray before the altars of the gods. There was little left to eat; many were sick and worn-out, and at times there was hardly any copal resin to burn to the gods. Raising their tribulated faces heavenward, the women cried: "Oh, Tzakol! Oh, Bitol! We kneel, lifting up our hearts to you. Lord, look upon us and hear our pleas! Take not your eyes from us, nor lose us from your sight. You who see in the darkness, in the heaven, and in the earth, give us the pledge of your word when night falls and at the dawning. Give us, too, the blue path, the one from which we were born and which you gave us. Let us live quietly and in peace with our children, with the good and pure in heart of our race, with the righteous in this life which you have given us. Oh, Thou, Jurakán-Chipí, Kuculjá, Managuak, Junapup, Tepeu, Gucumatz, Alom, Cojolom, Ixpiyacoc, and Ixmucané,

Great-grandmother of the Sun, Great-grandmother of the Day, show thyself and let day come."

But the gods had not yet expressed their final will, and therefore the men of Tulán had to move on and suffer still.

Meanwhile, in the region of Paxil, in a remote spot in the Heart of the Mountain, two venerable old people were clearing the ground. They were the lords of the dawn and the twilight, Ixmucané and Ixpiyacoc, who, after assembling in a bag the eight elements that were to work for seven days to form a new plant, were preparing to dig a hole in the earth with a stone knife. The eight elements were: a grain of gold, to transmit its color and its richness; a drop of deer's milk, to form the heart of the future seed; a hawk's talon, to give it the power to go everywhere; a drop of puma's blood, to give it endurance; a badger's vertebra, to make it adaptable, for the badger is an animal that can live in any climate; the shaft of a feather from a warrior's headdress, to give it courage; and, finally, a splinter of black jade, to insure it eternal life. All these they wrapped in a piece of a snake's sloughed skin to give it the property of renewing itself every year, and then, kneeling down, they buried it in the hole.

The rising sun found Ixpiyacoc and Ixmucané still praying at the foot of the grove of sapodilla, nance, cacao, matasano, pataxte, and cherimoya trees, for this remote spot in the Heart of the Mountain was like the mansion of happiness and well-being, and flowing with honey, too. To manifest itself the great work of the gods was waiting only for the sun to rise.

Suddenly the glittering pupil of the great eye that is the sky cast its luminous glance upon that patch of dark, fertile earth in the forest of Paxil, and all the virgin females, human and animal, felt the stir of an inexplicable quickening in their womb.

In the midst of a great silence on the part of all created things the tilled earth began to open, making way for a little lance-shaped leaf rolled upon itself. From the feathers of a cloud a drop of dew fell upon the tender shoot. In the rainbow of the dewdrop was the spirit of the new people that was coming into being. Corn had been created!

A ripple ran through the forest wall surrounding the sacred spot, and the wings of the wild turkeys drummed a long, joyous ruffle. The earth trembled, and to the south, beyond the ridge of mountains, Yaxcamul, the lord of volcanoes, roared with joy.

In a few moments the green tip of the lance began to rise, and when it was about twelve handspans high, it unfurled the beautiful plume of its tassel. Then, swaying in the soft wind, it proudly rocked its two ears of corn, like a young mother with a pair of twins at her breast. From the end of each ear peeped the blond fringe of its silken hair.

The miracle had come to pass!

The denizens of the towering trees—monkeys, parrots, tailor-birds, wild turkeys—hopped from branch to branch, voicing their wonder and delight.

Then the ancient Ixpiyacoc selected the four animals that were to carry the good news, Yac the wildcat, Utiú the coyote, Quel the parrot, and Joj the rainbird, and he said to them:

"My children, go out to meet the multitudes marching down from the north, and carefully take them the kernels of this plant which from now on will be their chief nourisher and the clay from which the legs, arms, and heads of the new people will be modeled."

Meanwhile old Ixmucané kindled a great fire to cook the first kernels of corn, and then ground the boiled corn of which new drinks would be brewed, and which, mixed with the blood of the tapir and the snake, would compose the blood and the flesh of the future generations.

Joli! Joli! Juquí! The white mass chuckled merrily, as it slipped under the roller in little waves, which seemed to become petrified as they lapped to the edge of the grinding stone. *Joli! Joli! Juquí!*

When all the corn was ground, the Great-grandmother prepared the mixture according to the magic formula. Then the Great-grandfather took it in his hands and began to mold the bodies of the four semigods: Balam-Acap, Balam-Quitzé, Majucutaj, and Inqui-Balam, who in turn would later engender the Quiché race.

When he had finished his work the Great-grandfather seated his dough men in a row in the shade of a red-leaved tree, and drawing the strength of day deep into his lungs, blew his divine breath upon their faces and brought them to life.

This was how, on one of the never-to-be-forgotten mornings of the infancy of America, corn came into being.

Its vigor will sleep forever under the stones of all the cities of the New World, in the strength of its men and the fecundity of its women. It is, has been, and will always be the treasure of the poor, the cornerstone of the fortune of the rich, and the most prized gift to mankind through their Indian race from the hands of the supreme givers and maintainers of life: Alom and Cojolom.

SALVADOR SALAZAR ARRUÉ

(1899–   )

SALVADOR SALAZAR ARRU has distinguished himself equally as writer and painter. He studied first in his native San Salvador, and later at the Corcoran School of Art in Washington. His pictures have been exhibited in this country and abroad.

His writing is characterized by an ingenuous grace and that same ironic tenderness which is typical of so many others of his generation. Despite his years of travel and residence abroad, it is in his own San Salvador that he finds his source of inspiration. *The Pot of Gold*, from his volume of short stories *Cuentos de barro*, is a touching and amusing revelation of the thought processes of what the author calls a "bone-lazy" Indian. But the idea of finding a pot of gold is as old as the day man tried to discover how to get rich without working—which probably dates back to the day of creation, or certainly to the fall.

The Pot of Gold *

[SALVADOR SALAZAR ARRUÉ]

JOSÉ PASHACA was a body that had been tossed into a skin; the skin was a skin that had been tossed into a shanty; the shanty was a *rancho* tossed on to the side of a hill.

Petrona Pulunto was the mother of that mouth.

"Son, open your eyes; I've even forgot what color they are."

José Pashaca wriggled and sometimes even stretched a leg.

"What you want, Mamma?"

"Son, you've got to find some work to do. You're just a bone-lazy Indian."

"Oh, Lord!"

But the good-for-nothing showed a slight improvement; from sleeping he took to sitting around, frowning, yawning.

One day Ulogio Isho came by with a thing he had found. It was of stone, shaped like a toad, which he had turned up while plowing. It

* Translated with the author's permission from *Cuentos de barro* by Salvador Salazar Arrué.

had a chain of round pebbles about its neck and three holes in its head, one for the mouth and two for the eyes.

"Did you ever see anything so ugly? It looks just like one-eyed Cande," he said with a guffaw.

And he left it for María Elena's children to play with.

But two days later old Bashuto happened by, and when he saw the toad, he said:

"These things were made a long time ago in the days of our grandparents. You bring up a lot of them plowing. And pots of gold too."

José Pashaca deigned to wrinkle the skin between his eyes, where other people have their forehead.

"What's that you say, *Ño* Bashuto?"

Bashuto took his home-made cigar out of his mouth and spat noisily and far.

"Just luck, my boy. You're going along plowing, and all of a sudden —*plocosh*—you turn up a buried pot. And there you are, rich as cream."

"No! You mean it, *Ño* Bashuto?"

"Just as sure as I'm sitting here."

Bashuto dragged at his cigar again with all the strength of his wrinkles, and became a cloud of smoke. Why, he'd seen people find pots of gold a thousand times, with his very own eyes. When he left, he left without realizing that he had scattered the seeds of what he had said behind him.

It so happened that about this time Petrona Pulunto died. José lifted up his mouth and carried it all around the neighborhood without any nutritive results. He lived on bananas he managed to steal, and decided he would look for buried pots of gold. To accomplish this, he got behind the tail of a plow and pushed. Both his eyes and the plowshare furrowed the earth. It was thus that José Pashaca became at one and the same time the laziest and the hardest-working Indian in the whole neighborhood. He worked without working, at least without realizing that he was working, and he worked so much that the colored hours always found him with his eyes on the furrow and his hands on the plow handle.

Like a louse of the hillside, he crawled up and down the black loam, always gazing so intently at the ground that it seemed he was planting his very soul in the soil. To be sure, nothing but laziness would have come up, because Pashaca knew he was the most worthless Indian in the valley. He was not working. He was looking for pots full of golden coins which went *plocosh* when the plow hit against them and vomited forth silver and gold.

As he grew, so did his obsession. Ambition more than hunger had straightened him up in his skin, and drove him to the slopes of the hills, where he plowed and plowed from the cock's crow that swallows up the stars to the hour when the hoarse, lugubrious cry of the *güa* in the fork of the ceiba goads the silence with its discordant note.

Pashaca shaved the hillsides clean. The *patrón*, awed by the miracle that had turned José into the best renter he had, gladly gave him all the land he wanted. And the Indian, musing on the buried treasure, furrowed the earth with eye ever alert to inform the eager heart waiting for the pot of gold like an enchanted carpet on which it should find its rest.

And Pashaca had to plant the fields, because the owner demanded his share. And for the same reason Pashaca had to harvest and sell the grain of his bountiful crops, carelessly tucking the money into a hole in the floor of the house, "just in case."

There was not another renter the equal of José. "He's made of iron," people said. "Look how he settled down once he set his heart on earning money. He must have a nice little pile laid by."

But José Pashaca never realized that he had a nice little pile. What he was looking for was that pot of gold, and as they were said to be buried in the fields, sooner or later he'd find it.

He had not only become a hard worker; in his neighbors' opinion he had even become generous. On days when he had no land of his own to plow, he helped out the others, telling them to go off and rest and he'd do their plowing. And he did a good job; his furrows were always so straight and deep it was a pleasure to look at them.

"Now, where the devil are you hiding?" the Indian muttered to himself, refusing to give up. "I'm going to find you, whether you like it or not, even if I kill myself in these furrows."

And that was just what happened. Not that he found the buried treasure, but that he killed himself.

One day, at the hour when the sky turns a tender green and the rivers are white stripes upon the plains, José Pashaca realized that for him there would be no pots of gold. His first warning was a fainting spell; he fell forward over the plow handle, and the oxen came to a halt as though the plowshare had caught in the roots of darkness.

José Pashaca was a sick man. But he did not want anyone to look after him. Ever since Petrona died, he had lived all by his lone.

One night, gathering up his little strength, he slipped out of the house, carrying all his money in an old jug. With his grubbing machete he began to dig a hole, slinking behind the bushes whenever he heard a noise. Every now and then he had to stop because of the pain, but then he would go back to work with renewed zeal. He set the pot in the hole, covered it carefully, patted down the dirt over it, and effaced all traces of his digging. Then raising his arms, aged before their time, to the stars, he uttered these words swathed in a deep sigh:

"Now nobody can say there are no more pots of gold to be found in the fields."

CARMEN LYRA

(1885–)

IT IS ONLY with our own Joel Chandler Harris that Carmen Lyra of Costa Rica can be compared. Both have related with incomparable charm and humor the doings of that scamp Brer Rabbit, and his friends—or victims—Brer Wolf, Sis Hen, Brer Fox. It was Harris's great modesty that led him to describe himself as a "cornfield" writer. Nothing is more difficult than to give a twice-told tale freshness, and there is no more exacting audience than children, although it should be quickly added that Brer Rabbit's public, like Alice's, is ageless. Carmen Lyra (the pen name of María Isabel Carvajal) has adapted the pranks and rogueries of this folk hero, whose origins would have to be sought in the tales of primitive India, to the Costa Rican background, just as Harris did to Georgia, employing all the localisms of dialect and setting, and has invested him with that same appeal which custom cannot stale. The prologue that precedes *Brer Rabbit, Businessman*, is as engaging as the story itself.

Carmen Lyra has devoted many years of her life to teaching, and has played an important part in the organization of the workers of Costa Rica. She is the author of a novel, *En un sillón de ruedas*, but her high literary reputation, both in Costa Rica and abroad, rests upon her *Cuentos de mi tía Panchita*, from which this selection is taken.

The Tales of My Aunt Panchita *

[CARMEN LYRA]

MY Aunt Panchita was a short, slight, little woman, who wore her gray hair in two braids, had a broad forehead and little, twinkling eyes. She

* Translated with the author's permission from *Los cuentos de mi tía Panchita* by Carmen Lyra.

was always dressed in mourning, and around the house she protected her black skirt with a snow-white apron. From her ears swung two of my baby teeth set in gold. Perhaps for this reason I once dreamed that I was tiny, tiny—the size of a bean—and that I was swinging in a golden swing fastened to one of Aunt Panchita's ears. I swung back and forth, tickling her withered face with my feet, which sent her into peals of laughter. She used to say that she had those teeth imprisoned there in punishment for the bites they gave her when they were fast in the mouth of their owner, who was a terrible little wild Indian.

Diligent and hardworking as an ant was the old lady, and ready to turn an honest penny at anything that came along. But this it must be said: she was not in the least like the smug ant of the fable, and on more than one occasion I have caught her sharing her provisions with some flibbertigibbet grasshopper.

She lived with my Aunt Jesusa, whose hands were crippled with rheumatism, in a neat little house near El Morazán. People always spoke of them as "the girls," and even their brothers Pablo and Joaquín, when they sent me to see them, would say:

"Go over to the girls—"

They made a thousand different kinds of sweetmeats, which sold like hotcakes and were famous all over the city. A big cupboard with glass doors which stood in the little entrance hall displayed the wares created by their hands for the delectation of the inhabitants of San José: boxes of the most delicious candied coconut and orange I have ever eaten in my life; *cidrachayote* preserves that often proved too strong a temptation for me to resist; little dolls and strange beasts of a snowy-white sugar paste such as I have never since encountered; cakes and tamales that attracted customers from distant sections of the city. There were glass jars holding fragrant cakes of Matina chocolate that made a drink whose taste was like nectar, and which crowned the cups with foam an inch high.

It was she who told me most of the stories that transported me to a land of wonder.

The other members of my family—sober, sensible people—scolded the old lady for filling the young fry's heads full of those tales of fairies, witches, ghosts which, in their opinion, were bad for the mind. These sound reflections seemed nonsense to me. All I can say is that none of my other relatives won my confidence; nor did their sensible conversation or their uplifting little stories, which almost always trailed some clumsy moral behind them, interest me in the least. My Uncle Pablo, who taught logic and ethics in one of the schools of the city, used to refer disdainfully to Aunt Panchita's tales as poppycock and rubbish. It may be that people who think like Uncle Pablo will have the same opinion of them, and they will be right according to their lights. But as for me, who have never been able to find a satisfactory explanation for the things that happen around me every minute, who look on in gaping-mouthed wonder every time I see a flower open, Aunt Panchita's "lies" are just as credible as the scientific explanations I have received from very solemn and learned professors.

What a world of colorful, ineffable suggestions was awakened in our childish imaginations by the words of her stories, many of which had been invented in a way the grammar would never have sanctioned, and which were meaningless to the minds of those weighed down with years and learning!

The tales of Aunt Panchita were humble iron keys that opened up treasure chests of dreams.

In the back yard of her house there was a well under a chayote vine that hung a canopy of coolness over the curb.

Often, especially during the heat of March, my mouth recalls the water of that well, the coolest, clearest it has ever tasted, and which is no more, for the heat has dried it up; and without intending to, at the same time my heart recalls the memory of the happiness I knew then, crystalline and cool, which is no more, for sorrow has dried it up.

Seated beside the well, the old lady told me lies that entranced me: at the bottom there was a crystal palace whose lamps were stars. In it there lived a king and queen, who had two beautiful daughters: one dark, with black hair that reached to her knees, and a mole shaped like a flower on her cheek; and the other fair, with golden hair that touched the ground, and a blue mole shaped like a star on her cheek. The fair one was my favorite, and the blue star-shaped mole on her cheek was a fountain of dreams to me.

My greatest pleasure was when Aunt Panchita took her bucket and started for the well. I skipped along in front of her, as though we were going to a festival.

What strange, fascinating sounds arose from that dark, deep hole in whose depths lights seemed to be winking on and off! (Now I know they were the flecks of sunshine that glinted through the foliage overhead, but then I believed they were the lamps the old lady had told me about.) The curb and the sides of the well were covered with a greenish-golden moss. The drops that fell from them made such charming music. Tin! Tan! Aunt Panchita said they were the silver bells the princesses' little dogs wore hanging from a gold chain about their necks.

If Aunt Panchita had on occasion been able to read my thoughts, she would have been horrified at the effects of her beguiling lies, and would have trembled for my life, for I wanted nothing so much as to go and play with the princesses and their dogs in the crystal palace. And the smile of deprecating triumph that would have curved the lips of Uncle Pablo, professor of logic and ethics, if he could have turned his glasses upon the fields of my fancy cultivated by his sister, who, according to him, had a couple of screws loose. Probably those of common sense and logic. Now I close my eyes, and the memory of the beloved old lady, a thousand times dearer to me than Uncle Pablo, in spite of the fact that she did not know there were such things as logic and ethics, seats itself in her little, low chair, while her busy fingers roll cigarettes. I am at her feet on the little leather stool Uncle Joaquín made for me. I can smell the tobacco cured with fig leaves, brandy, and honey. It is in a big room with whitewashed walls and a brick floor. Somewhere there hangs a picture of a shepherdess putting a garland of flowers upon her lamb. On a chest of drawers a bell glass protects a scene of the Passion from the inclemencies of the weather, and beside it sit two china hens, each in her own nest.

Among the stories were the ever-beloved *Cinderella*, *Puss in Boots*, *Snow White*, *Little Red Ridinghood*, *The Bluebird*, which later on I found in books. And other stories that perhaps are not to be found in books. Some of these I have since met, not in books, but on other lips.

Where did Aunt Panchita get them? What long-vanished imagination of America wove them out of scraps picked up here and there and bits of straw filched from tales created in the dim past of the Old World? She put into them the charm of her words and expression which disappeared with her.

Dear Aunt Panchita, who knew nothing of logics or ethics, but who had the gift of making children laugh and dream.

Brer Rabbit, Businessman

[CARMEN LYRA]

ONCE Brer Rabbit raised a crop of a bushel of corn and a bushel of beans, and as he was such a rascal he made up his mind to sell them for as much as he could get.

So early one Wednesday morning, he put on his big straw hat, slung his coat over his shoulder, and started down the road. He came to Sis Roach's house, and knock, knock. Sis Roach was roasting coffee, and she came out throwing her shawl over her head to keep from taking a chill.

"Who's there? Oh, Brer Rabbit! How are things going with you? Come in and sit down." And Sis Roach wiped off the end of the bench with her apron.

"Can't complain," answered Brer Rabbit, "I was just going by and thought I'd drop in to see if we could do a little business. What would you say if I told you I was selling a bushel of corn and a bushel of beans for two dollars? Did you ever hear the like? But needs must when the Devil drives!"

"Well, I'll think it over, Brer Rabbit. If I decide to take you up, I'll come over and let you know."

"Oh, no, Sis Roach. You'll have to make up your mind right now, or I'll look for another customer. I came here first because you know how much I think of you. If you want tnem, come to my house on Saturday around seven in the morning, for I have to go to town."

"What the devil, it's a deal. I'll be over for them on Saturday with my wagon. But don't go. The coffee is almost ready, and I have some tamales I just took out of the oven."

Brer Rabbit sat down, and in a little while Sis Roach was back with a pot of fresh coffee and a nice chunk of tamale.

With this to prop up his stomach, Brer Rabbit went on his way. He came to Sis Hen's house, and knock, knock.

"Who's there?" called out Sis Hen, who was busy getting lunch.

"It's me, Brer Rabbit. I've come to see if we can do a little business."

"Come in, come in, and sit down. Now, what kind of business is this?"

"I'm selling a bushel of corn and a bushel of beans for two dollars. Can you beat it? Just throwing the corn and the beans into the street, you might say. But I'm in a tight spot and I have to take what I can get. I came right over to your place, Sis Hen, because when all is said and done, we're good friends, and I always like to favor a friend."

Sis Hen got up to turn the tortilla on the griddle, and as she went back and forth she decided it was a good bargain, and she promised Brer Rabbit she would be over on Saturday about eight o'clock for her corn and beans. And she gave him a cheese she had made to taste.

Brer Rabbit went on his way and came to the house of Sis Fox, who was picking some chickens.

"Morning, Sis Fox. How's the world treating you?"

"Bless my soul if it isn't Brer Rabbit! Shanks' mare is right lively this morning. Come in, come in. We're just getting ready to eat."

Brer Rabbit came in, told Sis Fox the same yarn about the corn and the beans, saying that she was the first one he had thought of and here and there, and that if she wanted them she was to come around nine on Saturday, because he had to go to town. Sis Fox said all right, she would be there on Saturday with her money.

After a fine meal Brer Rabbit said good-bye and went on his way. He came to the house of Brer Coyote, who was just taking a big kettle of preserves off the stove.

"Hi there, Brer Coyote. What you know?"

"Why, Brer Rabbit, haven't seen you in a coon's age. It's better to walk in at the right time than be invited. Come on in and taste these preserves."

While he licked up the dish of preserves Brer Rabbit offered Brer Coyote his bushel of corn and beans for two dollars. They made the deal, and Brer Coyote was to come for them with his wagon on Saturday at ten o'clock.

Brer Rabbit said good-bye, and went on his way. He came to the house of Hunter Man, who was sitting on the porch cleaning his gun.

"Hunter Man, you're going to think I've gone plumb-dumb crazy, offering you a bushel of corn and a bushel of beans for two dollars. But I'm in debt up to my ears."

Hunter Man thought it over, and said he'd be over on Saturday with his two mules for the corn and the beans. Brer Rabbit told him to come about noon, because he had to go to town without fail that morning, and he wouldn't be back until around one.

Then Brer Rabbit moseyed along home. Saturday he got up bright and early and sat himself on the fence. The sun was hardly up when he saw Sis Roach coming down the road with her wagon.

Brer Rabbit told her to leave the wagon at the back of the house. He showed her the corn and the beans; Sis Roach pulled out her handkerchief with the two dollars tied in it, untied it, and handed him the money.

Then Brer Rabbit invited Sis Roach in, got down the hammock, which was hanging from one of the crossbeams, and said: "Come on, Sis Roach, and have yourself a little swing while you smoke this nice Havana cigar." And Sis Roach stretched herself out in the hammock and began to puff away.

Brer Rabbit was first in and then out of the house. Suddenly he rushed in with his hands to his head.

"Lord have mercy, Sis Roach! Sis Hen is coming down the road and she's headed this way!"

"Don't say that, Brer Rabbit," said Sis Roach, leaping out of the hammock. "God help me if she finds out I'm here! Hide me, hide me, Brer Rabbit! Oh, I can see myself in Sis Hen's craw!"

Brer Rabbit hid her in the oven and went out to meet Sis Hen. He told her to put her wagon in the shed, showed her the bushel of corn and beans, and received her two dollars. Then, winking and making signs, he pointed to the oven, and when she opened it, there was Sis Roach, who was down her crop before you could say amen. Then he invited her into the sitting room, had her get into the hammock, and gave her a Havana cigar.

Sis Hen was having a high old time when in rushed Brer Rabbit with his hands to his head: "Lord have mercy on us, Sis Hen! Guess who's coming down the road."

"Who, Brer Rabbit?"

"Sis Fox, and I don't know if she's coming for you or for me."

"For me, Brer Rabbit! Who would she be after? For mercy's sake, hide me!" And poor Sis Hen, scared out of her wits, rushed around, not knowing what to do.

Brer Rabbit hid her in the oven and went out to meet Sis Fox. He took her to the barn to leave her wagon, so she would not see the others, got her two dollars, and then did the same as before. Like the sly rascal he was, he kept pointing to the oven till Sis Fox opened it and finished off Sis Hen in the twinkling of an eye. While she lay rocking in the hammock, smoking a Havana cigar, Brer Rabbit was in and out, in and out, like a shuttle. One of these times he came in pretending he was scared to death.

"My God, Sis Fox, guess who's coming down the road!"

Sis Fox jumped out of the hammock. "Who, Brer Rabbit?"

"Brer Coyote. And I don't know if he's after you or after me."

"How can you be so dumb, Brer Rabbit? It's me he's after. Hide me, and please God he don't smell me!"

Brer Rabbit hid her in the oven and went out to meet Brer Coyote. After he got his two dollars he took him into the house.

"Stretch out in that hammock, Brer Coyote, and rest yourself while you smoke this nice little Havana. No need to be in a rush. You know how it is, we're here today and gone tomorrow, and nobody knows when the reaper cometh. For that reason I never hurry."

While he was puffing his cigar Brer Rabbit whispered in his ear: "Go take a look in the oven and see what I've got for you." Brer Coyote opened it, and there was Sis Fox playing possum. In a minute she was really dead, and Brer Coyote ate her up. He was still licking his chops when Brer Rabbit rushed in:

"God be merciful to sinners, Brer Coyote! Guess who's coming down the road."

"Who, Brer Rabbit?" yelled Brer Coyote, trembling at the look on Brer Rabbit's face.

"It's Hunter Man, with a gun this long. And I don't know if he's after you or after me."

"Oh, Brer Rabbit, he's after me. He's got it in for me. For pity's sake, hide me!"

"Well, get in the oven, and I'll shut the door."

Brer Coyote crawled in, with his heart going like a trip hammer, while Brer Rabbit went out to the gate to meet Hunter Man.

"I was beginning to think you weren't coming, Hunter Man," said the old whited sepulcher. "Come in, come in and rest yourself in this hammock, for you must be worn out. Have a cigar, and then you can look at the corn and the beans."

After Hunter Man had rested himself, Brer Rabbit whispered in his ear:

"Take your gun, Hunter Man, and have a look in the oven."

Hunter Man went to the oven, and what did he find there but Brer Coyote, whose shanks were knocking together so he couldn't stand up. Hunter Man took aim—bang—and good-bye, Brer Coyote.

Then they went out and loaded the corn and beans on the mules, and Hunter Man was the only customer who got what he had paid for. Brer Rabbit had seven dollars and a half for his bushel of corn and beans, and four wagons and four yoke of oxen, and he felt very proud of himself.

Always after Aunt Panchita finished this story, she would add sadly: "What a pity that Brer Rabbit should have got away with such wickedness! You know, I think it must have been Brer Fox, and the person who told me the story made a mistake, because Brer Rabbit was a mischief-maker, that's true, but not greedy for money, and not without the fear of God, no, not that!"

MARTÍN LUIS GUZMÁN

(1887–   )

THE MOST IMPORTANT event in the history of Mexico since the landing of Hernán Cortés in 1519 was the revolution of 1910. It has conditioned every phase of Mexican activity since it occurred. It has been the decisive influence, not only in the political, economic, and social life of the country, but in its literature, painting, and music as well.

Martín Luis Guzmán belongs to the generation of the revolution. He was a young man when Francisco I. Madero overthrew the seemingly unshakable power of Porfirio Díaz, and he lived the revolution in all its phases. But even though he was for a time with Pancho Villa,

Guzmán's role was that of a spectator rather than an active participant. It was difficult for him, a man of distinguished family and education, to reconcile many of the bandit-hero's acts with his own idealistic concept of what the revolution had set out to achieve, and he left Mexico. He spent a number of years abroad, in the United States, France, and Spain. Like Güiraldes and others of his contemporaries, Guzmán's outlook is both local and universal. His theme is Mexico, but his art is modern. *The Eagle and the Serpent,* his account of his revolutionary activities and his association with Pancho Villa and the other leaders of the movement, is one of the most dramatic and illuminating books that has been written on the Mexican revolution. In beautifully contained and measured prose, as cool and translucent as the air of the Mexican plateau, employing a cinematographic procedure, he highlights the essential truths, the powerful, often inarticulate forces that underlay the events. There is aloofness, but at the same time understanding. His *Memorias de Pancho Villa* is a remarkable account of Villa's awakening to social consciousness and his campaigns. It is written in autobiographical form, and if Villa had written it, it would have been as Guzmán set it down. This is how Villa spoke, thought, and acted.

As Guzmán himself says in the following selection from *The Eagle and the Serpent,* the legendary is often far more accurate than the strictly historical. This account of how Rodolfo Fierro, Villa's lieutenant and alter ego, disposed of a group of prisoners recalls the descriptions of the human sacrifices with which the Aztecs celebrated their victories.

The Carnival of the Bullets *

[MARTÍN LUIS GUZMÁN]

MY interest in Villa and his activities often made me ask myself, while I was in Juárez, which exploits would best paint the Division of the North: those supposed to be strictly historical or those rated as legendary; those which were related exactly as they had been seen, or those in which a touch of poetic fancy brought out their essence more clearly. These second always seemed to me truer, more worthy of being considered history.

For instance, where could one find a better painting of Rodolfo Fierro—and Fierro and Villa's movement were two facing mirrors that reflected each other endlessly—than in the account of how he carried out the terrible orders of his chief after one of the battles, revealing an imagination as cruel as it was fertile in death devices. This vision of him left in the soul the sensation of a reality so overwhelming that the memory of it lives forever.

That battle, which was successful in every way, had left not less than five hundred prisoners in Villa's hands. Villa ordered them to be divided into two groups: the Orozco volunteers, whom he called "Reds," and the Federals. And as he felt himself strong enough to take extreme measures, he decided to make an example of the prisoners in the first group and to act more generously with the second. The Reds were to be executed before dark; the Federals were to be given their choice of joining the revolutionary troops or returning home, after promising not to take up arms again against the Constitutionalist cause.

Fierro, as might have been expected, was put in charge of the execution, and he displayed in it that efficiency which was already winning him great favor with Villa, his "chief," as he called him.

It was growing late in the afternoon. The revolutionary forces, off duty, were slowly gathering in the little village that had been the objective of their offensive. The cold, penetrating wind of the Chihuahua plains was beginning to blow up, and the groups of cavalry and infantry sought protection against the groups of buildings. But Fierro—whom nothing and nobody ever held back—was not to be put out by a cool breeze that at most meant frost that night. He cantered along on his horse, whose dark coat was still covered with the dust of battle. The wind was blowing in his face, but he neither buried his chin in his breast nor raised the folds of his blanket around his face. He carried his head high, his chest thrown out, his feet firm in the stirrups, and his legs gracefully flexed under the campaign equipment that hung from the saddle-straps. The barren plain and an occasional soldier that passed at a distance were his only spectators. But he, perhaps without even thinking about it, reined his horse to make it show its gaits as though he were on parade. Fierro was happy; the satisfaction of victory filled his being; and to him victory was complete only when it meant the utter rout of the enemy; and in this frame of mind even the buffeting of the wind, and riding after fifteen hours in the saddle, were agreeable. The rays of the pale setting sun seemed to caress him as they fell.

He reached the stable-yard where the condemned Red prisoners were shut up like a herd of cattle, and he reined in a moment to look at them over the fence-rails. They were well-built men of the type common in Chihuahua, tall, compact, with strong necks and well set-up shoulders on vigorous, flexible backs. As Fierro looked over the little captive army and sized up its military value and prowess, a strange pulsation ran through him, a twitching that went from his heart or from his forehead out to the index-finger of his right hand. Involuntarily the palm of this hand reached for the butt of his pistol.

"Here's a battle for you," he thought.

The cavalrymen, bored with their task of guarding the prisoners, paid no attention to him. The only thing that mattered to them was the annoyance of mounting this tiresome guard, all the worse after the excitement of the battle. They had to have their rifles ready on their knees, and when an occasional soldier left the group, they aimed at him with an air that left no room for doubt as to their intentions, and, if necessary, fired. A wave would run over the formless surface of the mass of the prisoners, who huddled together to avoid the shot. The bullet either went wide or shot one of them down.

Fierro rode up to the gate of the stable-yard. He called to a soldier, who let down the bars, and went in. Without taking off his *sarape* he dismounted. His legs were numb with cold and weariness, and he stretched them. He settled his two pistols in their holsters. Next he began to look slowly over the pens, observing their lay-out and how they were divided up. He took several steps over to one of the fences, where he tied his horse to a fence board. He slipped something out of one of the pockets of his saddle into his coat-pocket and crossed the yard, at a short distance from the prisoners.

There were three pens that opened into one another, with gates and a narrow passage-way between. From the one where the prisoners were held, Fierro went into the middle enclosure, slipping through the bars of the gate. He went straight over to the next one. There he stopped. His tall, handsome figure seemed to give off a strange radiance, something superior, awe-inspiring, and yet not out of keeping with the desolation of the barn-yard. His *sarape* had slipped down until it barely hung from his shoulders; the tassels of the corners dragged on the ground. His grey, broad-brimmed hat turned rose colored where the slanting rays of the setting sun fell on it. Through the fences the prisoners could see him, his back turned towards them. His legs formed a pair of herculean, glistening compasses: it was the gleam of his leather puttees in the light of the afternoon.

About a hundred yards away, outside the pens, was the officer of the squad in charge of the prisoners. Fierro made signs to him to come closer, and the officer rode over to the fence beside Fierro. The two began to talk. In the course of the conversation Fierro pointed out different spots in the enclosure in which he was standing and in the one next to it. Then he described with gestures of his hand a series of operations, which the officer repeated, as though to understand them better. Fierro repeated two or three times what seemed to be a very important operation, and the officer, now sure about his orders, galloped off towards the prisoners.

Fierro turned back towards the center of the stable-yard, studying once more the lay-out of the fence, and the other details. That pen was the largest of the three, and the first in order, the nearest to the town. On two sides gates opened into the fields; the bars of these, though more worn-out than those of the farther pens, were of better wood. In the other side there was a gate that opened into the adjoining pen, and on the far side the fence was not of boards, but was an adobe wall, not less than six feet high. The wall was about a hundred and thirty feet long, and about forty feet of it formed the back of a shed or stalls, the roof of which sloped down from the wall and on the one side rested on the end posts of the lateral fence, which had been left longer, and on the other on a wall, also of adobes, which came out perpendicular from the wall and extended some twenty-five feet into the barn-yard. In this way, between the shed and the fence of the adjoining lot, there was a space closed on two sides by solid walls. In that corner the wind that afternoon was piling up rubbish and clanging an iron bucket against the well-head with an arbitrary rhythm. From the well-head there rose up two rough forked posts, crossed by a third, from which a pulley and chain hung, which also rattled in the wind. On the tip-top of one of the forks sat a large whitish bird, hardly distinguishable from the twisted points of the dry pole.

Fierro was standing about fifty steps from the well. He rested his eye for a moment on the motionless bird, and as though its presence fitted in perfectly with his thoughts, without a change of attitude or expression, he slowly pulled out his pistol. The long polished barrel of the gun turned into a glowing finger in the light of the sun. Slowly it rose until it pointed in the direction of the bird. A shot rang out—dry and diminutive in the immensity of the afternoon—and the bird dropped to the ground. Fierro returned his pistol to its holster.

At that moment a soldier jumped over the fence into the yard. It was Fierro's orderly. It had been such a high jump that it took him several seconds to get to his feet. When he did, he walked over to where his master was standing.

Without turning his head Fierro asked:

"What about them? If they don't come soon, we aren't going to have time."

"I think they're coming."

"Then you hurry up and get over there. Let's see, what pistol have you got?"

"The one you gave me, chief. The Smith & Wesson."

"Hand it over here and take these boxes of bullets. How many bullets have you got?"

"I gathered up about fifteen dozen today, chief. Some of the others found lots of them, but I didn't."

"Fifteen dozen? I told you the other day that if you kept on selling ammunition to buy booze, I'd put a bullet through you."

"No, chief."

"What do you mean: 'No, chief'?"

"I do get drunk, chief, but I don't sell the ammunition."

"Well, you watch out, for you know me. And now you move lively so this stunt will be a success. I fire and you load the pistols. And mind what I tell you: if on your account a single one of the Reds gets away, I'll put you to sleep with them."

"Oh, chief!"

"You heard what I said."

The orderly spread his blanket out on the ground and emptied on to it the boxes of cartridges that Fierro had just given him. Then he began to take out one by one the bullets in his cartridge-belt. He was in such a hurry that it took him longer than it should have. He was so nervous that his fingers seemed all thumbs.

"What a chief!" he kept thinking to himself.

In the meantime behind the fence of the adjoining barn-lot soldiers of the guard began to appear. They were on horseback, and their shoulders showed above the top fence-rail. There were many others along the other two fences.

Fierro and his orderly were the only ones inside the barn-yard; Fierro stood with a pistol in his hand, his *sarape* fallen at his feet. His orderly squatted beside him lining up the bullets in rows on his blanket.

The commander of the troop rode up through the gate that opened into the next lot, and said:

"I've got the first ten ready. Shall I let them out for you?"

"Yes," answered Fierro, "but first explain things to them. As soon as they come through the gate, I'll begin to shoot. Those that reach the wall and get over it are free. If any of them doesn't want to come through, you put a bullet into him."

The officer went back the same way, and Fierro, pistol in hand, stood attentive, his eyes riveted on the narrow space through which the soldiers had to come out. He stood close enough to the dividing fence so that, as he fired, the bullets would not hit the Reds that were still on the other side. He wanted to keep his promise faithfully. But he was not so close that the prisoners could not see, the minute they came through the gate, the pistol that was leveled at them twenty paces off.

Behind Fierro the setting sun turned the sky into a fiery ball. The wind kept blowing.

In the barn-yard where the prisoners were herded, the voices grew louder, but the howling of the wind made the shouts sound like herders rounding up cattle. It was a hard task to make the three hundred condemned men pass from the last to the middle lot. At the thought of the torture waiting for them, the whole group writhed with the convulsions of a person in the grip of hysteria. The soldiers of the guard shouted, and every minute the reports of the rifles seemed to emphasize the screams as with a whip-crack.

Out of the first prisoners that reached the middle yard, a group of soldiers separated ten. There were at least twenty-five soldiers. They spurred their horses on to the prisoners to make them move; they rested the muzzles of their rifles against their bodies.

"Traitors! Dirty bastards! Let's see you run and jump. Get a move on, you traitor!"

And in this way they made them advance to the gate where Fierro and his orderly were waiting. Here the resistance of the Reds grew stronger; but the horses' hoofs and the gun-barrels persuaded them to choose the other danger, the danger of Fierro, which was not an inch away, but twenty paces.

As soon as they appeared within his range of vision, Fierro greeted them with a strange phrase, at once cruel and affectionate, half ironical and half encouraging.

"Come on, boys; I'm only going to shoot, and I'm a bad shot."

The prisoners jumped like goats. The first one tried to throw himself on Fierro, but he had not made three bounds before he fell, riddled by bullets from the soldiers stationed along the fence. The others ran as fast as they could towards the wall—a mad race that must have seemed to them like a dream. One tried to take refuge behind the well-head: he was the target for Fierro's first bullet. The others fell as they ran, one by one; in less than ten seconds Fierro had fired eight times, and the last of the group dropped just as his fingers were touching the adobes that by the strange whim of the moment separated the zone of life from the zone of death. Some of the bodies showed signs of life; the soldiers finished them off from their horses.

And then came another group of ten, and then another, and another, and another. The three pistols of Fierro—his two and that of his orderly—alternated with precise rhythm in the homicidal hand. There were six shots from each one, six shots fired without stopping to take aim and without pause, and then the gun dropped on to the orderly's blanket, where he removed the exploded caps, and reloaded it. Then, without changing his position, he held out the pistol to Fierro, who took it as he let the other fall. Through the orderly's fingers passed the bullets that seconds later would leave the prisoners stretched lifeless, but he did not raise his eyes to see those that fell. His whole soul seemed concentrated on the pistol in his hand, and on the bullets, with their silver and burnished reflections, spread out on the ground before him. Just two sensations filled his whole being: the cold weight of the bullets that he was putting into the openings of the barrel, and the warm smoothness of the gun. Over his head one after another rang out the shots of his "chief," entertaining himself with his sharpshooting.

The panic-stricken flight of the prisoners towards the wall of salvation—a fugue of death in which the two themes of the passion to kill and the infinite desire to live were blended—lasted almost two hours.

Not for one minute did Fierro lose his precision or aim or his poise. He was firing at moving human targets, targets that jumped and slipped in pools of blood and amidst corpses stretched out in unbelievable positions, but he fired without other emotion than that of hitting or missing. He calculated the deflection caused by the wind, and corrected it with each shot.

Some of the prisoners, crazed by terror, fell to their knees as they came through the gate. There the bullet laid them low. Others danced about grotesquely behind the shelter of the well-head until the bullet cured them of their frenzy or they dropped wounded into the well. But nearly all rushed towards the adobe wall and tried to climb it over the warm, damp, steaming heaps of piled-up bodies. Some managed to dig their nails into the earth coping, but their hands, so avid of life, soon fell lifeless.

There came a moment in which the mass execution became a noisy tumult, punctuated by the dry snap of the pistol-shots, muted by the voice of the wind. On one side of the fence the shouts of those who fled from death only to die; on the other, those who resisted the pressure of the horsemen and tried to break through the wall that pushed them on towards that terrible gate. And to the shouts of one group and the other were added the voices of the soldiers stationed along the fences. The noise of the shooting, the marksmanship of Fierro, and the cries and frantic gestures of the condemned men had worked them up to a pitch of great excitement. The somersaults of the bodies as they fell in the death-agony elicited loud exclamations of amusement from them, and they shouted, gesticulated, and gave peals of laughter as they fired into the mounds of bodies in which they saw the slightest evidence of life.

In the last squad of victims there were twelve instead of ten. The twelve piled out of the death pen, falling over one another, each trying to protect himself with the others, in his anxiety to win in the horrible race. To go forward they had to jump over the piled-up corpses, but not for this reason did the bullet err in its aim. With sinister precision it hit them one by one and left them on the way to the wall, arms and legs outstretched, embracing the mass of their motionless companions. But one of them, the only one left alive, managed to reach the coping and swing himself over. The firing stopped and the troop of soldiers crowded into the corner of the adjoining barn-lot to see the fugitive.

It was beginning to get dark. It took the soldiers a little while to focus their vision in the twilight. At first they could see nothing. Finally, far off, in the vastness of the darkling plain they managed to make out a moving spot. As it ran, the body bent so far over that it almost seemed to crawl along on the ground.

A soldier took aim. "It's hard to see," he said as he fired.

The report died away in the evening wind. The moving spot fled on.

Fierro had not moved from his place. His arm was exhausted, and he let it hang limp against his side for a long time. Then he became aware of a pain in his forefinger and raised his hand to his face; he could see that the finger was somewhat swollen. He rubbed it gently between the fingers and the palm of his hand and for a good space of time kept up this gentle massage. Finally he stooped over and picked up his *sarape*, which he had taken off at the beginning of the executions. He threw it over his shoulders and walked over to the shelter of the stalls. But after a few steps he turned to his orderly:

"When you're finished, bring up the horses."

And he went on his way.

The orderly was gathering up the exploded caps. In the next pen the soldiers of the guard had dismounted and were talking or singing softly. The orderly heard them in silence and without raising his head. Finally he got slowly to his feet. He gathered up the blanket by the four corners and threw it over his shoulder. The empty caps rattled in it with a dull tintinnabulation.

It was dark. A few stars glimmered, and on the other side of the fence the cigarettes shone red. The orderly walked heavily and slowly and, half feeling his way, went to the last of the pens and in a little while returned leading his own and his master's horses by the bridle; across one of his shoulders swung the haversack.

He made his way over to the stalls. Fierro was sitting on a rock, smoking. The wind whistled through the cracks in the boards.

"Unsaddle the horse and make up my bed," ordered Fierro. "I'm so tired I can't stand up."

"Here in this pen, chief? Here . . . ?"

"Sure. Why not?"

The orderly did as he was bidden. He unsaddled the horse and spread the blankets on the straw, making a kind of pillow out of the haversack and the saddle. Fierro stretched out and in a few minutes was asleep.

The orderly lighted his lantern and bedded the horses for the night. Then he blew out the light, wrapped himself in his blanket, and lay down at the feet of his master. But in a minute he was up again and knelt down and crossed himself. Then he stretched out on the straw again.

Six or seven hours went by. The wind had died down. The silence of the night was bathed in moonlight. Occasionally a horse snuffled. The radiance of the moon gleamed on the dented surface of the bucket that hung by the well and made clear shadows of all the objects in the yard except the mounds of corpses. These rose up, enormous in the stillness of the night, like fantastic hills, strange and blurred in outline.

The blue silver of the night descended on the corpses in rays of purest light. But little by little that light turned into a voice, a voice that had the irreality of the night. It grew distinct; it was a voice that was barely audible, faint and tortured, but clear like the shadows cast by the moon. From the center of one of the mounds of corpses the voice seemed to whisper:

"Oh! Oh!"

The heaped-up bodies, stiff and cold for hours, lay motionless in the barn-yard. The moonlight sank into them as into an inert mass. But the voice sounded again:

"Oh . . . Oh . . . Oh . . ."

And this last groan reached to the spot where Fierro's orderly lay sleeping and brought him out of sleep to the consciousness of hearing. The first thing that came to his mind was the memory of the execution of the three hundred prisoners; the mere thought of it kept him motionless in the straw, his eyes half open and his whole soul fixed on the lamentation of that voice:

"Oh . . . please . . ."

Fierro tossed on his bed.

"Please . . . water . . ."

Fierro awoke and listened attentively.

"Please . . . water . . ."

Fierro stretched out his foot until he touched his orderly.

"Hey, you. Don't you hear? One of those dead men is asking for water."

"Yes, chief."

"You get up and put a bullet through the sniveling son-of-a-bitch. Let's see if he'll let me get some sleep then."

"A bullet through who, chief?"

"The one that's asking for water, you fool. Don't you understand?"

"Water, please," the voice kept on.

The orderly took his pistol from under the saddle and started out of the shed in search of the voice. He shivered with fear and cold. He felt sick to his soul.

He looked around in the light of the moon. Every body he touched was stiff. He hesitated without knowing what to do. Finally he fired in the direction from which the voice came. The voice kept on. The orderly fired again. The voice died away.

The moon floated through the limitless space of its blue light. Under the shelter of the shed Fierro slept.

ALFONSO REYES

(1889–   )

ALFONSO REYES has represented his native Mexico as ambassador in various countries, European and American. And it is no exaggeration to say that at all times, wherever he is, he exemplifies the finest human qualities his own land and all Latin America can offer. "To know him was to love him, to name him was to praise." Scholar, poet, essayist, his entire life has been dedicated to learning and to understanding. There is a Renaissance quality about the vastness of his culture and the multiplicity of his interests. In his refinement, his good taste, and the keenness of his sensibilities, he is very Mexican; and in his understanding, of the heart as well as the head, he is a citizen of the world. Anyone who has known him accounts his acquaintanceship a privilege. His conversation is a delight, and, if he had not written a single line, he would deserve immortality for one of his phrases: "There is only one race I believe in—the human race." He is the author of many works, essays, poems, erudite studies, but one of his best known is the *Visión de Anahuac*, an evocation of the Aztec civilization at its moment of culminating splendor, just before the Conquest, from which the following selection has been taken.

Vision of Anahuac (1519) *

[ALFONSO REYES]

THE loss of the native poetry of Mexico must be mourned as irreparable. Scholars may unearth certain isolated fragments of it, or weigh the relative fidelity with which others were turned into Spanish by the missionary fathers. But none of this, important though it be, can ever make up for the loss of this native poetry as a group and social expression. Our knowledge of it boils down to conjectures, to the ingenuous narrations preserved by friars who may not always have understood the poetic rites they were describing, as in the case of what we imagine of the fabulous early years of Netzahualcoyotl, the prince whose kingdom was seized by usurpers, and who dwelt for a time in the company of the forest, nourishing himself on its fruits, the while he composed songs to solace his exile.

Nevertheless, certain curious proofs remain of what may have been the reflection of nature in that poetry, which, despite probable confusion and adulteration, would seem to be based on certain authentic, unmistakable primitive elements. Of these are the old poems written in Nahuatl, the kind the Indians sang on their festive occasions, and to which Cabrera y Quintero alludes in his *Escudo de Armas de Mexico* (1746). Memorized, they handed on from one generation to another the most minutely detailed legends of their origins, as well as precepts of conduct. Those who first discovered them passed them over in silence, regarding them as compositions designed to honor the powers of darkness. The existing text of the few we possess could not be an exact translation of the original, inasmuch as the Church declared punishable, although it tolerated because unable to root it out, the genteel custom of reciting these poems at banquets and dances. In 1555 the Provincial Council ordered them submitted to the ministers of the gospel for examination, and three years later the Indians were once more forbidden to sing them without the permission of their parish priests and bishops. Of the few at present extant—for of those Fray Bernardino de Sahagún is reported to have published only their mention has remained—author and origin are alike unknown, as well as their date of composition, although it is believed that they are genuinely native, and not, as some have believed, transmogrified versions of the missionary friars. Scholars are agreed that they were collected by some friar to be submitted to his superior; and that, though composed prior to the Conquest, they were set down shortly after the old tongue had been put into its equivalent Spanish characters. Changed and remote as they have reached us, these songs reveal a tone of sensual aware-

*Translated with the author's permission from *Visión de Anahuac* by Alfonso Reyes.

ness which, in truth, hardly befits the missionary fathers, simple, apostolic souls engaged in the spreading of the faith, whose piety exceeded their imagination. When treading such uncertain ground, however, we must be on guard against the surprises typical of the times. It is to be hoped that the striking similarity between these poems and certain passages of the *Song of Songs* is purely coincidental. We have been made extremely wary by that collection of *Aztecas* containing Pesado's paraphrasis of native poems, and in which the critics claim to have discovered the influence of Horace on Netzahualcoyotl!

In the old Nahua songs the metaphors preserve a certain boldness of imagery, a certain apparent incongruity; they evince a trend of thought that is non-European. Brinton, who translated them into English and published them in Philadelphia in 1887, claims to have discovered a certain allegorical sense in one of them. The poet ask where inspiration is to be sought, and answers himself, like Wordsworth, in the great lap of Nature. The whole world seems to him a responsive garden. The song is entitled *Ninoyolnonotza:* it is a close-knit meditation, a melancholy delectation, a long, voluptuous play of fancy in which the reactions of the senses are transmitted into a search for the ideal:

Ninoyolnonotza *

I. SONG AT THE BEGINNING

1. I am wondering where I may gather some pretty, sweet flowers. Whom shall I ask? Suppose that I ask the brilliant humming-bird, the emerald trembler; suppose that I ask the yellow butterfly; they will tell me, they know, where bloom the pretty, sweet flowers, whether I may gather them here in the laurel woods where dwell the tzinitzcan birds, or whether I may gather them in the flowery forests where the tlauquechol lives. There they may be plucked sparkling with dew, there they come forth in perfection. Perhaps there I shall see them if they have appeared; I shall place them in the folds of my garment, and with them I shall greet the children, I shall make glad the nobles.

2. Truly as I walk along I hear the rocks as it were replying to the sweet songs of the flowers; truly the glittering, chattering water answers, the bird-green fountain, there it sings, it dashes forth, it sings again; the mocking bird answers; perhaps the coyol bird answers, and many sweet singing birds scatter their songs around like music. They bless the earth pouring out their sweet voices.

3. I said, I cried aloud, may I not cause you pain ye beloved ones, who are seated to listen; may the brilliant humming-birds come soon. Whom do we seek, O noble poet? I ask, I say: Where are the pretty, fragrant flowers with which I may make glad you my noble compeers? Soon they will sing to me, "Here we will make thee to see, thou singer, truly wherewith thou shalt make glad the nobles, thy companions."

* Translation from Nahuatl by Daniel G. Brinton, *Ancient Nahuatl Poetry*, Philadelphia, 1887.

4. They led me within a valley to a fertile spot, a flowery spot, where the dew spread out in glittering splendor, where I saw various lovely fragrant flowers, lovely odorous flowers, clothed with the dew, scattered around in rainbow glory, there they said to me, "Pluck the flowers, whichever thou wishest, mayest thou the singer be glad, and give them to thy friends, to the nobles, that they may rejoice on the earth."

5. So I gathered in the folds of my garment the various fragrant flowers, delicate scented, delicious, and I said, may some of our people enter here, may very many of us be here; and I thought I should go forth to announce to our friends that here all of us should rejoice in the different lovely, odorous flowers, and that we should cull the various sweet songs with which we might rejoice our friends here on earth, and the nobles in their grandeur and dignity.

6. So I the singer gathered all the flowers to place them upon the nobles, to clothe them and put them in their hands; and soon I lifted my voice in a worthy song glorifying the nobles before the face of the Cause of All, where there is no servitude.

Whatever the historic faith to which one subscribes (and I am not of those who dream of an absurd perpetuation of the native tradition, nor do I even put too much faith in the survival of the Spanish) we are linked to the race of yesterday, without entering into the question of blood, by a common effort to master our wild, hostile natural setting, an effort which lies at the very root of history. We are also linked by the far deeper community of the daily emotions aroused by the same natural objects. The impact on the sensibility of the same world engenders a common soul. But even if one refused to accept as valid either the one or the other, neither the fruits of a common effort, nor the results of a common outlook, it must be allowed that the historic emotion forms a part of our modern life, and that without its glow our valleys and our mountains would be like an unlighted theatre. The poet sees, as the moonlight shimmers on the snow of the volcanoes the shade of Doña Marina outlined against the sky, pursued by the shadow of the Archer of Stars; or dreams of the copper axe on whose sharp edge the heavens rest; or thinks to hear, in the lonely desert, the tragic weeping of the twins the white-robed goddess bears upon her back. We must not ignore the evocation, nor turn our backs upon the legend. Even if this tradition were not ours, it is at any rate, in our hands, and we are its sole repository. We must never renounce, Oh Keats, a thing of beauty, the creator of eternal joys.

MEXICAN CORRIDOS

THE *corrido* is not the exclusive patrimony of Mexico. It is to be found in all the Hispanic countries, but it is in Mexico that it flourishes with greatest vitality. It has its origins in the ballads of the Middle Ages, the *romances*, which the German philosopher and historian Hegel, called "a necklace of pearls" in Spanish poetry. The conquistadors brought them to America, and they immediately became acclimated to the new terrain. It is anonymous folk poetry, sung by minstrels or street singers to the accompaniment of guitar or harp, in which the people express their admiration for their heroes or relate some dramatic episode of national or local importance. Although the *corrido* still exists everywhere, it now lacks creative power and is in the nature of a vestige of the past, except in Mexico. When, with the revolution, the Mexican people came to the fore, they brought with them their own art. For them the *corrido* was not a mere repository of tradition, even though its form and music were traditional, but a living vital thing. It is a form of folk history. It encompasses everything: the exploits of a highwayman, the death of a bullfighter, Maximilian and Carlotta's misadventures, the revolution. Matters of international interest come in for attention, and we have the *corrido* of the Spanish Republic, the attack on Pearl Harbor, the defeat of Germany. The people gather about to hear them sung by the *mariachis*, those bands of strolling minstrels, as they did in the Middle Ages. They have an epic value, for they interpret events in and outside Mexico from the people's point of view. This same point of view has had a decisive influence on modern Mexican painting and literature. Before the revolution there were two levels of culture, that of the folk and that of the educated minority; in Mexico they have now become fused into one.

The three following *corridos* are among the most typical and best known. *The Ballad of Heraclio Bernal* relates the adventures and death of a Mexican Robin Hood. *The Ballad of Lucio Vázquez* employs the old theme of the son who refuses to heed his mother's warning and meets his death, and that of Felipe Angeles, Villa's commander of the artillery, and one of the most sympathetic figures of the Revolution, tells of his capture and execution.

The Ballad of Heraclio Bernal

The year eighteen ninety four
And the port of Mazatlán,
For the first time here is sung
The tragedy of Bernal.

Heraclio Bernal he said
Sitting his sorrel so gay
I'm going to be the boss
Of Mazatlán port one day.

Heraclio Bernal he said
Riding out toward Saucillos
I have silver in my pocket,
And bullets in my belt, oh!

Heraclio Bernal he said
Riding toward Sonora town
This hide I carry with me
Will make a fine drum to play on.

Fly, little dove, fly away,
To the tip of the nopal,
They're offering ten thousand pesos
For the capture of Bernal.

To some poor folk in the hills,
Without a cent of their own,
He gave five hundred pesos
To see that they had a home.

Heraclio Bernal he said
When he'd meet a muleteer,
I never rob a poor man,
My silver with him I share.

From Torreón in Coahuila
To the very strand of the sea,
He went wherever he pleased,
And was stopped by nobody.

But once up in the sierra
They came on him by surprise,
On him and the Indian Fabián,
Closing in on every side.

The Indian Fabián he said,
Will this business never end,
This is a trap set for us
By the Rochas of Copalquín.

Heraclio Bernal he said,
Sitting his chestnut so grand,
Now we will shoot our way out,
And ride into Mazatlán.

And of those seven Rochas,
Who set out to bring them in,
Only three made it back home
Healthy, and with a whole skin.

Heraclio Bernal he said,
On the way to Mazatlán,
Not a hair of our heads was touched,
And look at the shape they're in.

Don Crispín García he said,
Commander of Mazatlán,
Give me two squads of the Mounted,
And the Guardia Nacional.

Give me two squads of the Mounted,
And the Guardia Nacional,
We're on our way to Durango
To get Heraclio Bernal.

In Mazatlán port they killed him,
The cowards, and in the back,
For Crispín García, the dog
Was equal to more than that.

Even lying in his coffin,
When they saw him dead and all,

Both the Mounted and the soldiers
Still paled with fear of Bernal.

Now the rich folk of the coast
Don't cower in bed with fright,
They finished off brave Bernal,
Now they can sleep sound at night.

Not a girl that does not sigh,
From Altata to Mapimí,
They killed Heraclio Bernal,
His like no more will they see.

How handsome was brave Bernal
Astride his coal black horse,
He never robbed a poor man,
He opened to him his purse.

Fly, little dove, fly away,
To the walnut tree so tall,
The roads are sad and forlorn,
They killed Heraclio Bernal.

What a fine sight to behold,
Bernal on his stallion roan,
His forty-four in his hand,
Thirty-five men against one.

Fly, little dove, fly away,
Fly up to the olive limb,
Even Don Porfirio Díaz
Regretted not meeting him.

This is the end of my song,
This the sad tale they relate,
Of brave Heraclio Bernal,
His bold deeds and tragic fate.

The Ballad of Lucio Vázquez

The peacocks flew toward the Sierra
Mojada, high, high they flew,
Lucio Vázquez was done to death
Because of a maiden untrue.

Nine was the hour by the clock,
At the table sat young Lucio,
In walked some friends, his trusted friends,
To invite him to a fandango.

Then his mother she spoke and said:
Son of my life, stay home,
Don't go, my son, whom I love so dear,
Fear weighs on my heart like a stone.

Weep not, weep not, Mother my own,
Your tears make me suffer sore,
I want to see the faithless one,
Whom I love every day more.

Up they mounted and off they rode
Toward the Sierra Mojada dim,
But when they reached the dance hall
His rival was waiting for him.

Eleven was the hour by the clock,
And everyone dancing so gay,
Dancing, too, was the faithless one
Whom Lucio loved more every day.

They invited Lucio to have a glass,
He refused to drink that night,
The angry words flew thick and fast,
And they stepped outside to fight.

Three stabs they fetched him in the back,
In his heart they sank the blade,
They did him to death, a treacherous death,
Just as his mother had said.

The peacocks flew toward the Sierra
Mojada, high, high they flew,
Lucio Vázquez was done to death
Because of a maiden untrue.

The Ballad of Felipe Angeles

Nineteen hundred and twenty,
A year to remember well,

They put to death in Chihuahua
A most valiant general.

In the station of La Mora
Captain Sandoval, they say,
Learned that Felipe Angeles
Had just come through that way.

On the slopes of La Brisa,
The general and his band,
Twenty men in all,
Prepared to make a stand.

There he lost ten dragoons
Of the twenty in his squad,
And with those that were left,
Into the hills he fled.

Of the ten that remained,
Four he sent out in advance,
With orders to be on the watch,
In case an ambush was planned.

The advance guard was taken
By that Captain Sandoval,
And they led him to the hide-out
Of the valiant general.

Felipe Angeles Trujillo
And the rest of the prisoners
To Chihuahua without delay
Were instantly transferred.

Angeles sent an appeal
To the Congress of the State,
Hoping that august body
Would save him from his fate.

But being a military offender,
His appeal it did deny,
To his comrades he then said
This means that I must die.

The United States government plead
That pardon they would give,
And the widow of Madero,
To the hapless captive.

When they read him the sentence,
Of the penalty he must meet,
There before them all
To his lips he raised the sheet.

Overhead soared the swallows,
As he in prison lay,
His thoughts turned toward his old folks,
And his artillery days.

It was in the artillery
His military career began,
In a very short time he rose
To the rank of general.

The clock ticks off the hours,
Near the execution drew,
Steady your guns, my lads,
At my heart aim straight and true.

At my heart aim straight and true.
Show me no faces sad,
Never dishonor a man like me
By shooting him in the head.

With this I take my leave,
By the leaves of the walnut tall,
They put to death in Chihuahua
A most valiant general.

PART V

Brazil

Brazil

FINE as is the motto on Brazil's flag, "*Ordem e Progresso*," a more fitting device would have been: "The last shall be first." From the outset there has been a quality of manifest destiny about Brazil's development. It had been discovered in 1500 by Portuguese explorers seeking a quicker and safer route to the East. The other nations trying to find this route were gambling on the hope of getting a share of this rich trade and breaking Portugal's monopoly; for the latter it was a more vital need, because India was already hers. This intrepid little nation clinging to the fringe of Europe, before the other great powers were out of their swaddling clothes, had constituted herself the first modern state and had embarked on a career of discovery, exploration, and colonization that blazed the trail for all the others. By the beginning of the sixteenth century she was firmly entrenched in many parts of Africa, the Azores, Madeira, the Pacific islands, and India. Slight importance was at first attached to Brazil. It was not a passage to India. The early coastal explorations revealed nothing in the way of rich native kingdoms or immediate wealth, whereas India was pouring fabulous treasures into Portugal. But when foreign pirates began to make landings on Brazil's shores, Portugal decided to colonize it.

If not the dregs of Portugal, as has on occasion been asserted, it was not members of the first families—at least not members in good standing—who came out to settle Brazil. Anyone with influence at the court or some wire he could pull managed to join an expedition to India or secure a government appointment there. A slow trickle of what in those days were considered undesirables began to flow into Brazil: people in trouble with the law (and offenses considered little more than misdemeanors today could easily land one in prison); newly converted Jews desirous of putting as much distance as possible between themselves and the Inquisition; members of the lower classes who had nothing to lose and everything to gain by a change. Agriculture was the only occupation that could be followed in the new land, and on their arrival they were granted allotments of land, where they settled and began raising sugar cane, coffee, and stock. Since the uncivilized, nomadic Indians that inhabited Brazil were poorly fitted for the hard work required, and as the Jesuits very soon began to dispute the right of the colonists to utilize their services, gathering them into missions where the only white men permitted were the priests, Negro slaves began to be imported in great numbers.

The first white settlers brought no women with them, and from the beginning miscegenation flourished. The country had to be settled, there were not enough Portuguese, they were spread over a vast area, and so a population that was a mixture of white, Indian, and Negro quickly developed. As the distinguished Brazilian sociologist, Gilberto Freyre, says in *The Masters and the Slaves:*[1] "As to their miscibility, no colonizing people in modern times has exceeded or so much as equaled the Portuguese in this regard. From their first contact with women of color, they mingled with them and procreated mestizo sons; and the result was that a few thousand daring males succeeded in establishing themselves firmly in possession of a vast territory and were able to compete with great and numerous peoples in the extension of their colonial domain and in the efficiency of their colonizing activity. Miscibility rather than mobility was the process by which the Portuguese made up for their deficiency in human mass or volume in the large-scale colonization of extensive areas. For this they had been prepared by the intimate terms of social and sexual intercourse on which they had lived with the colored races that had invaded their peninsula or were close neighbors to it, one of which, of the Mohammedan faith, was technically more highly skilled and possessed an intellectual and artistic culture superior to that of the blond Christians."

Along with the development of a Brazilian race, if one may employ this questionable term for lack of a better, came the quick growth of a national consciousness. Whereas Spain had organized her colonies to the last degree, transplanting to them all her institutions and droves of functionaries, almost smothering them with solicitude, Brazil was very loosely governed. The country was divided into several provinces, known as *capitanías*, under the nominal authority of a representative

[1] Alfred A. Knopf, 1946.

appointed by the crown, but the real rulers of the country were the sugar barons, the *senhores de engenho*, who ruled their estates like feudal lords. Many even had their own militia. It was with an army made up of these troops—Negro slaves, Indians, small farmers rallied by the Jesuits against the heretic invaders—that they drove out the French and the Dutch who had managed to establish themselves along the coast. In the case of the Dutch, this was done without the approval of Portugal, which was reluctant to antagonize Holland, but the Brazilians refused to play the game of European politics, probably unaware of the rules, and established the principle of "Brazil for the Brazilians." When the fight was over and the Dutch were driven out— leaving behind them a number of light-haired mestizos—all the disparate elements that had participated in it were conscious of having fought for a common cause: the defense of their country. It was the beginning of the birth of a nation.

At the same time that the masters of the plantations were securing the north from foreign invasion, the ruthless, enterprising men of the south, the *bandeirantes*, principally from São Paulo, exploring for gold and precious stones, and doing a lively slave trading in Indians on the side, were establishing the western and southern boundaries of Brazil.

Life was primitive, hard, and dangerous; there was little time or opportunity for book learning, and it is not surprising that during its early centuries of existence Brazil produced very little in the way of literature. There is nothing even remotely comparable with that which flourished so abundantly in Spanish America during the sixteenth and seventeenth centuries. It is only in the middle of the eighteenth century that Brazilian literature gets under way, with Santa Rita Durão's epic poem *Caramarú*, which relates the adventures of one of the first Portuguese in Brazil and the despair of the native women over his departure, swimming after his ship in an attempt to lure him back, and Basilio da Gama's *Urugai*. In both, the element of Indianism, which is to be such an outstanding feature of Brazilian literature, is strong.

The transfer of the court of Portugal to Brazil in 1807, because of the menace of a French invasion under Napoleon, acted as a strong stimulus in the development of Brazil's culture. It was a moment of prosperity and intellectual activity. Schools and academies were established, learning and literature flourished. With the advent of Romanticism a real Brazilian literature began to develop. This universal trend fitted in admirably with the natural inclinations of the people. The taste for the exotic, the primitive, the legendary, and the supernatural was completely familiar to the Brazilian; he had only to look about him to find all these elements flourishing and alive. He had been formed, at least in his subconscious, in an atmosphere of folklore, a blend of Negro superstitions, witchcraft, Indian legends, reinforced by a strong Celtic leaning toward the supernatural inherited from his Portuguese ancestors. All of this found immediate expression in Brazil's growing literature, and is present in nearly every important Brazilian writer down to the present day. One notable exception is Machado de Assis, Brazil's greatest nineteenth-century writer, and one of the great novelists this continent has produced. His novels were psychological studies, and except that the characters are Brazilian, he might be a French or English writer of the period. It would be impossible to know from his works that Machado de Assis was a mulatto.

There is a vigor and abundance to nineteenth-century and contemporary Brazilian literature that is in keeping with the vitality of the land. More and more it deals with the problems of the reality of Brazil. There is a great variety to it, as might be expected from a land so vast and diversified. It is characterized by the same traits the Brazilian people exemplify: urbanity, irony, a sly humor, a supple spirit of compromise, a tolerance, and a distaste for violence. (It must not be forgotten that the transformations that engendered such bitter and prolonged struggles in Spanish America and in our own country, namely, the independence and the abolition of slavery, were accomplished in Brazil without bloodshed.) Through it there runs an ardent belief in the Brazilian way of life, and a love of its folklore and tradition. It is regrettable that exigencies of space make it necessary to allot to Brazil the same space as to other Latin American countries, for, in reality, as observed before, it is a continent within a continent.

EUCLIDES DA CUNHA

(1866–1909)

"IF I HAD TO CHOOSE just one book to be translated into other languages as representative of my country and of my people, I would pick *Os Sertões*," says the distinguished Brazilian novelist and critic Érico Veríssimo. It is a work that is difficult to define. It is not a novel, or a history, or a sociological study, and yet it is all these, and more. It is an account of the activities of a half-demented mystic, Antonio Conselheiro, a combination of the early Church prophet, Montanus, Savo-

narola, and a crude, spellbinding revivalist. His austerity, his reputed
miraculous powers, and his eloquence had given him a remarkable
ascendancy over the poor, ignorant, superstitious inhabitants of
Brazil's northern backlands, the *sertões*, and they followed him about
the country. They founded a village, Canudos, to which converts
flocked, many of them in trouble with the law, and it became known as
a sanctuary for fugitives from justice. They carried on depredations
throughout the region, robbing and plundering to get materials and
money for their religious enterprises. The Brazilian government had
not taken Antonio Conselheiro's activities too seriously, though the
Church had been vigorously protesting, until he began to preach
against the republic, exempting his followers from observing its laws
or paying taxes. A detachment of federal troops was sent against him,
only to meet complete defeat at the hands of the rebels. Finally, after
a number of unsuccessful attempts, Canudos was stormed, but it never
surrendered. Antonio Conselheiro's followers died to a man in defense
of their leader and his teachings.

Euclides da Cunha, soldier, military engineer, and journalist, had
been sent out by his newspaper to cover the campaign. *Os Sertões* was
the fruit of his observation. It is a study of this neglected region of
Brazil, of its geography, society, and ethnology, reporting of the highest
order, and a psychological analysis of the "Messiah" and his followers
in relation to their Brazilian background. The only other comparable
book in Latin American literature is Sarmiento's *Facundo*. Da Cunha's
death in a duel at the age of forty-three was a grievous loss for his
country.

Os Sertões, published in 1902, marked an epoch in Brazilian literature.
As Veríssimo says, "Many of the literati who had their eyes turned
toward Europe and who were concerned merely with esthetic problems
left their ivory towers and stepped down to earth. . . . After the publication of *Os Sertões* there sprang up throughout Brazil, with the
uxuriance of tropical flora, a regional literature whose heroes were
countryfolk and whose landscapes were native, as native were, too,
their problems, conflicts, and passions."

In the following description of Antonio Conselheiro, da Cunha has
given us not only a masterly physical and psychological portrait of the
prophet, but an equally memorable study of the genesis of a legend.

Antonio Conselheiro, the "Counselor"

[EUCLIDES DA CUNHA]

AND there appeared in Bahia that somber hermit. He was terrifying to
behold, with his hair hanging down to his shoulders, a long, unkempt

beard, a face like a death's-head, glittering eyes, garbed in a habit of blue cotton, and in his hand the classic pilgrim staff.

For a long time nothing was known of his existence. An old *caboclo* who was imprisoned in Canudos during the later days of the campaign gave me a little information about him, but vague and imprecise. The *sertões* of the inland of Pernambuco knew of him a year or two after he left Crata. From the words of this witness I came to the conclusion that while still a young man, Antonio Maciel had made a vivid impression on the imagination of the dwellers of that region. He appeared among them without any definite purpose, a wanderer. He made no reference to his past. He rarely spoke, and when he did, it was in brief phrases or monosyllables. He roved about aimlessly, from one ranch to another, indifferent to life and danger, eating poorly and irregularly, sleeping in the open air beside the road, in a prolonged, severe penance.

He gradually became something supernatural or bewitched to the minds of those simple people. When this strangely aged man, who was only a little more than thirty years old, appeared among the cattle herders, their songs ceased and their guitars were silenced. It was only natural. He suddenly loomed up—squalid and emaciated—in his long, plain blue habit, silent, like a specter, from the wasteland inhabited by ghosts.

He went on his way leaving the superstitious countryfolk awed and apprehensive.

He acquired an ascendancy over them without making any effort to do so. In a primitive society in which, by reason of its racial composition and the influence of the nefarious "holy missions," life rested on a basis of miracles they could not fathom, his mysterious mode of life began to create an atmosphere of supernatural prestige about him which, perhaps, aggravated his deranged temperament. Little by little all this domination which he unintentionally exercised on others seems to have taken hold on him. All the conjectures and legends by which he was soon surrounded stimulated the growth of his aberration. His madness acquired outward form. He saw it reflected in the intense admiration and unquestioning respect that in a short time made his word law in all disputes and quarrels and converted him into the supreme authority in all decisions. This attitude on the part of the multitude spared him the ordeal of trying to understand his own mental state, the painful effort of self-analysis and that obsessive introspection which drives an unhinged mind to madness. The multitude recast him in its own image, created him, enlarged him beyond all human proportions, and launched him upon a sea of errors two thousand years old. It needed someone who should translate its own vague idealism and guide it along the mysterious paths that lead to heaven. The evangelist emerged, but inhuman, an automaton. This agitator was a puppet. He acted passively, like a sleepwalker. But in his behavior he reflected the obscure, formless aspirations of three races.

And he acquired such dimensions that he projected himself into history.

From the *sertões* of Pernambuco he proceeded to those of Sergipe, appearing in the city of Itabaiana in 1874.

He arrived there, as everywhere, unknown and arousing distrust by reason of his strange attire: a long, unbelted tunic, a hat with a wide, drooping brim, and sandals. On his back hung a knapsack in which he carried paper, pen, and ink, and two books, a *Brief Missal* and *The Hours of Mary*.

He begged his bread, but he always refused to take more than he needed for the day. He sought out the loneliest ranches. He never accepted any bed but the bare boards or, lacking this, the hard earth. He wandered about like this for a long time until he appeared in the *sertões* to the north of Bahia. His fame was growing. He no longer traveled by himself. The first of the faithful were following him on his uncharted route. He did not call them. They came of their own free will, happy to share with him his life of privation and suffering. For the most part they were the dregs of humanity, of doubtful antecedents, averse to work, a troupe of life's outcasts, adept in the ways of laziness and thievishness.

One of the disciples carried on his back the only temple that then existed of this puny new religion: a roughly carved cedar altar on which was an image of Christ. When they stopped along the roadside they hung it from the branch of a tree, and there they knelt in prayer. As they entered the hamlets and villages they bore it triumphantly aloft, intoning a chorus of litanies.

In 1876 the Counselor, as he was known, appeared in the town of Itapicuru de Cima. His fame had become widespread. A document published that year in the capital of the Empire bears witness to this:

There has appeared in the *sertão* of the north a man who calls himself *Antonio the Counselor*, and who exerts a great influence on the lower classes, utilizing for this end his mysterious aspect and his ascetic habits, which make a great impression on the ignorance of these simple-minded people. He has let his hair and beard grow long, he wears a cotton tunic and eats very little, looking almost like a mummy. He goes about in the company of two women converts, and he spends his life praying and preaching and giving advice to the multitudes that gather to hear him wherever the priests permit it. By playing on their religious sentiments he attracts the people and does what he likes with them. He shows himself to be a man of intelligence, though devoid of culture.

These remarks, which were the exact truth, published in a journal hundreds of miles away, are eloquent testimony to the fame he was acquiring.

Meanwhile in this town of Itapicuru his extraordinary career almost came to an end. That same year, to the consternation of the faithful, he was arrested. This came about as the result of a false accusation that his strange life and past domestic difficulties justified to a certain point. He was said to have killed his wife and his own mother.

It was a gruesome tale. It was said that his mother hated her daughter-in-law and set about to work her ruination. With this in mind she told her son that his wife was unfaithful to him; and as he demanded proofs of her guilt, she proposed to supply them without delay. She advised him to pretend that he was going away on a trip, but to remain in the neighborhood and at night he would see the seducer who was dishonoring his home. The poor wretch, following her advice, rode several miles away from the town and then, taking a roundabout lonely route back, hid in a place he had selected where he could see what took place and act quickly.

There he remained hidden for hours until, late in the night, he saw a shadowy figure approach his house. He saw it creep up and climb into one of the windows. Before it could get through he felled it with a shot.

With one bound he was in the house and with another shot he killed his wife, who was asleep.

Then he turned back to discover the identity of the man he had killed. And he saw, to his horror, that it was his own mother, who had disguised herself as a man to carry out her diabolical plan.

Aghast, crazed, he immediately fled, leaving everything he owned, to the *sertões* of the interior.

The popular imagination had begun to create a legend about his life, giving it a vigorous touch of tragic originality.

Nevertheless the fact remains that in 1876 the law laid hold of him just as the evolution of his spirit had reached its climax and he was sunk in a dream from which he was never again to awaken. The ascetic was emerging, full stature, from the rude discipline of fifteen years of penance. He had reached perfection in his apprenticeship of martyrdom, a profession so highly recommended by the old Church fathers. It was the result of brutally binding himself over to hunger, thirst, fatigue, and every form of pain and misery. There was no suffering he did not know. His leathery skin was stretched over his insensible flesh like a battered and cracked coat of mail. It had been anesthetized by its sufferings. It was lacerated and scarred by disciplines more severe than a hair shirt; it had been dragged over the stones of the road, it had been charred by the blazing heat of the drought, numbed by the cold morning dew, had known only momentary rest in the bone-breaking beds of the rough hills.

His prolonged fasts brought him many times to the brink of death. The perfection of his asceticism would have surprised Tertulian, that gloomy advocate of the slow elimination of the flesh, "ridding himself of his blood, that heavy, importunate burden of the soul eager to flee. . . ."

For a person undergoing this training in suffering, that prison order was but a trifling incident. He received it with indifference. He forbade his followers to defend him. He gave himself up. He was taken to the capital of Bahia. There his strange appearance, his corpselike face, as rigid as a mask, expressionless and unsmiling, his eyelids drooping over his sunken eyes, his strange garb, his revolting appearance, that of an unburied corpse, in the long tunic like a dark winding sheet, and the lank, dusty hair falling about his shoulders, mingling with the unkempt beard, which hung to his waist, made him the object of general curiosity.

As he was led through the streets, people exclaimed and made signs to ward off the evil eye, while devout old women crossed themselves and fell back in fear.

The judges questioned him in amazement. He was accused of old crimes he had committed in his native region. He listened to the questions and accusations without answering a word, in stony silence. It was later learned that the guards who had brought him in had beaten him on the road. He did not voice the slightest complaint. His was the lofty indifference of a stoic. Only on the day he was to be embarked for Ceará—and I have this from a person of complete reliability—did he ask the authorities to protect him from the curiosity of the crowds, the only thing that bothered him.

On reaching his native town the charges against him were proved to be groundless and he was placed at liberty. And that same year he appeared in Bahia once more among his followers, who had been waiting for him. His return, on the very day he had prophesied when he was arrested, so it was said, assumed the character of a miracle. His influence became thrice what it had been.

Then for a time (1877) he wandered about the *sertões* of Curaca, making his headquarters in Chorrochó, a village of a few hundred inhabitants, whose lively fair attracted the majority of the people of that region of San Francisco. A beautiful chapel, still standing, tells of his stay there. And perhaps more deserving of veneration is a little tree at the entrance to the village which for a long time was the object of extraordinary devotion. It was a sacred tree. Its shadow cured the ills of the faithful; its leaves were an unfailing panacea.

The multitude vouched for a great series of miracles to which the unhappy wretch probably had never given a thought.

From 1877 to 1887 he wandered about those *sertões*, from one end to the other, even reaching the seacoast, in Villa do Conde (1887). There is probably not a city or village in this whole region where he did not make his appearance. Alagoinhas, Inhambupe, Bom Conselho, Geremoabo, Cumbe, Mucambo, Massacara, Pombal, Monte-Santo, Tucano, and other settlements saw him arrive, accompanied by the troupe of the faithful. In nearly all he left a trace of his passage: in one the rebuilt walls of a ruined cemetery; in another a restored church; farther on, a chapel, always beautiful.

His entrance in the towns, followed by the contrite multitude, in silence, bearing images, crosses, and banners of the Lord, was solemn and impressive. The people deserted their shops and farms. They swarmed into the place where he was, and for a time, overshadowing the local authorities, the humble, wandering penitent took command, became the sole authority.

Sheds covered with branches were erected in the public square, and in the afternoon the faithful intoned their prayers and litanies; and when the gathering was great a platform was constructed in the middle of the market place so the words of the prophet could be heard from all sides and edify the faithful.

There he stood up and preached. It was an extraordinary experience, according to witnesses who are still living. It was a barbarous, hair-raising oratory, made up of fragments from *The Hours of Mary*, disconnected, abstruse, with astounding Latin quotations, pouring forth in disjointed phrases a confused, tangled mixture of dogmatic advice, commonplace precepts of Christian morality, and weird prophecies.

It was grotesque and terrifying. Imagine a clown carried away by a vision of the Apocalypse!

Using few gestures, he would talk for a long time, his eyes fixed on the ground, without looking at the multitude, which was spellbound by the rush of words, which varied from nerve-racking exhortations to a wearisome singsong.

It would appear that he was often bemused by the effect of some significant phrase. He would pronounce it and then become silent, raising his head and suddenly opening his eyelids wide; then his deep, black, shining eyes could be seen, and the brilliant glitter of his glance. Nobody dared to look upon him. The crowd, overawed, lowered its eyes, under the strange hypnotic spell of that terrible insanity.

It was on such occasions that this tormented wretch performed his only miracle: he managed not to make himself ridiculous.

In his preaching, in which he successfully competed with the wandering Capuchin fathers of the missions, he upheld a vague, incongruous system of religion. Whoever heard him could not avoid suggestive historical comparisons. On rereading the unforgettable pages of Renan's *Marcus Aurelius*, in which he brings to life, through the power of his style, the mad leaders of the religious sects of the first centuries of Christianity, one can see in the Counselor's teachings the complete revival of their extinct aberrations. It would be impossible to find a more faithful reproduction of the same system, the same metaphors, the same hyperboles, almost the same words. It is a beautiful example of the similarity of evolutionary phases among peoples. This retrogade of the *sertão* is the living copy of the mystics of the past. One can experience, looking at him, the marvelous effect of a perspective of centuries.

He does not belong to our time. He belongs with all those stragglers whom Fouillée, in a felicitous phrase, calls the "runners on the field of civilization who fall farther and farther behind."

He was a dissenter cast in the same mold as Themison. He rose in rebellion against the Church of Rome, and he hurled invectives against it, employing its own arguments: it had forsaken its glory and was following Satan. His moral teaching was an interlinear translation of that of Montanus: chastity carried to the point of utter horror of woman, while at the same time there was absolute tolerance for free love, leading almost to the extinction of marriage.

In the Phrygian, as perhaps in the man from Ceará, this was the result of an unhappy conjugal experience. Both severely forbade the young women to do anything that enhanced their beauty. They fulminated against fancy wearing apparel, and both of them, above all, against elaborate hairdressing; and what is very curious, they both fixed the same punishment for this sin, the demon of the hair: a piercing crown of thorns for the offenders.

Beauty was to them a snare of Satan. The Counselor missed no opportunity to show his invincible repugnance for it. He never looked at a woman. He talked with his back turned even to pious old women who would have exercised a restraining influence on a satyr.

This similarity with the past grows even more impressive as one examines the absurd concepts of this mad apostle of the *sertões*. Like his predecessors, he appeared when it was believed that the world was coming to an end, that the millennium was at hand; and he had the same terror of the antichrist, whose presence could be felt in the universal collapse of life. The world was approaching its close.

The faithful were to abandon all their possessions, all that might defile them with the slightest trace of vanity. As all worldy goods would be engulfed in the imminent catastrophe, it would be rash folly to treasure them. Let them give up their fleeting pleasures and make their lives a stern purgatory, unsullied by the sacrilege of a smile. The Judgment Day was at hand.

He prophesied years of disaster to follow one after another: [1]

> . . . *In 1896 a thousand flocks will flee from the meadows to the desert, and then the desert will become a meadow, and the meadow a desert.*
> *In 1897 there will be much pasture and little stubble, and a single flock and a single shepherd.*
> *In 1898 there will be many hats and few heads.*
> *In 1899 the waters will turn to blood, and a planet will appear in the east with a ray of sun that the branch will confront on the earth, and the earth in some spot will be confronted by the heavens. There will come a great rain of stars, and that will be the end of the world. In 1900 the lights will go out. God says it in the Gospels: I have a flock that is wandering outside the fold, and it must be brought together so there will be but one flock and one shepherd.*

Like those of old he believed he had been sent to do the will of God, and that it was Christ Himself who had prophesied his coming:

> *In the ninth hour, as He sat resting upon the Mount of Olives one of the disciples asked Him: "Master, what shall be the sign of the end of the world?" And He answered: "There shall be many signs in the Moon and the Sun and the Stars. And an angel will be sent forth by My eternal Father, preaching at the gates, building towns in the desert, building churches and chapels, and giving advice. . . ."*

Through all this wild maundering, together with the religious Messianic concept, there was the Messianism of the race, urging him on to rebellion against the republican form of government:

> *Verily, verily I say unto you, when nation shall rise against nation, Brazil against Brazil, England against England, Prussia against Prussia, from the depths of the sea Don Sebastian will come forth with all his army.*
> *From the beginning of the world which he enchanted with all his army and restored in war.*
> *And when he was enchanted he buried his sword in a rock, up to the hilt, and said: "Farewell, World."*
> *Until a thousand and so many to two thousand years you will not come.*

[1] These prophecies were written out in a number of little notebooks that were found in Canudos. These I have quoted were copied from one of them that belonged to the adjutant of the officer in charge of the campaign.

On that day when he comes forth with his army, he will put all those of this play republic to the sword. The end of this war will come in the Holy House of Rome and the blood will run loin-deep.

Prophecy had, as can be seen, the same accent in him as when it first appeared in Phrygia, moving westward. It foretold the same Last Judgment, the downfall of the mighty, the destruction of the godless world, and the coming of the millennium.

Is there not to be seen in all this a marked trace of Judaism? It seems indubitable. This return to the golden age of apostles and prophets, this revival of old illusions, is nothing new. It is the ever recurring return of Christianity to its Hebrew cradle. Montanus is reproduced throughout history, changed in this respect or the other, depending on the character of the different nations, but revealing in his very revolt against the ecclesiastical hierarchy, in his approach to the supernatural, in his vision of heaven, the outlines of the primitive dream of the old religion, before it had been distorted by the canonized sophists of the Church councils.

Following the example of his predecessors in the past, Antonio Conselheiro was a pietist, waiting for the coming of the reign of heaven on earth, which had been promised, ever delayed, and finally completely forgotten by the orthodox Church of the second century. His creed had little to do with Catholicism, which he hardly understood.

In keeping with the mission he had taken upon himself, after delivering these homilies, he ordered penances, which were generally to the benefit of the locality. Neglected churches were restored; abandoned cemeteries were repaired; beautiful new edifices were built. The stonemasons and carpenters worked for nothing; stores donated the materials; the multitude brought in the stones. For days on end the workmen busied themselves with their pious tasks, and their wages were credited to them in heaven.

When the work was finished, the messenger of God suddenly departed—whither? Anywhere, taking the first road deeper into the *sertões*, over the endless plains, without even looking back at those who followed him.

He was unperturbed by the hostility of his dangerous adversary the priest. According to reliable testimony, the clergy, in general, encouraged or at least allowed him to practice, without return of any sort, all those acts from which they derive their income: baptisms, confessions, feasts, and novenas. They showed indulgence toward the absurdities of the possessed saint, who at least helped them to eke out their meager sustenance. In view of this, the archbishop of Bahia, in

1882, to bring to an end this tolerance, not to say barely disguised protection, sent out a circular to all the priests of his see:

> *It has come to our knowledge that a person known as Antonio Conselheiro is going about among the parishioners of this see, preaching to the people who flock to hear him superstitious doctrines and excessively rigid moral concepts with which he is disturbing the consciences and undermining, not a little, the authority of the clergy in those regions. Therefore we order Your Reverence not to tolerate this abuse among your parishioners, advising them that we absolutely forbid them to gather to hear his preachings, for in the Catholic Church it is the mission of the ministers of religion alone to instruct the people, and a layman, however learned and virtuous, has no authority to do this.*
>
> *Meanwhile let this serve to increase your zeal in the exercise of your preaching duties so that your parishioners, properly instructed, will not be swept off their feet by every passing wind of doctrine. . . .*

But the intervention of the Church was futile. Antonio Conselheiro continued his mad apostolate without let or hindrance through the *sertões*. And as though he wished to keep green the memory of the first persecution he had suffered, he always came back to Itapicuru, where the police authorities finally appealed to the government in a report which, after giving a brief summary of the antecedents of the agitator, says:

> *. . . He made his camp in this vicinity and soon he was building a chapel at the expense of the town.*
>
> *Although this work may be an improvement, even a necessary one, for the town, it is not worth the agitation and unrest; and from the state the people are in, the apprehension of great disturbances is more than justified.*
>
> *In order that you may judge what Antonio Conselheiro is, I need only tell you that he is followed by hundreds and hundreds of people who listen to him and follow his orders in preference to those of the parish priest.*
>
> *There are no limits to their fanaticism, which is so great that it may be affirmed without fear of error that they adore him, as though he were a living God.*
>
> *On the days of sermons, prayers, and litanies, over a thousand people come together. In the building of this church, which involves weekly wages of almost a hundred thousand milreis, ten times the amount that should be paid, people from Ceará are employed, to whom he gives his absolute protection, tolerating and covering up their violations of the law, and this money comes from the credulous and ignorant, who not only do not work, but sell what little they have, and even steal so that nothing may be lacking, without mentioning the large sums that have been collected for other buildings in Chorrochó, in the region of Capim Grosso.*

Then it goes on to describe the latest outrage of the fanatics:

Owing to a misunderstanding between Antonio Conselheiro's followers and the priest of Inhambupe, they have armed themselves as though they were going into battle, alleging that they believe the priest is going to the place called Junco to kill him. It frightens those who have to go by to see those scoundrels armed with clubs, knives, daggers, shotguns, and God help anyone who is suspected of being hostile to Antonio Conselheiro.

As far as can be gathered, this report, couched in such alarming terms, received no answer. No measures were taken until the middle of 1887, when the diocese of Bahia intervened once more, the archbishop writing to the governor of the province to urge that measures be taken to curb "a person known as Antonio Vicente Mendes Maciel who is preaching subversive doctrines, and doing great harm to religion and the state, distracting the masses from their religious duties and dragging them after him, trying to convince them that he is the Holy Ghost, etc."

In the face of this complaint, the governor of that province addressed himself to one of the ministers of the empire, asking that the madman be confined in an insane asylum in Rio. The minister answered the governor, adducing the extraordinary argument that there was no vacancy in that institution, and the governor, in turn, communicated this cogent decision to the archbishop.

This was the beginning and the end of the legal measures taken during the empire.

The Counselor continued his demoralizing apostolate without interference, acquiring an ever greater hold on the popular imagination. The first legends began to crop up. I shall not give a complete list of them.

He founded the settlement of Bom Jesus; and the astounded people told that on a certain occasion, when they were building the beautiful church that is there, ten workmen were struggling in vain to lift a heavy beam into place; whereupon the Chosen One climbed upon the wood and then ordered just two men to raise it up; and that which so many had been unable to do was done by the two quickly, without any effort. . . .

Another time—and I heard this strange tale from persons who had not fallen under his spell—he came to Monte-Santo and ordered that a pilgrimage be made to the top of the mountain, where there was a little chapel. The ceremony began in the afternoon. The multitude laboriously toiled up the steep slope, chanting hymns of praise, stopping at the Stations of the Cross, imploring forgiveness. He marched at the head of the procession, grave, awe-inspiring, his head uncovered, the wind blowing his long hair about, supporting himself on his inseparable staff. Night fell. The penitents lighted torches, and the procession formed a luminous pathway along the ridge of the mountain. When they reached the cross at the summit, Antonio Conselheiro, panting, sat down on the first step of the rude stone stairway and fell into an ecstasy, raptly contemplating the sky, his gaze lost in the stars. . . .

The first wave of the faithful crowded into the little chapel, while the rest remained outside kneeling upon the jagged rocks.

Then the dreamer got to his feet, showing signs of great fatigue. Between the respectful rows of the faithful he made his way into the chapel, his head bowed in humility, drawing his breath with difficulty.

As he approached the altar he raised his pale face, framed by his disheveled hair. A shudder ran through the astounded multitude. Two tears of blood rolled slowly down the immaculate visage of the Blessed Virgin. . . .

These and other legends are still related in the *sertões*. It is only natural. Antonio Conselheiro summed up in his mad mysticism all the errors and superstitions that form the lowest common denominator of our nationality. He attracted the inhabitants of the *sertões*, not because he dominated them, but because they were dominated by their own aberrations. He was favored by his surroundings, and at times, as we have seen, he even achieved the absurdity of being useful. He was serving the ends of old, irresistible ancestral impulses; and dominated by them, he revealed in all his acts the placable disposition of an incomparable evangelist. In fact, his neurosis was benumbed by an astonishing placidity.

One day the priest of a congregation of the *sertões* saw arrive at his door a man, thin to the point of emaciation, exhausted, with long hair falling about his shoulders and a long beard down his breast: the traditional figure of the pilgrim, lacking neither the traditional cross hanging from the rosaries at his belt, the worn, dusty cloak, the canteen of water, nor the long staff. . . .

The priest offered him food; he accepted nothing but a piece of bread. He offered him a bed, but he preferred a board, on which he lay down without blankets, dressed, without even untying his sandals.

The next day this strange visitor, who until then had spoken few words, asked the priest to allow him to preach on the occasion of a feast that was to be held in the church.

"Brother, you are not ordained; the Church does not permit you to preach."

"Then let me perform the services at the Stations of the Cross."

"I cannot do that either," answered the priest. "I am going to do that."

At this the pilgrim looked at him fixedly for a while and, without speaking a word, took from beneath his tunic a cloth. He brushed the dust from his sandals and departed.

It was the classic reproach of the apostles. . . .

Meanwhile the growing reaction he was encountering began to eat into his soul. Completely masterful by nature, he began to show irritation at the slightest obstruction.

Once, in Natuba, in the absence of the priest with whom he was not on good terms, he ordered stones to be brought to repair the church. The priest arrived, saw that his sacred domains had been invaded, and in exasperation decided to put a stop to the infringement of his authority. Being a practical man, he appealed to the people's selfishness.

A few days before, the town council had ordered the inhabitants to pave the walks of their houses. The priest told the people they could use the stones that had been brought up for that purpose.

This time the Counselor did not limit himself to brushing the dust off his sandals. At the gates of the ungrateful city he uttered his first curse and departed.

Some time later, at the request of this same priest, a local political figure sent for him. The church was falling into ruin, the cemetery was overgrown with weeds; the parish was poor. Only one who controlled the credulous as did the Counselor could repair this state of affairs. The apostle accepted the invitation, but he laid down his own terms, recalling with a haughtiness in contrast to his former meekness the affront he had received.

He was growing bad.

He looked upon the republic with evil eyes, and preached rebellion against the new laws. From 1893 he assumed a belligerent attitude that was completely new. It began with a matter of slight importance.

The autonomy of the municipalities having been established, the town councils of the interior of Bahia posted on bulletin boards, which took the place of newspapers, edicts regarding the levying of taxes and so forth.

When these innovations were introduced, Antonio Conselheiro was in Bom Conselho. The imposition of the tax exasperated him, and he planned an immediate answer to it. He gathered the people on a holiday and, amidst seditious shouting and volleys of rifle fire, he ordered the bulletin boards burned in a bonfire in the public square. His voice was heard above the "auto-da-fé," which the authorities were too pusillanimous to interfere with, openly preaching rebellion against the laws.

Later he realized the gravity of what he had done. Leaving the town, he took the Monte-Santo road to the north.

The event produced a strong effect in the capital, and a considerable force of police was sent out to apprehend the rebel and dissolve the rioting groups, whose number at this time did not exceed two hundred. The police overtook them in Massete, a desolate desert spot between Tucano and Cumbe in the foothills of the mountains of Ovo. The thirty members of the pursuing force attacked the crowd of miserable-looking penitents, certain of dispersing them with their first shots. They were dealing, however, with the fearless *jagunços*. They were completely routed and took to flight, their commanding officer in the lead.

Unfortunately this little battle was to be repeated on a larger scale many times later.

After their victory the faithful resumed their march, following the prophet in his hegira. They did not seek the towns as before. They made for the desert.

The rout of the troops would be followed by more vigorous persecutions, and with the protection of the wilderness they counted on being able to defeat their new adversaries by drawing them on into the hills. Without loss of time eighty soldiers of the line set out from Bahia. But they did not proceed beyond Serrinha, where they turned back without venturing into the desert. Antonio Conselheiro did not build up false hopes with this inexplicable retreat that saved him. He led the horde of the faithful, which was joined every day by dozens of proselytes, along the paths to the *sertão*, following a fixed route. He came to know the *sertão* well. He traveled it from one end to the other in an uninterrupted pilgrimage that lasted twenty years. He knew of hidden refuges where he would never be found. Perhaps he had marked them out earlier, foreseeing future vicissitudes.

He headed straight for the north. The faithful went with him. They did not ask where he was leading them. And they crossed steep sierras, sterile plateaus, and bare hills on the march day after day, in time to the chanting of hymns and the slow step of the prophet.

AFFONSO ARINHOS DE MELO FRANCO

(1868–1916)

A THOUGHTFUL study of comparative folklore reinforces one's belief in the doctrine of original sin. It seems the only tenable explanation of men's perverse determination to emphasize differences between peoples when the similarities are so great. As Gabriela Mistral, the great Chilean writer, said to her fellow Latin Americans: "In the hour of suffering we are one, we all groan in the same iron grip." And not only in the hour of suffering. So many of our beliefs, aspirations, interpretations of the universe are so similar in all races, in all religions, under the most varied external circumstances that any people or nation attempting to assert an innate superiority over others is wilfully blind or woefully ignorant.

In this beautiful legend of the Amazonian Indians which follows, the distinguished Brazilian journalist and historian Affonso Arinhos de Melo Franco gives us an American version of the sirens whose fatal allure the wily Ulysses combatted by stopping his men's ears with wax and having himself lashed to the mast, or of the bewitching Lorelei maiden of the Rhine.

The Yara

[AFFONSO ARINHOS DE MELO FRANCO]

JAGUARARI, the son of the chieftain of the Manáus, was as beautiful as a cool morning when the sun is shining on the waters of the Amazon. He was as strong and agile as the gold-black puma, the lord of the jungle, but he far surpassed him in his boldness as a hunter, and his daring in the face of the enemy. When he sailed his canoe, slipping so lightly over the still waters that the prow, like a bird's wing, hardly touched the surface, the shy herons, for the pleasure of seeing him, did not fly away from the bank, and the friendly *jacamins* came to greet him, fluttering along the ground.

In the great festivals with which the different villages of the Manáus, called together by the beating of the great drum made of a hollow tree trunk, celebrated the admission of the youths to the rank of warriors, none of the young braves equaled Jaguarari in pride of bearing, keenness of sight, and strength of arm.

The unerring arrow from his tense bow halted the swift flight of the peccary, dropped the bounding ocelot in its tracks, and the dart from his blowgun brought the preying hawk to the ground.

The old men loved him, the girls dreamed of him at night, the braves admired him, and their songs foretold how Jaguarari—may the day be distant!—would go to receive his supreme reward in the Blue Mountains, where the brave have their eternal mansion.

When the leafy *mamaurana* flowered he would glide along the bank in his canoe under the green foliage shading the stream, and the playful breezes would shake the branches and shower down on the black hair of the chieftain's son a rain of blossoms.

But many a purple twilight his canoe, reddened by the glow of the setting sun and checkered by the flickering shadows of the trees that lined the stream, failed to return to Taruman point, but remained on the water, alone and silent, until midnight.

"What kind of fishing is this, my son, that lasts into the night, at an hour when only the Devil Anhangá goes about the land and the waters? Have you never heard his fearful voice carried on the howling wind? Son, my beloved son, Anhangá scatters upon the grass and the leaves of the bushes the seeds of the sorrows that kill."

These were the words of his sorrowing mother when she saw her son return to his home in the dead hours of the night and sit huddled in his hammock, his legs hanging, his elbows on his knees, unsleeping, his sad, sunken eyes gazing out on the darkness, the river, the night, the realm of darkness.

To these pathetic words of his mother, Jaguarari responded with a brief glance, a glance from those sad, sunken eyes, contracted as with a vertigo of the depths.

"Son, it was not long ago, only a little while back, that happiness fluttered over your eyes like the wild ducks about the lake. Why did it fly away? Why did it go to build its nest so far from you and from me?"

"Mother," he murmured, in a voice so low as to be barely heard, with a helpless gesture.

And his body, fresh and full of sap like a palm tree, withered away, withered away; the gnawing termites had stung him in the heart.

He still accompanied the chieftain on his hunting expeditions, and his arm did not tremble at the roar of the spotted leopard. But as the afternoon lengthened, he left the company of the young braves who were setting snares for wild birds and fled the company of those who followed the course of the river, casting their fishing nets.

Alone, he leaped into his little canoe and sped toward Taruman point, where from the distance his comrades could see him, his eyes fixed on the mirror of the waters, solitary and sad, like the pensive heron.

One day his mother, her heart heavy with sad forebodings, said:

"Son, the evil spirits have poisoned the air you breathe, The *acauan* have been singing by the door. Your father wants to build another village for our people far from here. Only in that way will the bird of happiness flutter in your eyes again—"

After a long silence Jaguarari answered with a sigh:

"Mother, I saw her. I saw her, Mother, floating among the flowers like the water lilies on the lagoon. She is beautiful like the moon on a night when there is not a cloud in the sky. I saw her. Mother, her hair is the color of the flower of the *pau d'arco*, and gleams like the sun. Her face is pink like a flamingo's feathers and the flower of the coconut tree. The song of the birds that sing most sweetly cannot equal hers. Mother, no man in all the villages of the Amazon has ever seen or will ever see anything so beautiful as she. When she sings, the waterfall of Taruman hushes its roar to listen to her, I am sure. Oh, Mother, she looks at me and holds out her arms to me. Then the waters divide, and she descends to her home that was left there by the sky, long, long ago, when the sky spread all around us like a flowery mead, before it rose to form an arch above our heads with its starry vault. But I want to see her again; I want to hear her song once more."

The terrified mother cried:

"Oh, flee, flee that cursed spot. Never again let your canoe reach the point of Taruman. Flee, my son. You have seen the Yara. Her song is fatal. Flee, Jaguarari! It is the Yara. Death lurks in her green eyes."

And, sobbing, the old Indian woman threw herself on the ground.

The next day, at the hour in which the turtle doves fly high above the houses, cleaving the air as they seek their nocturnal haven, Jaguarari's canoe slipped swiftly down the waters of the black river.

The lads of the tribe who saw him pass said:

"There goes Jaguarari to fish for *tucunaré*."

But suddenly from a group of women who had gone to the river with their water jars there came a cry:

"Come, everyone. Come and see."

The young men rushed to the spot and stood rooted to the ground, gazing into the horizon reddened by the setting sun. The canoe of the chieftain's son, all aglow, was cutting through the water, and Jaguarari was standing up, his arms outspread, like a wild bird about to take off in flight. The canoe seemed to be rushing straight toward the sun, as though it would hurl itself into the flaming disk. And beside the young warrior, clasping him like a vine, stood a white figure, of beautiful form, in a halo of silvery light that contrasted with the ruddy gleam of the setting sun, and crowned with long loose golden tresses.

"The Yara! The Yara!" they all shouted with one voice, the braves and the maidens of the Manáus, as they ran back to the village.

This was the last time anyone saw the chieftain's son sailing the dark waters of the river.

GUSTAVO BARROSO

(1888–   )

GUSTAVO BARROSO has had a distinguished career as novelist, short-story writer, historian, and journalist. He has been the editor of several of the leading newspapers of his country, contributor to many and correspondent of *La Nación* of Buenos Aires and the London *Times*.

Mr. Barroso is from Ceará, that remote northwestern province of Brazil which Euclides da Cunha describes so vividly in *Os Sertões*. Like so many others of his epoch, he has been keenly interested in searching for the roots of Brazilian nationalism, which led him to a study of its folklore. In a number of his works he has described with great vigor and color the types and customs of his region that are fast disappearing under the impact of the forces of civilization. Many of the scenes and episodes, allowing for local differences, might be from our own frontier days. The following selection from his volume *Terras de Sol* is a fine, masculine description of a stirring past that is now gone.

The Cattle Drovers *

[GUSTAVO BARROSO]

IN its gradual penetration inland from the coast, civilization is eliminating, little by little, the traditional types and effacing or transforming old customs. The disappearance of these elements is hastened by the slight esteem in which we hold the oral traditions of the people, and the indifference Brazilians, in general, feel for all this. For this reason, it will not be out of place to perpetuate these old traditional figures that

* Translated with the author's permission from *Terras de sol* by Gustavo Barroso.

are dying out. Many of them sprang up in the backlands in consequence of some rebellious movement, and when this had died out they disappeared. This was the case of the *balaios*, rebellious rustics who formed a kind of jacquerie; the *calangros*, followers of families engaged in a feud; the *quebra-kilos*, ignorant backlanders who stubbornly and unreasonably opposed the introduction of the decimal system of weights and measures; and the *jagunço*. For some time now the term *jagunço* has become synonymous with the backlander of the North. Nothing could be more erroneous. The backlander of the North was never so dubbed. *Jagunço* was the name given to the inhabitants of Canudos, the fanatical supporters of Antonio Conselheiro; or at most, the backwoodsman of Bahia. It was the denomination of a certain group, but never a general name.

One of the most original of these vanished types that existed in the backwoods of Ceará was the cattle drover. Progress has done away with him.

Before the railroad of Baturité connected the interior of that state with the capital, all business transactions of the remote backlands was with Recife and other cities of Pernambuco, and the means of communication was by horseback over the highways. The herds were driven to the famous and bustling fair of Pedras de Fôgo, between Parahyba and Pernambuco. The cattleman of Ceará sent his herds to the fair of Parahyba; there he sold them, and with the money bought merchandise and articles that had a quick sale in the backlands. Many of the stock raisers drove their own herds; others—the majority—had men especially hired for this work.

These men, who liked this half-wild life they led, enjoyed the complete confidence of the men they worked for; they were absolutely honest, strong, daring, and brave.

Today the railroads have brought about a great change. The herds are no longer sent to Pedras de Fôgo. The reason for the cattle drover's existence disappeared, and he has vanished from the scene.

He was a celebrated figure. He lives in the memory of the people, who relate his prowesses with great admiration for his cool courage in the face of danger and his ability to get himself out of a tight corner.

Because of the commercial activity across vast areas sparsely populated and even more sparsely policed, the region was infested with highwaymen. They rarely set upon the drover when he was traveling with the herds, preferring to wait until the return trip, when he came back with merchandise and money, to demand their heavy tribute. Many of the leaders of such gangs were wealthy landowners, who preyed upon travelers after the manner of the medieval barons, who imprisoned Genoese peddlers, Jewish merchants, and the royal tax collectors. Travel through these regions was dangerous. It required astuteness and courage. The drovers possessed both.

One of them left behind him a fame that will never die. He was born in the town of S. Francisco da Uruburetama, and for that reason he was known as Xico of S. Francisco. He was a dark half-breed, with a snub nose, quick-witted and strong, calm and courageous. He affected a great modesty, speaking with a slow drawl, and when any of his exploits was recounted in his presence, he kept silent, greatly embarrassed. He was always complaining of being old, good for nothing, timid. He wore a leather outfit, chaps, hat, jerkin, and breaking the monotonous brown of the leather garments, a long chest protector of wildcat fur, with yellow and black markings. From his belt hung a *parnahyba*, a long, razor-sharp machete; and his inseparable companion was a "bell-mouthed" shotgun, a kind of Catalonian blunderbuss in wide use at that time, always loaded with a heavy charge of lead bullets.

Once Xico was driving a big herd that belonged to a rich rancher to Pernambuco. He had as his helpers five or six herders, undependable and cowardly. Every so often along the road there were corrals where the drovers could camp. Not far from one of them there lived the worst bandit of that whole region, the terror of the plains, to whom it was necessary to pay tribute in cattle or money to get by unharmed. The covetous thief owned four plantations, each with its sugar mill— the Diamond, the Brilliant, the Star, the Orient—and commanded a gang of followers as perverse as himself.

Xico took no notice of the fears of his helpers. At one of the corrals he shut in the cattle and made camp. He built a big fire and prepared the evening meal. Night was falling, and as happens in those latitudes, almost without twilight, quickly, dense and black. The owls were beginning to hoot in the woods, and the shy goatsuckers were fluttering through the trees. In the distance the foxes were barking. Amidst the dark foliage the yellow eyes of the whippoorwills gleamed. All the nocturnal animals were making their sinister rounds.

The drover had finished eating, had lighted his pipe, and stretched his hammock between two trees. Then he sat down with his shotgun resting on his knees. The fire crackled, the flames died down and then sprang up anew. The herders sat or squatted about the fire, talking.

Some time went by like this. Suddenly, the distant sound of hoofbeats broke the silence. The riders were carrying arms and wearing spurs. Then came the crackling of twigs and the rustle of leaves under heavy heels. The herders turned livid, trembling with fear. These must be the bandits. Xico remained imperturbable, without moving from where he sat. Finally out of the darkness there emerged five faces, brutal, scowling, terrifying, red in the flickering flames of the fire. The light was reflected off the burnished muzzles of pistols and shotguns. The leader of the sinister band stepped forward, his corpulent frame seeming to fill the whole clearing. He was dressed in leather like the others, with a chest protector of mottled leopard skin, fastened at the neck with clasps of silver. His harsh good evening had a menacing tone. Only the drover failed to show the slightest uneasiness, and asked quietly, indifferently, like one who is resting and does not wish to be disturbed:

"What can I do for you?"

"How much do you want, you, for that spotted heifer in the corral?"

In those days cattle sold very cheap. Xico took in the thinly veiled intention of the highwayman and answered shortly:

"Twenty thousand reis."

"Will you take fifteen?"

"No. I wouldn't sell it to my father for that price, if he was alive."

"Well, I'm only paying fifteen. You hear me?"

Calmly, as though the conversation were being carried on under the hospitable shade of his own roof, the half-breed replied firmly:

"I'm not selling at that price."

"All right. I'll give you twenty—on time. You pick up the money on your way back."

Imperceptibly Xico was pulling himself into a sitting position in the hammock.

"On time? Not me. You can hit the road, partner. We're not doing any business."

The highwayman's face turned as red with anger as though the flames of the fire had licked it. He, the terror of the plains, aroused no fear; nor, on bended knee, did this contemptible drover offer him the tribute he was in the habit of receiving. He glanced around him. The herders were trembling in fearful expectation. Xico was the only man among them. Pulling down his bushy brows in a threatening frown, the bandit exploded in a spate of insults, threats, oaths. Then in the vaunting, boastful tone of the bandit of the backlands, giving vent to his wounded pride, he shouted:

"You must be looking for trouble! Do you know who you are talking to? I am the famous João Ferrabraz, the master of four sugar plantations. I'll have you beaten by my followers. I'll throw you into the furnace of the Brilliant, I'll run you through the press of the Diamond, I'll drop you into the vats of the Star, I'll have you ground up in the mills of the Orient . . ."

Xico got to his feet with a roar, raising his gun:

"And I am Xico Francisco de S. Francisco, a drover of Ceará, the son of all the devils! One sneeze from my gun and you will see the stars at noon and give a somersault so high in the air it will be three days before you come down."

He leaped back and took aim. A shot rang out. The bandit fell to the ground with his brains oozing out. His followers and the herders took to the woods, one as frightened as the others.

On another occasion a young fellow was going from Cariry to Pernambuco with a large sum of money. He was looking for a mule driver he could trust, a man who was brave and honest. They told him about Xico. The young man hired him for the trip, in spite of his vehement protestations that he was good for nothing, and not brave. But he had been so highly recommended, and at the moment the traveler could not find anyone else. They set out across the vast backland at a steady trot. For two days they had traveled uneventfully. The night of the second day they came to a region that was practically uninhabited, without a house or cabin to be seen. They swung their hammocks close to the fire, under the branches of the trees. In a little while the young fellow was nodding sleepily; Xico sat in his usual position, puffing away at his pipe. They had brought with them two valises with clothing and supplies; in one of them was the package of money hidden in a corner. They had laid them on the ground close by. The horses, hobbled, were grazing a little way off. The bells about their necks gave out a faint tinkle.

Suddenly, swiftly, out of the dense shadows there appeared two highwaymen with leveled guns.

The poor lad cast an agonized glance at Xico. But the latter in a loud, cynical tone said to him:

"Didn't I tell you I was a coward? Why did you depend on me? Now get out of this the best way you can."

Then turning to the two bandits, who saw in him an accomplice:

"The money is in that dark valise. The key is in the kid's left pants' pocket. And the money is in the right-hand corner of the valise. Now, don't bother me. You know everything."

The boy, frozen with fear, did not make the slightest move or say a word. He was utterly astounded; the wind had been completely knocked out of his sails. Was this, then, the famous drover of Cariry, the upright man, the model of loyalty and courage?

One of the bandits snatched the keys out of his pocket, and both of them, eagerly, greedily, bent over the lock of the valise. As cool as a cucumber, Xico raised the gun to his face, took aim, and blasted the

two of them with unerring aim. Then, laughing, he said to the lad
who was even more amazed than before:

"Didn't I tell you I was a coward? There's the proof."

This is what the vanished cattle drovers were like.

JOSÉ BENTO MONTEIRO LOBATO

(1889–   )

AT THE END of World War I, Brazil was in a state of literary doldrums.
Its writers spent their time polishing their imitations of European
models or their own classics. But this was only the calm before the
powerful winds of the contemporary movement that completely
freshened the air. In the vanguard of this literature, this authentically
Brazilian production, stands José Bento Monteiro Lobato. He was a
lawyer who, detesting his profession, had gone to run a coffee plantation he owned near São Paulo. Possibly he might have gone on being
a planter the rest of his life but for a severe forest fire that broke out
in the vicinity. Deeply upset by this disaster, he wrote a letter to the
editor of the leading newspaper of São Paulo on the subject. Whether
the letter had any practical effects on the control of forest fires is not
on record, but it launched Monteiro Lobato on his literary career. The
editor was so impressed by the contribution that he published it and
asked the author for further articles. A second sketch, *Urupés*, a wryly
humorous study of Jeca Tatú, Lobato's name for the Brazilian counterpart of Jeeter Lester of *Tobacco Road*, won him national fame. Jeca
Tatú was the symbol of Brazil's forgotten man. He was lazy, shiftless,
improvident, completely indifferent to everything that was going on,
for he had no stake in anything. Jeca Tatú was an indictment of the
government. Monteiro Lobato is the link between the analytical,
sociological novel of the end of the nineteenth century and the modern
novel with its acute social sense, the tendency in modern literature
everywhere.

Monteiro Lobato left his plantation and moved to São Paulo, where,
in addition to continuing his own writing, he founded a magazine and
a publishing house that brought out the works of the younger gener-

ation of writers who were just beginning, many of whom later won distinction.

It is as a writer of short stories that Monteiro Lobato excels. He manages to inject humor and compassion into the most tragic and pathetic of his tales about the Brazilian countryfolk of the São Paulo region, whom he knows so well. *The Vengeance of the Redwood*, with its deft interweaving of an old superstition into a neighborhood quarrel that begins so ludicrously and ends so tragically, is a perfect example of his art.

The Vengeance of the Redwood *

[JOSÉ BENTO MONTEIRO LOBATO]

THE town was somewhat skeptical about the whole affair. Nevertheless, for months the chief topic of conversation of the neighborhood was João Nunes's mill at Varjão. Especially in the vicinity of the Porungas, for Pedro Porunga, a miller of considerable reputation, snorted with laughter every time he described the goings-on at the mill.

Porunga and Nunes were neighbors, living on their respective farms, separated by Nheco Hill—and by an old quarrel. Once Nunes, one Sunday, had started a water hare; but as the animal crossed the crest of the hill, it ran head on into one of the young Porungas, who happened to be cutting wood there. One blow of the ax and the hare was dead mutton.

So far, so good.

But he ate it without sending even a quarter as a gift to its legitimate owner. Yes, legitimate, for when all is said and done, that hare was a well-known character. As sly as a vicar, it was, according to Nunes, and there was not a hound or trap it did not laugh at. It always got away. The folks on the other side of the hill knew all this. The doings of a wily old hare are always a favorite topic of conversation among hunters. A well-known hare, a resident on Nunes's property, it was Nunes's hare, no question about it. And on the very day when by a happy chance he had caught it off guard, for that young Porunga to do that!

"He's nothing but a kid."

"Yes, but didn't his father back him up? Didn't he go around laughing and saying: 'That's Nunes's hard luck.' " They would pay for it.

That was how the bad feeling started. The hill dated back to slightly more remote times, when the surface of the earth was solidifying.

The dissension was aggravated by what might be termed a kind of

* Translated with the author's permission from *Urupés* by José Bento Monteiro Lobato.

caste rivalry. Nunes belonged to the class of those who run down at the heel as the result of too much rum in the head and too many skirts around the house. He had only one son: José Benedito, nicknamed Pernambi, a little squirt knee-high to a grasshopper, though he was a good seven years old. There was a whole drove of girls—María Benedita, María da Conceição, María da Graça, María da Gloria, a string of eight Marys. All those women around the house got on Nunes's nerves, and on the days when he had been hitting the bottle harder than usual, he threatened to drown them all in the lake, like a litter of kittens.

His consolation was Pernambi, whom he spoiled to death. As soon as he was big enough, he should go to the field with him to help him with mattock and grub hoe, while all those good-for-nothing females sat idling around, combing the lice out of each other's hair in the sun. He made the boy his boon companion and taught him to drink. At first he made wry faces at the taste of the stuff, which amused his father greatly, then very quickly acquired the habit. He drank and he smoked, with a foolish expression on his face, and looked as though he did not have sense enough to come in out of the rain. He carried a knife at his belt too.

"A man who doesn't drink, doesn't smoke, and doesn't carry a knife isn't a man," Nunes affirmed.

And conscious of the fact that he was a man, the young hopeful beat his sisters, spat between his teeth, called his mother names, and did many other things that befit a man.

On the other side of the hill it was the exact opposite. Never much of a hand for the bottle, Pedro Porunga had married a sensible woman who had given him six in family, all sons.

It was only natural that he should prosper. Every September he planted three fields of corn, he had two grist mills, a sugar grinder, his patch of manihot, his canefield, besides a mare and two brood sows. He used a double-barreled gun for hunting, a Laporte model. There wasn't another like it. He lived in a new house, well roofed with good thatch, built with plummet and line, by the side of the road. The beams and doors were of carved wood, and the inside walls, plastered by hand, were something to see.

By this time Nunes—poor Nunes—did not plant even one field. He had had a mare, but he traded her off for a pig and an old shotgun. After they had eaten the pig, all that was left to show for his trade was the single-barreled, muzzle-loading shotgun that generally missed fire.

His house, with unhewn beams and doors of cracked *embaúba*, the corners black with soot, gave promise of turning into a tumble-down shack in the not too distant future.

Pigs, none. Chickens, very few.

It profited the dog, Brinquinho, little to be known as the best rabbit hound in the neighborhood. His stomach and backbone met, and he was a walking mass of fleas. The poor animal could not take ten steps without sitting down in a vain attempt to catch one of his out-of-reach tormentors. Let him forage for his food! A dog is a shrewd animal, and the woods are full of silly rabbits! And everything else around Varjão was in pretty much the same shape.

One day somebody told Nunes that Pedro Porunga was planning to buy a she-donkey with a saddle and everything. That was a body blow for Nunes. Porunga was getting too big for his breeches.

"So, that's what he's bragging about now!" he stormed. "Well, I'll show those Porungas who João Nunes Eusebio dos Santos of Ponte Alta is."

And he suddenly began to display an unwonted activity.

His wife was amazed at the change that had come over her husband, and she was torn between doubt and hope.

"Is this fire going to last? Who can tell?"

Nunes was planning big things. He was going to plant three fields of corn, fix up the house, build a hominy mill—

At this his wife pursed her lips dubiously.

"A mill? *Che*, what a hope!"

Nunes, who had the bit between his teeth, shouted:

"You wait, woman, I'm going to have a hominy mill, I'm going to put in a cane grinder, I'm even going to set up a flour mill. I'll make those Porungas gnaw their wrists with envy. You just wait and see."

To everyone's amazement the promise did not remain idle words. Nunes fixed up the house after a fashion, cleared a field that had been growing to underbrush for eight years, and, making a supreme effort, planted two and a half bushels of corn.

Pedro Porunga soon heard about his boast. He laughed and predicted:

"An old nag's last spurt. It won't last."

The year started off well. The rains came on time, so that by January the corn flaunted its banners high and the stalks were heavy with ears.

Nunes was nearly beside himself he was so happy. Radiating satisfaction, he visited the fields, pulling up the suckers, showing all his yellow teeth as he grinned to himself, feeling the tender ears, with their golden silk showing through. Holding his lower jaw in his hand, he would give himself over to his dreams of future prosperity, balancing the debits and the credits in his mind. The debits were already out of the way. Nothing but credits remained. Back in the house, he said to his wife:

"What a crop of corn I'm going to harvest this year!"

Now he had to set up the mill. The corn ground into hominy would bring him double profits. Wasn't that how the Porungas had made their money, in hominy? But one doesn't undertake a thing as important as that pell-mell. One has to think it over, figure things out. Here Nunes gave his imagination free rein. The *chóó-pan* of the future mill echoed inside his head like the refrain of angel music.

"I'll show that Porunga he's not the only miller in the world. I'm going to get my *compadre* Teixeirinha of Ponte Alta to help me with it."

His wife clapped her hands to her head.

"Holy Virgin! You must be crazy. Why, Teixeirinha's only got one arm—"

"*Bééé*," Nunes brayed at her in indignation. "You shut up. What does a woman know about such things."

"All right. But afterwards don't come complaining."

"*Bééé*," answered her husband, ending the discussion.

This roar was the concluding argument in Nunes's dealings with the family. When that "*bééé*" sounded, wife, daughters, Pernambi, Brinquinho the dog stole silently away. They had learned from painful experience that the sequel was the whack of a stick. And they preferred to let bad enough alone.

With the silence of his wife good sense fell silent too, for Teixeirinha the One-Armed, was a slipshod carpenter, one of those who make a living at odd jobs and repairs. Only to a drunken fool like Nunes would it occur to entrust the building of a hominy mill to a broken-down whamper-jaw like that, crippled and blind in one eye, to boot. But he was Nunes's *compadre*, and that was all there was to it. *Bééé.*

Nunes spent another week in "imaginative" work. He would sit slowly scratching his head, puffing away at a long cigar, in a brown study, with his eyes on the cornfield and his thoughts on the future. Finally he made up his mind. He set out for Ponte Alta and brought back with him the old carpenter with his one-armed kit of tools.

The question left to be decided was what wood to use. On his land there was nothing but second growth. Big trees that could be used for the mill, there were none, except the redwood on the boundary line, an old dead tree that had been tacitly respected by both parties. He was going to cut it down without any explanations to the Porungas—just as they had done with his hare.

It would serve them right. Nunes chuckled to himself as he made plans to chop down the tree at night, so that the next morning, when the Porungas realized what had happened, not even St. Anthony could do anything about it.

"That's settled. I'm going to chop down the redwood."

No sooner said than done. That same night two axes hacked away at the tree, and it was not yet day when the redwood crashed to the ground, falling on Nunes's land.

As soon as it was light, the Porungas, who had heard the chopping, showed up to find out what was going on. When they saw the trick that had been played on them, Pedro, the spokesman for the group, called out:

"Who told you you could do that?"

"The hare," Nunes snapped back, defiantly.

"The hare is the hare, but that redwood was the boundary mark, half mine, half yours."

"Well, I want to use my half. I'm leaving yours there," replied Nunes, pursing his lips in the direction of the red stump.

But Pedro was not finished.

"You son-of-a-bitch! I don't know what's the matter with me that I don't—"

"Well, I know that I'm on my land, and I'll let daylight into the first bastard that crosses the line."

The verbal exchange grew hotter. They called each other every name they could lay their tongues to. The women put in their two cents. With his shotgun in his hand, radiant in the midst of the hubbub, Nunes said to his one-armed assistant:

"You go on about your work, *compadre;* I can take care of these pumpkinheads by myself."

In the end the Porungas abandoned the field—to avoid bloodshed.

"Keep the tree, you flannelmouthed drunk, but you'll weep tears of blood over it before you're done—"

"*Bééé!*" roared Nunes triumphantly.

The Porungas went home muttering among themselves, followed by Nunes's victorious glances.

"See what cowardly trash they are, *compadre?* Lots of talk, but when it comes to doing—that's another story."

And he had the old man's eyes popping out with his accounts of the fights he had been in, the heads he had broken, the bullies he had made knuckle under, the devil knows what.

"The day is ours, *compadre.* Let's get out of here and wet our whistles."

The wetting of the whistles turned into the most complete bender anyone could recall. Nunes, Teixeirinha, and Pernambi celebrated their triumph until the three of them passed out on the ground. With the last of the series of Marías hanging to her flaccid breast, the wife looked at the sight and shook her head misgivingly:

"Mother in Heaven, what kind of a mill is going to come out of this?"

The next day, when their heads were clear again, the ywent back to the redwood, blood brothers. The liquor had cemented a friendship of years' standing, but the building of the mill began with great bodily fatigue. Nunes spent the days watching his *compadre* cut up the tree with his single arm. It was an unfailing source of wonder to him to see how the mangled stump helped out the good arm. Old Teixeirinha cited instances all going to show what a worthless lot the Porungas were, and Nunes adduced additional proof.

After the tree was trimmed, Teixeirinha got a string, which he dipped in a sticky paste of soot. "Take hold of this end, *compadre*," said the old man. "Now this one, that's the idea." Then, with the doubled string between his fingers, he lashed at the wood, marking it with black lines.

Nunes revealed a real vocation as a bit cooler. Bit coolers are carpenters' "kibitzers." They sit around on the bench by the hour watching the shavings drop as the plane smooths a board or the chisel hollows out a furrow. They pick up the adze, run a finger over the edge of the blade, and inquire: "Is it a Greaves? What did you have to pay for it?" And when the bit is removed from the wood, hot with friction, they snatch it up and blow on it to cool it off, with an air of great efficiency.

While he was doing this, Teixeirinha was clumsily hollowing out the tip bucket with axe and adze. Then he bored the holes in the crossbeam and fashioned the pestle. When these were ready he went to work on the mortar. He hacked and he chopped, and in three days he had it done. All that was left was to fix up the grooved fork in which the crossbeam played.

"Have you ever heard about the bad-luck tree, *compadre?*"

Nunes knew nothing about it. Nunes knew nothing about anything except putting a bottle to his mouth and running down the Porungas. Without interrupting his measuring of the fork, Teixeirinha told the story he had heard from his father, Teixeirão the lumberjack, a famous woodsman in his day.

" 'In every stretch of woods,' the old man used to say, 'there is the bad-luck tree that punishes men for their wrongdoings. I have lived in the woods all my life, I have worked with every kind of tree, I have cut down *embaúvas*, *embirussús*, even balsam firs, which are rare around here. The nights I slept on a platform in the trees! I was like a wood animal. And from all my dealings with trees I came to the conclusion that they have souls, like people.' "

"Well, I'll be damned."

"That's what the old man said; me, I've got no opinion in the matter. 'They've got a soul,' he used to say, 'because they feel pain and weep. Haven't you heard trees groan as they fall? And others weep red tears that run down and turn to resin. They've got a soul, because in this world everything is a child of God.' "

"Could be—"

" 'And,' he said, 'in every woods there is a tree, nobody knows which, a kind of champion to avenge the others. That's the bad-luck tree. The poor wretch that lays an axe to its heart might just as well commend himself to the devil, for he's a goner. He'll get hurt, or have his head cracked by a falling branch, or if nothing happens to him at the time, something will when he goes to use the lumber. He can't get away from it. It's no good for him to be on his guard. Misfortune will rope him, if not today, tomorrow. He's a marked man.' "

"That's what the old man said—and I've seen a lot of queer things myself. Remember when they were cutting down the big fig tree, and Chico Pires's son was killed? He was cutting down a *gúamarim* when all of a sudden he lets out a yell. Everybody rushed over, but the boy's chest was caved in. What had happened? How did it happen? Nobody could figure it out. When I thought it over, I said to myself: 'The bad-luck tree.' I can't tell you how many cases like that there have been. There was Sebastiãozinho at Ponte Alta. He built himself a house, and he himself cut the ridgepole. Didn't it fall down and crush his head? For that reason my father, knowing these things, always tried to find out first whether there had already been some misfortune in the vicinity. This was to see if the bad luck had already happened or was still lurking around, so as to be on his guard."

With this and other tales of the same sort, Teixeirinha beguiled the working hours while he put the finishing touches on the mill.

At last the mill was ready. Nunes was in high spirits. The first step in his dreams of prosperity had been realized. All that had to be done now was to set it up—which was nothing—and he patted the redwood affectionately.

"There we are. Nice, isn't it. I'm going to call it the Champion— the Champion of the Porungas—yellow bellies, bastards!"

They quit work early that day to celebrate their achievement at the expense of a keg of brandy, which they finished off between them.

Days later, the mortar firmly set in place, well adjusted, the grinder received water. The sluice was opened, a foaming stream rushed into the tip bucket, filled it, and overflowed into the spillway. The beam creaked in the socket and pulled up the pestle. The water poured out of the tip bucket—*Chóó!* The pestle banged down on the mortar—*pan!*

Nunes was beside himself with satisfaction.

"Now, you lousy Porungas, now you see who João Nunes Eusebio of Ponte Alta is!"

But this rejoicing was not enough for him, nor the handclapping and yelling of the children, nor the yapping of Brinquinho, who, frightened by such goings-on, was barking, out of range of kicks. He wanted more. He ran and got the shotgun, loaded it, and pointing it "across the way," pulled the trigger. But the old broken-down muzzle-loader did not seem to share his happiness; it blew off the cap, but there was no report. Nunes held it in position a few minutes longer, waiting for the shot. Irritated by its failure, he hurled it away, calling it every name he could think of. Then he happened to remember three firecrackers that had been left over from some religious festivity. He went and got them and set them off in the direction of the Porunga farm.

"Get a whiff of that powder, you jack rabbits!"

Unfortunately the firecrackers were damp and fizzled out without exploding.

"Nothing wants to help us, *compadre!* Let's see how the keg behaves."

It behaved all right. So well, in fact, that before long they were stretched out on the ground, snoring like two anteaters.

The next day Teixeirinha left for Ponte Alta, to Nunes's great regret, for he had enjoyed his company. As for the mill, there was no corn yet, so it had to wait until the crop was ready to make its debut.

The summer rains came to an end. Fall set it, cool, clear. The leaves of the corn began to turn yellow, the ears drooped heavy. The harvest began. Full of impatience, Nunes shelled the first basket and started the grinder. Alas, there is no unalloyed happiness in this world. The mill did not work too well. The yield of hominy was poor. The beam was out of proportion to the tip bucket and did not move freely. The pestle, either because it was too light or because the groove was not true, pulled to the left, scattering the corn all over the ground. And as though that were not enough, with the first rain the mortar began to leak. It had been hollowed out of cracked wood. It was no good.

Nunes, with a face down to the ground, restraining his anger, tried to fix things up as best he could. He lightened the counterweight on the beam, he increased the flow of water, he tightened something here, he loosened something there, he filled in the cracks. He spent days in a somber struggle with the mill's exasperating tricks. But the devilish contraption responded to every adjustment by behaving worse.

Finally the poor man exploded. He began to vomit a stream of insults against that knave of a carpenter.

"May that one-armed devil rot in hell—"

It would be impossible to set down here all the names he called him. The milder ones can go on paper, but the stronger ones will have to remain at Varjão. And not names alone, threats. He would go to Ponte Alta and cut him to pieces with his machete, he would poke his other eye out, he would—

In one of these outbursts his silly wife made the terrible mistake of saying:

"I told you, I warned you. But would the mule listen to me?"

God help us! That was all Nunes had been waiting for. His wife was suddenly transformed into the hated carpenter. Grabbing up a stick of wood, he gave her such a beating as would have taken the kinks out of a Negro.

"Take that, you dog! Take that, you devil's leavings! I'll teach you to build mills, you filthy pig! God damn the day—"

The woman ran limping off into the woods, followed by the smaller Marías. For eight days she poulticed herself with salt to cure her bruises. But Nunes improved considerably as a result of this diversionary activity. He had let off all his pent-up steam.

The news of all these happenings came to the Porungas' ears. Pedro was jubilant; he wanted to see with his own eyes the rattletrap of a mill that was avenging him so perfectly. He thought up a plan, and one day he crossed the hill in the direction of his rival's place. He was home in an hour, laughing till the tears ran down his face.

"Come listen, folks, if you want to hear something good. You never saw anything like it. As I came over the top of the hill, I could hear the noise—*chóó-pan*—it was pounding like the devil. I said to myself: one thing about it, it sure makes a noise.

"I went on. Nunes, looking as though he had lost his last friend, was sitting by the door shelling corn. When he saw me, he started to get up, with the most amazed look on his face.

" 'How are you,' says I, holding out my hand to him. 'Two grown men, and neighbors in the bargain, can't go on like this the rest of their lives, with their noses in the air. Bygones are bygones. Shake!'

"He cut his eyes in the direction of the pounding, and very embarrassed, stuck out his hand without opening his mouth.

" 'Bring some coffee,' he yelled into the house.

"I took one look at the kitchen. It was swarming with women. I began to talk, and he'd answer, but you could see he wasn't in much of a mood for conversation. Finally I said to him: 'How's the mill, neighbor? Working all right?' Nunes turned as yellow as a fallen leaf.

" 'Pretty good.'

" 'I'd like to see it,' I said, 'if I'm not being too nosey.'

" 'Go ahead,' he answered, without moving from his place.

"I went. Mother of God! That was never a mill, either here or on the devil's acre. It's nothing but a bunch of sticks and stones tied together with withes. The beam is nine handspans long, and from the tip bucket to the mortar is ten."

"Haw, haw, haw," roared his audience, all experts on mills.

"And the pestle is too light; it weighs less than fifty pounds. The fork is set wrong and is out of plumb. There's so much corn scattered around that the ground is white with it. The pestle pulls to one side. Sweet Jesus, what a mess!"

The Porungas drooled with satisfaction.

"But it does make a noise?"

"Christ, worse than a thunderstorm. But grind? In a pig's eye! Not three quarts a day. I tell you, folks, you have to see it to believe it."

The faces of the Porungas, which had been clouded over since the incident of the tree, were now wreathed in happy, malicious smiles. It was their turn now. They thought up all kinds of jokes and wisecracks. They added comic touches of their own to the shortcomings of the mill. They trimmed it up like a Maypole. To the general description of old Porunga, the younger ones each contributed his bouquet, until the poor mill was the laughingstock of the neighborhood. The word "Roarer" had become the synonym for everything ridiculous or harebrained.

The tittle-tattle finally got around to Nunes's ears. His pride, which had grown so high-flown during the period of his dreams of grandeur, was drying up like a fruit picked too green. Unable to avenge his humiliation, he began to develop a sullen hatred of the "Roarer," which kept up its heavy pounding—*chóó-pan*—day and night, in a dull rotation whose practical results were negligible. To soothe his spirits, Nunes doubled the doses of brandy.

His wife did what she could to keep the place going, but she was sick at heart, in rags, and could see no future ahead for her husband.

Pernambi, a small edition of his father, had got completely out of hand. There was always a cigarette dangling from his lips, and every day his hand fell heavier on the little girls.

Brinquinho was completely at sea. He would sit back on his haunches, bewildered, cocking his head first to one side, then to the other, trying to figure out what had happened to his folks.

This went on for months.

Finally the tragedy fell. Whether it was the malefice of the tree or not, the fact is that the innocent paid for the guilty with Biblical justice. One day Nunes heard that José Cuitelo of Pedra Branca had named a scabby mare he owned "Roarer." That was the last straw.

"Even that yellow dog of a Cuitelo," he groaned, reaching out his hand for the bottle.

He took a long swallow. Then he called out:

"Pernambizinho, come here. Have a drink with your father."

The boy did not wait for a second invitation; he took a pull at the bottle, and then another and another, smacking his lips. The rest of the bottle found its way into his father's gullet. Half drunk, the boy hung around for a little while and then went off. Nunes stretched himself out in the sun to sleep.

It was an unpleasant day in August. The sky was heavy with the smoke of the burning brush. A dull, copper-colored sun hung heavy in the west. Charred leaves whirled slowly through the air.

An hour had gone by. The drunken man woke up and looked about him with glazed eyes.

"Where's Pernambi?" he asked his daughters, huddled together on the doorstep.

They knew nothing of their brother's whereabouts.

"Call Pernambi," muttered the father, drowsing off again.

One of the girls set out to look for her brother.

Nunes could hardly keep his eyes open; his head bobbled around as though his neck were broken. The spittle was running out of the corner of his mouth, and his words came out moist, vague and unco-ordinated.

Suddenly, a blood-curdling scream in the distance threw the household into a panic.

The wife, aghast, rushed to the door, and when she had located the direction of the scream, she started to run. The daughters followed her, making for the mill.

There was a tragic silence. Then more screams, a chorus of screams, screams of despair.

"Oh, my son, my poor little son!" came the mother's shriek from afar.

Nunes tried to get to his feet, pulling himself up by the frame of the door.

"Now, what's the matter?" he growled.

Nobody answered. There was no one there to answer. But in the direction of the mill the screaming grew louder. The drunken man set out toward it, stumbling as he walked. On the way he ran head-on into his wife, who was running back, her hair disheveled, talking wildly to herself.

"What has happened, woman?"

The poor mother glared at him, her eyes stabbing him with uncontrollable rage.

"What has happened? This is your work, you drunken devil! This is your drink, you good-for-nothing, you stinking dung! Go and see, go and see, go and see, you wretch—"

Nunes managed to stagger to the mill. An awful sight met his eyes. Surrounded by the screaming girls, the skinny body of Pernambi hung face down over the mortar. His two legs hung limply over the side—and the pestle went on indifferently rising and falling, *chóó-pan*, grinding a red paste of meal, brains and skin . . .

The alcohol fumes cleared from his head. Half beside himself, he rushed for the axe, grinding his teeth, howling:

"Your day has come, you monster!"

What a scene! Roaring with rage, the crazed father rained blow after blow upon the murderous mill. One against the pestle—take that, Bluebeard!—another against the beam—I'll kill you, you devil!—another on the mortar—you contraption of hell! One after the other, ten, twenty, a hundred axe slashes such as the stoutest lumberjack could never have dealt.

The chips flew all around, red splinters and chips of the man-eating redwood.

The tragic duel between the demented father and the inert apparatus went on for a long time. When finally the cursed mill was a heap of wreckage, the pitiful *caboclo* fell to the ground, clasping to his bosom the limp body of his son. Instinctively his hand reached toward the bottom of the mortar, feeling for the little head that was missing.

JOSÉ LINS DO REGO

(1901–   )

IN A RECENT interview, José Lins do Rego, author of the great series of novels, *Menino de Engenho*, *Doidindho*, *Bangué*, *Moleque Ricardo*, and *Usina*, which comprise *The Cycle of Sugar Cane*, admits that his has been a happy life. Wealthy, of distinguished family, gifted, his lines have been laid in pleasant places. But his own good fortune has not blinded him to the sufferings of others less privileged. "I know that I love mankind," he says, "because I loathe the forces of oppression and injustice with all the strength of my body and all the purity of my soul."

There is a strong autobiographical element in all Lins do Rego's work. His novels deal with the life of a sugar plantation, a counterpart of the one owned by his grandfather where he grew up, indulged and petted by the old slaves who had remained on the plantation after the emancipation, and with the young Negroes as his playmates. So strong an impression did this life make on the sensitive boy that at times his novels seem a direct transcription of the reality he had lived. His characters are so alive, his language is the living speech he had heard on the lips of his early associates. His works are a repository of the customs, traditions, folklore that were ingrained in this society. Many of the scenes he describes recall Katherine Anne Porter's fine tales of Southern plantation life.

Lins do Rego has the social consciousness of his generation, though he is too much of a novelist to be a propagandist. But the evils and abuses engendered by a feudal system resting on the more or less benevolent exploitation of the many by the few are clearly pointed up by the facts.

The two following selections from *Menino de Engenho* are tender evocations of persons and scenes that will soon be "long ago and far away."

Old Totonha *

[JOSÉ LINS DO REGO]

FROM time to time old Totonha happened along at the plantation. And that was a red-letter day for the small fry. She lived by her fairy stories. Tiny and shriveled, so light that a puff of wind could have carried her away, she walked miles and miles on foot, from one plantation to another, a living edition of the *Arabian Nights*. The gift she had for storytelling, and how she could throw herself into the part of all the different characters! Without a tooth in her head, but with a voice that gave every shade of tone to her words.

For me there was nothing in the world that could compare with her tales. She knew how to pick her audience. She did not like to tell them when Cousin Silvino was around, because he was noisy and made remarks in the middle of the story. Not me; I sat silent, motionless before her. With a listener of this sort, old Totonha never tired. She would repeat the stories, tell still another, pass from one to the other, and always with that smile of hers, like that of the grandmother pictured in story books. And her stories were unique; nobody could tell them like her. There was a personal touch in the inflections of her

* Translated with the permission of the publisher, José Olympio, from *Menino de Engenho* by José Lins do Rego.

voice and a human quality about the kings and queens of her tales. Her Hop o' My Thumb was different from all others, and her witch that fattened children to eat them was more cruel than anybody else's.

Old Totonha possessed the dramatic gift. She ran the whole scale from sublime to ridiculous without ever forcing the situation, making it seem the most natural thing in the world. Her memory was prodigious. She recited whole tales in verse, interpolating here and there fragments of prose, like footnotes. There was the story about the man sentenced to death. The bells were already tolling for the poor wretch, who was on his way to the gallows. He had been accused of killing another. All the evidence was against him. As the procession passed before his house, where his wife stood at the door in tears, with her nursing babe in arms, the infant stopped suckling and began to talk in verse, revealing what had really happened and thus saving its innocent father. Old Totonha recited the verses spoken by the baby in a tone so grief-stricken that it was almost unbearable. My eyes would fill with tears at the sound of that puling lament of the nursing babe.

There was always a king and a queen in her tales, and a gallows and magic. And a great deal of life, with its wickedness and its kindness, in those heroes and scoundrels, the latter always coming to a horrible end. And the most interesting thing was the local color old Totonha managed to give all her descriptions. When she talked about some far-off kingdom, it was as though she were telling about some fabulous sugar plantation. The rivers and forests where her characters moved and had their being bore a marked resemblance to the Paraiba and the woods of Rôlo. Her Bluebeard was the master of a plantation of Pernambuco.

The story of the stepmother who buried the little girl was her masterpiece. The father had to take a long trip and leave his daughter, whom he loved better than anything in the world, with his second wife. When he left he charged his wife to take the best care of his daughter. She was a little girl with golden hair, beautiful like a princess. But the stepmother hated her, because she was jealous of her husband's love for the child. As soon as he was gone she began to ill-treat the little girl. It was she who had to go to the river for water, look after the pigs, sweep the house. She had no more time to play with her dolls. She looked like a servant with her unkempt hair and her dirty clothes. One day her stepmother sent her out to the fig tree, to stand there with a stick in her hand and drive the birds away from the fruit. And the little girl stayed there day after day, hungry, driving the birds away. The wood pigeons, the ones that wash the clothes of Our Lord, would come and talk with her and tell her stories of Heaven. One day she was looking up at the beautiful blue sky and the joyful, singing birds. In the shade of the fig tree, drowsy with the noonday heat, she fell asleep, dreaming of her father, who was far away, and of the toys he would bring her when he came back. And the birds came and pecked the figs of the fig tree. That was what the stepmother had been waiting for. She gave her such a whipping she half killed her, and then buried her alive by the riverbank. When the father returned he wept his heart out over the news of the death of his daughter. The stepmother told him the child had taken ill as soon as he set foot out of the house.

"There was nothing we could do to save the poor little thing."

But one morning the hay gatherer of the plantation went out to mow hay for the horses. In the middle of the field he saw a clump of very green grass growing. As he went to cut it down, out of the earth came a faint voice from far, far away. At first he thought his ears were playing a trick on him, and he started to cut it down again. Then a sad voice, like that of a soul in torment, began to sing:

> Hay gatherer of my father,
> Do not cut off my hair
> That my loving mother combed.
> My stepmother buried me,
> Because of the figs
> That the little birds ate.

The hay gatherer was astounded and ran quickly to tell the plantation owner. They came back with a mattock and began to dig in the ground. There they found the little girl as green as a leaf of the woods. Her hair had grown into green grass. Her eyes were full of dirt, and her fingernails were black and very long. The plantation owner wept like a man out of his mind, hugging and kissing his little daughter. They held a celebration that lasted for many days. The Negroes danced the *coco* for two weeks. Many slaves were set free. And they tied the stepmother to the hind legs of two wild colts, and the pieces of her were scattered on the ground and rotted.

There were also the stories of Jesus's travels with his disciples. Jesus came to a poor farmhouse one evening with his companions. The owners were so poor it would break your heart. They didn't even have a piece of bread to offer their guests. Jesus sent Peter to bring their sack of provisions.

"Master, the sack is empty."

"Man of little faith, go get the sack."

St. Peter knew there was nothing left in the sack, but he went anyway. And at the door he found two bags of flour and meat.

In these stories St. Peter never believed anything he did not see,
and he was always being scolded by Our Lord.

Old Totonha knew a poem about the shipwreck of the *Baía*, off the
coast of Pernambuco. One of the survivors described the disaster he
had witnessed:

Oh, what a day of Judgment,
Oh, what a day of horror.
Only the stones did not weep,
Because they feel no pain . . .
Come, boatswain and coxswain,
Pilot and Captain,
Let us go see our *Baía*,
If she's going down or no.

Episode after episode was narrated; children wailing and clinging to
their mothers; the anguished cries of the dying; the water rising in the
ship; an old woman floating on a chicken coop; a rich miser by the
name of Pataca-Lisa running back to his stateroom for his money and
never returning: he went to the bottom with his riches. The whole
poem abounded in a wealth of detail. And the old woman's expressive
voice made it seem that the tragedy was at our very doorstep. This
grim song gave me the shivers. It was then that I developed my fear of
ship travel because of the horror of those scenes connected with the
sinking of the hapless *Baía*.

When Totonha left to visit the other plantations I waited eagerly
for her to return with her stories that were always new to me. For she
possessed a gift that time could not wither nor custom stale.

The Masters and the Slaves *
[JOSÉ LINS DO REGO]

THE old slave quarters were still standing. Some twenty bedrooms, all
opening on to a long porch. The Negresses who had belonged to my
grandfather all stayed on at the plantation, even after the emancipation, in the "street," as they called their quarters. There they lived until
one by one they died of old age. I knew four of them: Fat María,

* Translated with the permission of the publisher, José Olympio, from *Menino
de Engenho* by José Lins do Rego.

Generosa, Galdina, and Romana. My grandfather went on feeding and clothing them. And they worked for nothing, as contented as when they were slaves. Their daughters and granddaughters succeeded them in their duties with the same devotion to the Big House and the same passivity of kindly domestic animals. It was in the street that the young ones of the plantation had their friends, the pickaninnies who were their playmates, the Negro women who had been their wet nurses, in whose affectionate arms they had been reared. There we were all one, receiving from the older women the same scoldings, the same pettings as their own children. Weren't we all foster brothers? I did not have any foster brothers, because I had been born in the city, far from the healthy udders of those good Holsteins. But my mother's wet nurse, Aunt Generosa, as we called her, acted as my grandmother. She lavished care upon me and quarreled with the others on my account. When they threw up to her that she always took my part, she always had the same answer:

"Poor little thing, he has no mother."

We invaded the quarters, playing in the women's old trunks, with their boxes they kept in a hole in the wall which held their rosaries, their tawdry bits of jewelry, their miracle-working charms.

On the adobe walls there were always images of saints, and in a corner the bed of bare boards, where for more than a century they had lain with their men and borne their children.

I never knew the husband of any of them, and yet they were pregnant most of the time, perpetuating the species without thought and without fear. The young ones slept in stinking hammocks; the whole room had the stench of a latrine. The floor was damp with the nightly urinations. Yet it was there that we were happy, as though we were in a palace.

The odd thing was that we of the Big House were under the leadership of the young colored boys, the *moleques*. They directed us, even bossed us around in all our games, for they could swim like fish, ride any kind of a horse, kill birds with a slingshot, went swimming whenever they felt like it, and asked nobody's permission to go where they pleased. They could do everything better than we could: fly kites, spin tops, play the castanets. The one thing they did not know was how to read. But this did not seem important to us. We longed to be free, barefooted, bareheaded, our own masters, as the *moleques* were at all hours. At times they took advantage of their ascendancy over us, of their fascination for us. They put us up to stealing things from the Big House, oranges, sapote plums, pieces of cheese. They traded us their slingshots and tops for our pilferings from the pantry. And they introduced into our conversations the exciting theme of sex. Through them I began to understand what men did with women, and where babies came from. They were first-class tutors in natural history. We pursued our studies around the stables. There was a wagon shed, where the old conveyances of the plantation were stored. We turned it into a kind of kindergarten brothel. There we lost our youthful innocence in these brutal conversations, in our lewd contacts with the young Negro lads. The women, however, behaved with great circumspection in front of us. They never said an improper word when we were around. They would be engaged in their own private conversations, but as soon as we appeared on the scene, they would change the subject. The men would come to see them in the room where they lived with their children. My cousin Silvino told us one day what he had seen in the Negress Francisca's room:

"Zé Guedes was making the bed creak."

Every year they had a child. Avelina had children by Zé Ludovina, by João Miguel the distiller, by Manoel Pedro the sugar refiner. They had inherited the fecundity of their slave mothers. That was how I grew up, in the midst of these people, with a full knowledge of their men, their quarrels, their ailments.

One place we never went was the room of Fat María. We never had anything to do with that old Negress. It was impossible to understand what she was saying; she babbled some kind of jargon, and at lunch and dinner time she would come out of her hole, dragging herself along with the help of a stick, to get her provisions. She was from Mozambique, and though she had been in Brazil for eighty years, she spoke a language of her own, Portuguese mixed with I don't know what. I was afraid of the old woman. She reminded me of the witches in old Totonha's stories. Her room exuded a stench of carrion. On Midsummer Night Eve it was only at her door that no bonfire was lighted. The Devil danced with her all night long. I could not get it out of my head that there was something infernal about that Negress, for she never revealed a human trait, any resemblance to other people. Everybody on the "street" was afraid of Fat María. In the afternoon she used to sit on a box at the door of her hut and smoke her long reed pipe, always alone, muttering God knows what to herself.

Old Galdina was another story. She too was African, from Angola, and walked with crutches, for she had broken a leg playing blindman's buff with the children. She had been my grandfather's nursemaid, and we all called her Granny. The other Negresses were very fond of her. Aunt Galdina was the great lady of the "street." They never raised their voice when they talked to her, and they addressed her as *"Vossa Mercê."* I was always at her heels to get her to tell me stories of the African coast. She was ten years old when they stole her from her father. A brother of hers sold her to the slave traders, and they had branded her on the face with a red-hot iron. She would tell about the voyage, which had lasted so many days, the grown Negroes shackled and the children loose. In the daytime they brought them above deck to get air, and they could see the sea and the sky. She had become used to life aboard ship and was happy. The schooner was as swift as a liner. Then one day they reached port. It was a long time before anyone bought her. The buyers preferred grownups or well-developed girls.

Granny told us how she had seen the souls of the dead in the shape of white birds. On the voyage these souls at night circled above the heads of the shackled slaves. And she taught us the words she remembered of her native tongue. On Christmas Eve they yoked the oxen to the cart so Aunt Galdina could go to mass in Pilar. And they gave her old blankets for her bed. She would cry like a child about anything. When they wanted to catch any of us and give us a whipping, it was to her that we always ran. She would plead for her "grandchildren" with tears in her eyes.

Old Generosa was the cook at the Big House. Nobody could touch a pot in the kitchen except her. And if anyone trespassed on her territory she would fly into a rage, even if it was the white folks. She had I don't know how many children and grandchildren. She was tall, with arms like a man, and could lift a caldron of preserves off the stove without asking help from anybody. She shouted all the time, but we did what we pleased with her. She was as good as her preserves and her puddings. We only had to whisper to her what we wanted, and she would give it to us, paying no attention to the meddlesome snooping of my greataunt Sinhazinha.

"The boss of the kitchen is the one who stands over the stove."

And when they tried to question her about anything, she would snap back:

"Anybody who doesn't like it can lump it. Slave days are over."

It was she who distributed to the boys who herded the cattle their rations of meat, flour, and meal. She bellowed at them as she did so, calling every one of them a scoundrel. But they paid no attention to old Generosa's bad humor. The boys knew she had a heart like a lump of sugar. Afterwards she gave them remedies for their colds and their wounds and mended their ragged clothing.

The slave quarters of Santa Rosa did not disappear with the emancipation. They remained a part of the Big House, with their Negresses turning out good wet nurses and faithful servants uninterruptedly.

MARIO DE ANDRADE

(1893–1945)

ANY PERSON wishing to acquaint himself with Brazil's rich and varied folklore must begin with the works of Mario de Andrade, whose premature death deprived Brazil of one of its most talented writers at the very height of his career. One of the most cultivated men of his generation, poet, essayist, sociologist, musicologist, novelist, the emphasis in all his work is laid upon that which is authentically Brazilian. Not only did he cultivate a new artistic nationalism in his own work and in that of the group of young writers on whom he has had such a marked influence; he organized and took part in trips into the remoter regions of Brazil to collect the folk songs of the people and make films of their customs and activities before they disappeared.

Famous as he is for his poetry, essays and short stories, his penetrating criticism of art and music, it is his novel *Macunaíma*, "the story of a hero without any backbone," that gives him a place by himself in Brazilian literature. This legendary figure out of Brazil's remotest folklore, an engaging rascal, shameless, gay, unabashed, becomes a national symbol. Andrade cuts across all boundaries of time and space, making a completely modern figure of his hero. It is an insuperable record of Brazilian myths, symbols, and customs, filled with riotous humor and written in a language that is typically, authentically Brazilian.

The following selection gives the flavor of Andrade's unique style.

Macunaíma *

[MARIO DE ANDRADE]

IN the depths of the jungle, Macunaíma, one of our folk heroes, was born. He was black—jet black—the child of midnight. At a moment when everything was hushed listening to the murmur of the Uraricoera, the Tapanhumas squaw brought forth an ugly man-child. This child was the one known as Macunaíma.

Even as an infant he did amazing things. First of all, he did not

* Translated with the permission of the publisher, José Olympio, from *Macunaíma* by Mario de Andrade.

talk until he was six. When they urged him to talk, he would answer:
"Oh, I'm too lazy—" and that was all he said. He sat in the corner
of the cabin, he climbed up on the platform bed, watching the others
work, especially his two brothers; Maanape, who was getting on in
years, and Jiguê, who was in the prime of manhood. His pleasure was
pinching off ants' heads. He spent most of his time lying down, but if
he caught sight of money there was nothing Macunaíma would not do
for a penny. And he would wake up when the family went down to the
river to bathe, all together and naked. All the time they were there he
would keep diving under the water, and the women would give squeals
of pleasure because they said the stream was full of fish. When any of
the young women came near to caress him, Macunaíma would put his
hands where he was not supposed to and the girls would run away.
He spat in the men's faces. However, he did respect his elders, and he
never missed the *murúa*, the *porace*, the *tore*, the *bacororo*, the *cucuicogue*,
all the religious dances of the tribe.

When he went to bed he climbed up into his little hammock, always
forgetting to pass water first. His mother's hammock was under his
cradle, and our hero pissed down on the old woman, scaring away the
mosquitoes. Then he fell asleep, dreaming bad words, shocking things,
and kicking his feet in the air.

When the sun stood high in the noonday sky the favorite topic of
conversation among the women was the mischievousness of our hero.
The women laughed indulgently, saying: "A thorn has a point even
when it's little," and at a tribal feast King Nago made a speech and
told people our hero was smart.

When he was six years old they gave him water in a gourd of his own,
and Macunaíma began to talk like everybody else. And he asked his
mother to stop grating manihot and take him for a walk in the woods.
His mother told him she could not leave the manihot. Macunaíma
whined all day long. He went on crying that night too. The next day
he waited with one eye shut until his mother started to work. Then he
asked her to put aside the reed basket she was weaving and take him
for a walk in the woods. The mother did not want to, because she had
to finish the basket. And she asked her daughter-in-law, Jiguê's wife,
to walk with the child. Jiguê's wife was a good-looking girl by the name
of Sofará. She approached him warily, but this time Macunaíma behaved himself and did not put his hands where he was not supposed to.
She swung the papoose up on her back and carried him to the foot of a
tree by the riverbank. There the water slowed down to pick out
syncopated music among the leaves of the *javarí*. It was very beautiful
along the bank, with all the gulls and little gulls flying over the water.
The girl dropped Macunaíma on the grass, but he began to whine that

there were too many ants there and asked Sofará to carry him to the slope of the hill in the forest, and the girl did. But as soon as she put the boy down on the rushes, the wake-robins, the spiderwort of the forest carpet, he suddenly began to grow and was changed into a handsome prince. They stayed there for a long time.

When they got back to the cabin the girl seemed all tired out from carrying the papoose on her back. Our hero had frolicked a lot with her. She had just put Macunaíma in his hammock when Jiguê came in from fishing, and his wife would not do any work. Jiguê got mad, and after he had picked the ticks off himself, he gave her a good thrashing. Sofará took it and did not open her mouth.

Jiguê did not suspect anything, and he began to weave a rope out of *curauá* fiber. He had seen the fresh track of a tapir and wanted to set a snare for it. Macunaíma asked his brother for some of the fiber, but Jiguê answered him that it was not for children to play with. Macunaíma began to cry, and they all spent a bad night.

The next day Jiguê got up early to set the snare, and, seeing that the boy was still in a bad humor, he said to him:

"Good morning, darling of the others."

Macunaíma stayed in his hammock, scowling.

"Don't you want to talk to me?"

"I don't want to have anything to do with you."

"Why?"

Then Macunaíma asked for some *curauá* fiber. Jiguê gave him an evil look and told his wife to give the boy some of the thread, and the girl did. Macunaíma thanked her and went to ask the witch doctor to weave a rope for him and blow lots of tobacco smoke on it.

When it was all ready Macunaíma asked his mother to leave the *cachiri* she was brewing and take him to walk in the woods. The old woman was too busy, but Jiguê's wife artfully said to her mother-in-law that she would be glad to help out. And she went off to the woods with the papoose on her back.

When she threw him on the rushes and the wake-robins and the spiderwort, the boy began to grow and grow and turned into a handsome prince. He told Sofará to wait for him and he would come back and they would do some frolicking. And he went to the water hole where the tapir came down to drink, and set his snare. They had no more than got home when Jiguê too came back from setting his trap for the tapir. His wife did not want to do any work. Jiguê got very mad, and when he had pulled the ticks off himself, he gave her a good whipping. Sofará endured the whipping patiently.

The next day the dawn was just coming up over the trees when Macunaíma woke everybody up with a great hubbub, telling them to come, to come quickly to the water hole and see the tapir he had caught. But none of them believed him, and they went about what they had to do.

Macunaíma was very cross and asked Sofará to go down to the water hole just to take a look. The girl did and came back telling everybody that there really was a big tapir in the trap and it was dead. The whole tribe hurried down to get the animal, marveling at the boy's sagacity. When Jiguê arrived with his empty snare and found them all cutting up the game, he helped. And when he divided up the meat he did not give Macunaíma a single piece, nothing but offal. The hero swore vengeance.

The next day he asked Sofará to take him for a walk, and they stayed in the woods until it was dark. The minute she dropped the boy on the rushes he turned into a lusty prince. They frolicked together. After they had frolicked three times, they ran about the woods having lots of fun together. First they poked each other, then they tickled each other, then they buried each other in sand, then they burned each other with lighted straws. What fun they had! Macunaíma picked up a *copaiba* stick and hid behind a *piranheira* tree. When Sofará came running past, he hit her in the head with the stick. The girl fell at the foot of the tree, nearly dying of laughter. She grabbed him by the leg. Macunaíma howled with delight, clinging fast to the huge trunk. Then the girl got his toe between her teeth and bit it off. Macunaíma, laughing till the tears ran down his face, spattered her all over with blood from his foot. Then he took hold of a liana that was hanging like a trapeze, and with a leap swung himself to the top branch of the *piranheira*. Sofará climbed after him. The slender branch swayed back and forth with the weight of the prince. When the girl climbed up there, they had another frolic swinging back and forth in the sky. Afterwards Macunaíma wanted to play a trick on Sofará. He bent her body back as hard as he could push, but the branch broke, and both of them came tumbling out of the tree and knocked themselves silly on the ground. When our hero recovered his senses he looked around for the girl, but she was not there. He was getting to his feet to look for her when out of the branches above his head came the terrifying howl of a jaguar piercing the silence. Our hero was paralyzed with fright, and he closed his eyes so he would not see himself devoured. Then he heard a giggle and a gob of spit hit him in the breast; it was the girl. Macunaíma began to throw rocks at her, and when they hit her, Sofará screamed with excitement, sprinkling him with the blood from her cuts. Finally a rock caught her in the side of the mouth and knocked out three teeth. She leaped up in the branch of a tree and jumped down—

whoosh!—right on the stomach of our hero, who wrapped himself around her, roaring with pleasure. And they had another frolic.

The star Papaceia was shining in the sky when the girl came home, all worn out from carrying the papoose on her back so long. However, Jiguê, who had become suspicious, had followed the two of them into the forest and had seen the transformation and all the rest. Jiguê was very stupid. He was as mad as he could be. He grabbed up a braided leather whip and brought it down with all his might on our hero's rump. The screeching was so terrible that the night shrank and many birds fell to the ground with fright and were turned into stones.

When Jiguê had worn himself out beating him, Macunaíma ran off into the woods, chewed some thistle root, and got all well. Jiguê took Sofará back to her father and climbed into his hammock and had a good sleep.

A NOTE ON THE TYPE
IN WHICH THIS BOOK IS SET

This book is set in Monotype BASKERVILLE, *a facsimile cutting from type cast from the original matrices of a face designed by John Baskerville. The original face was the forerunner of the "modern" group of type faces.*

John Baskerville (1706–75), of Birmingham, England, a writing-master, with a special renown for cutting inscriptions in stone, began experimenting about 1750 with punch-cutting and making typographical material. It was not until 1757 that he published his first work, a Virgil in royal quarto, with great-primer letters. This was followed by his famous editions of Milton, the Bible, the Book of Common Prayer, and several Latin classic authors. His types, at first criticized as unnecessarily slender, delicate, and feminine, in time were recognized as both distinct and elegant, and his types as well as his printing were greatly admired. Four years after his death Baskerville's widow sold all his punches and matrices to the Société Littéraire-typographique, which used some of the types for the sumptuous Kehl edition of Voltaire's works in seventy volumes.

Composed, printed, and bound by Kingsport Press, Inc., Kingsport, Tennessee.